PRINCIPLES OF ELECTRICITY

for Students of Physics and Engineering

COLLEGE OUTLINE SERIES

PRINCIPLES OF ELECTRICITY

FOR STUDENTS OF PHYSICS AND ENGINEERING

Eugene George Key

Associate Professor of Engineering

East Los Angeles College

BARNES & NOBLE, INC. NEW YORK
PUBLISHERS BOOKSELLERS SINCE 1873

Reprinted 1971

L. C. catalogue card number: 66–23153

SBN 389 00042 6

Manufactured in the United States of America

To my children

Linford Eugene

Robert Ellis

Jenifer Margaret

George David

Barbara Ann

ABOUT THE AUTHOR

Eugene George Key is Associate Professor of Engineering at East Los Angeles College. He received the degrees of B.S. in Arts and Sciences from Illinois Institute of Technology and B.S. in Electrical Engineering from Northwestern University.

Professor Key, a licensed professional engineer, has had varied and extensive practical experience as an engineer and mechanical designer in private industry and for government agencies. He holds the rank of Lieutenant Colonel in the United States Air Force Reserve, and while on active duty during World War II he wrote and edited technical handbooks for the Air Force. He has published some twenty articles on technical subjects in *Power Plant Engineering* (now *Power Engineering*) and *Design News* magazines, and is the author of two other books, *Elementary Engineering Mechanics* and *Mars Mountain*, a science fiction work. Professor Key is a member of the American Society of Engineers and Architects, the National Science Teachers Association, the American Society for Engineering Education, and the Los Angeles College Teachers Association, and is listed in *The International Yearbook and Statesmen's Who's Who*, *Who's Who in the West*, and *Who's Who in Commerce and Industry*.

PREFACE

The need for a book to help students understand the fundamental principles of electrical engineering became very apparent to me during several years of teaching courses in electricity and magnetism (physics), electronics, and electrical and electronic drafting. Many times during my teaching of these courses, students asked me to recommend books that would help them understand the textbook coverage of some of the material. I had to admit that I knew of none currently in print. Several students countered: "Then why don't you write one?" Now, at last, I have done so.

This book is intended to assist the college student who wants to be an engineer, a physicist, or an engineering technician. It should be of value to students who are now studying electricity and magnetism (physics), elementary electronics, elementary electricity, or electrical circuits, or are planning to study any of these courses in the near future. It should also be helpful to anyone in or out of school who wants to learn the principles of electricity by home-study methods. Engineers and technicians will find the book a useful reference guide in their work where circuits are involved.

Instead of concentrating only on dry theory, I have tried to relate theory to the practical application of the principles of electrical engineering in the work that most electrical engineers have to do. Consequently, some subjects often omitted from standard textbooks are included, such as the three-wire system, the four-wire delta-connected three-phase system, over-current and under-voltage protection of alternating-current motors, and simplified—but practical—methods of conducting a short circuit study for an industrial plant and its distribution system. References are made to facts that engineers know or should know, and to occasional simplified means of computing quantities such as currents in d-c and a-c systems.

A knowledge of mathematics through algebra and trigonometry is all that is required to solve the problems in this book. In Chapter 8 calculus is employed to show the derivation of some of the equations needed in alternating-current circuits, and in Chapter 10 calculus notation is used as a shorthand method of expressing what happens in a magnetic circuit. However, calculus is not necessary in the actual solutions of the problems based on these derivations, even though it was needed to put together the equations that make the solutions possible.

I wish to thank many people who helped in the preparation of this book. Dr. John R. Nicklin, formerly Associate Professor of Chemistry, and Dr. Milford R. Lehman, Chairman of the Chemistry Department at East Los Angeles College, contributed their time and knowledge to the review of the material in Chapter 6. Others on the faculty of East Los Angeles College who helped directly or indirectly are Dr. Dewey C. Duncan, Chairman of the Mathematics Department (now retired); Anthony F. Klute, Instructor in Engineering; Robert T. Weiss, Instructor in Architecture; and Richard S. Kenealy, Associate Professor of Physics. I also wish to thank Vancil (Jack) Foust, laboratory assistant in the Physics Department at the college, for suggestions from the student's viewpoint.

My wife, Winifred, assisted me with the typing of the manuscript, particularly with the tables and the longer equations. Our five children—Linford, Robert, Jenifer, George, and Barbara—helped in many ways. I also gratefully acknowledge the encouragement given me throughout my teaching and writing career by Dr. Douglas Bruce Pearce, now Supervisor, Advisement Service, Los Angeles City Schools.

Eugene George Key

San Gabriel, California

CONTENTS

TABLES

TABULATED BIBLIOGRAPHY OF STANDARD TEXTBOOKS

This Outline is keyed to standard textbooks in two ways.

1. If you are studying one of the following textbooks, consult the cross references here listed to find which pages of the Outline summarize the appropriate chapter of your text. (Roman numerals refer to textbook chapters, Arabic figures to Outline pages.)

2. If you are using the Outline as your basis for study and need a fuller treatment of a topic, consult the pages of any of the standard textbooks as indicated in the Quick Reference Table on pages xviii–xxi.

Del Toro, *Principles of Electrical Engineering*, Prentice-Hall, 1965.
I (4–18, 22–27); III (16–18, 85–89, 110–123); IV (9–16, 123–131, 54–72); V (113–123, 131–135); VI (139–180, 185–202); XIV (225–254); XV (260–274); XVI (292–299, 316–320).

Fitzgerald and Higginbotham, *Electrical and Electronic Engineering Fundamentals*. McGraw-Hill, 1964.
I (1–31); II (139–154); III (154–160); IV (160–184); V (185–198); VI (110–129); XI (225–252); XII (260–272); XIII (292–294, 296–298); XIV (316–320); XVI (32–33).

Fowler and Meyer, *Physics for Engineers and Scientists*. 2nd ed. Allyn and Bacon, 1961.
VIII (1–5); IX (119–123, 99–105); XV (6–18); XVI (225–236); XVII (236–250); XIX (1–5, 225–235, 110–125, 139–152).

Freier, *University Physics*. Appleton-Century-Crofts, 1965.
XXIII (1–5); XXIV (119–123); XXV (99–105, 77–82, 6–9); XXVI (105–108, 9–16, 22–30); XXVIII (225–233); XXIX (240–246, 110–116); XXX (246–250); XXXII (143–160, 260–262).

Gray and Wallace, *Principles and Practice of Electrical Engineering*. 8th ed. McGraw-Hill, 1962.
I (4–5); II (1–4); III (225–231); IV (5–31, 54–62, 85–89); V (41–51);

VI (231–240, 248–254); VII (240–246, 110–116); XVIII (99–108); XIX (27–30, 41–43, 77–85); XX (139–145); XXI (155–163, 171–174); XXII (145–155, 160–163, 166–174); XXIII (139–143, 157–160, 166–174); XXIV (185–198); XXV (260–272); XXVI (282–296); XXVII (296–303); XXVIII (316); XXIX (316–320).

Halliday and Resnick, *Physics*. Wiley, 1966.

XXVII (1–4); XXX (119–123, 126–131); XXXI (5–9); XXXII (9–16, 22–27, 121–123); XXXIII (225–236); XXXIV (236–240); XXXV (240–246); XXXVI (110–116); XXXVII (246–254).

Hammond, *Electrical Engineering*. McGraw-Hill, 1961.

I (4–9, 16–18, 110–116, 119–123, 22–24); II (139–160); III (116–119, 123–129, 131-135); IV (155–163); V (113–123); VI (166–178, 188–198); VII (27–31, 54–67); IX (1–4); XVI (225–230, 240–242, 246–248, 252–254); XVII (230–246, 260–268, 277–282); XVIII (230–240, 296–303, 316–320).

Jackson, *Introduction to Electric Circuits*. 2nd ed. Prentice-Hall, 1965.

I (1–2, 4–5); II (4–5, 100–108); III (5–9, 77–93); IV (16–18); V (9–16, 22–27); VI (27–33, 54–72); VII (225–240, 246–254); IX (110–119, 240–246, 123–126); X (119–123, 126–131, 1–4); XI (143–145, 152–155); XII (146–152); XIII (139–143); XIV (155–160, 166–174); XV (160–163); XVI (166–174); XVII (174–178); XVIII (260–274, 294–296); XX (185–221); XXI (163–166, 178–180).

Johnson, *Introduction to Electrical Engineering*. International Textbook, 1965.

I (1–18, 110–116, 119–125, 152–154); II (139–143, 155–157, 22–24, 174–178); III (54–72); IV (116–119, 123, 131–135); XII (225–227, 246–248); XIII (227–231, 250–252, 296–299, 260–265).

Marcus, *Basic Electricity*. 2nd ed. Prentice-Hall, 1964.

I (1–4); III (4–9, 16–18); IV (9–16, 22–24); V (225–230, 252–254); VII (143–145, 152–155); VIII (145–152, 157–163); IX (110–116, 147, 119–123, 148–150, 123–128, 155–157, 174–178); XI (296–299); XII (99–101, 105–108); XIV (77–80); XVI (260–265, 271–272); XVII (296–299).

Romanowitz, *Electrical Fundamentals and Circuit Analysis*. Wiley, 1966.

I (1–10, 22–24, 225–230, 240–243, 101–105, 16–18); II (99–101, 105–108); III (77–89, 92–93); IV (10–16, 24–31, 41–43); V (54–72); VI (230–240, 245–254); VII (243–245, 110–119, 123–126); VIII (119–123, 126–131); IX (139–174); X (32–36); XI (174–178); XV (178–180); XVII (260–284); XVIII (185–221); XIX (296–303).

Sears and Zemansky, *University Physics.* 3rd ed. Addison-Wesley, 1964.
XXIV (1–2); XXV (3–4); XXVII (119–123, 126–129); XXVIII (6–9, 77–80, 82–85, 16–18); XXIX (5–6, 9–16, 32–33); XXX (225–230); XXXI (230–236); XXXII (230–240); XXXIII (240–246, 110–119, 131–135); XXXIV (246–254); XXXV (143, 178, 260–262).

Siskind, *Electrical Circuits: Direct and Alternating Current.* 2nd ed. McGraw-Hill, 1965.

I (1–5); II (6–9, 77–89, 93–94); III (5–18, 99–101, 105–108); IV (22–31, 54–72); V (225–240); VI (246–254); VII (32–35); VIII (110–119, 242–245); IX (119–123, 126–131); X (143–160); XII (139–143, 166–174); XIII (174–178); XVI (260–262); XVIII (185–221); XIX (178–180).

Skilling, *Electrical Engineering Circuits.* 2nd ed. Wiley, 1965.

I (1–18, 22–30, 85–89, 110–116, 119–123, 225–230, 236–240); II (143–152, 157–160, 116–119, 123); III (139–143); IV (143–163); V (166–178); X (260–265); XIV (178–180); XX (185–201, 209–219, 284–293).

Slurzberg and Osterheld, *Essentials of Electricity—Electronics.* 3rd ed. McGraw-Hill, 1965.

II (1–9, 16–18); III (100–101, 105–108); IV (6–16, 22–27, 77–89, 32–33); V (225–254); VII (160–163, 185–193, 260–269); VIII (110–119, 123–126); IX (119–123, 126–131); X (139–160, 166–175, 59–62); XI (174–178).

Timbie and Pike, *Essentials of Electricity.* 3rd ed. Wiley, 1963.

I (1–5); II (5–6); III (9–16); IV (225–230); VI (22–30, 67–68); VII (16–18); VIII (99–108, 54, 59–62); IX (77–85, 27–30).

Turner, *Basic Electricity.* 2nd ed., enlarged. Holt, Rinehart and Winston, 1963.

I (1–5); II (5–18, 22–27, 85–89, 100–108); V (225–233, 236–240, 246–248, 250–254); VI (143–155, 178–180); VII (119–123, 126–129); VIII (110–116, 123–126); IX (155–163, 174–178); X (260–262, 294–296); XI (296–299, 316–320); XII (185–196); XVIII (32–33).

Weber, White, and Manning, *Physics for Science and Engineering.* 1st ed., revised. McGraw-Hill, 1957, 1959.

XXVI (1–5); XXVIII (99–108, 5–9); XXIX (9–16); XXX (32–33, 85–89, 90–91); XXXI (225–240); XXXIII (246–254); XXXIV (41–47); XXXV (242–246); XXXVI (260–262); XXXVII (119–123, 126–129); XXXVIII (143–163, 174–175).

QUICK REFERENCE TABLE

All figures refer to pages.

CHAPTER IN THIS BOOK	TOPIC	Del Toro	Fitzgerald & Higginbotham	Fowler & Meyer
1	**Electrical Fundamentals**	3–15 77–78 92–96 101–107	5–11 13–16	128–157 260–278
2	**Kirchhoff's Laws of Current and Voltage**	17–20	18–30 493–497	270–278
3	**Power and Energy**	72–73	11–13	266–267
4	**Circuit Calculations**	107–133	24–32	
5	**Resistance and Temperature**	74–75	16–17	
6	**Conduction of Electricity in Solids and Liquids**			165–166
7	**Inductance and Capacitance in Direct-Current Circuits**	12–13 15–17 140–178	169–183	344–348
8	**Alternating-Current Circuits**	184–226 232–234	41–120 139–147	349–354
9	**Three-Phase Circuits**	242–252	147–161	
10	**Magnetism**	573–609	330–352	285–297 304–319
11	**Alternating-Current Machinery**	614–644	356–372 392–401 407–412 438–446	

TO STANDARD TEXTBOOKS

See pages xv–xvii for complete titles.

Freier	Gray & Wallace	Halliday & Resnick	Hammond	Jackson	Johnson
251–260 280–281 301–304	3–8 25–28	663–700 708–729 770–797	1–22	20–31 46–53 62–63 82–84 85–88 240–252	1–4
291–294	30–34	798–802	28–30	84 90–91 110–113 124–127	16–19
	53–56			68–76	
	34–39			116–124	
	210–218			53–59	
277–280 281–282 289–291	193–209			33–43	
	81–86 256–260	802–808 899–907	69–87	211–234 256–274	
	220–256 260–289		40–58	283–300 303–390 409–426	4–26
	290–316			472–505 511–527	232–237
310–331 335–339	58–76	814–827 844–880	404–425 462–479	132–180	206–216
	317–390 416–426		432–436 451–458	459	230–232 245–250

QUICK REFERENCE TABLE

All figures refer to pages.

CHAPTER IN THIS BOOK	TOPIC	Marcus	Romanowitz	Sears & Zemansky
1	Electrical Fundamentals	1–33 39–46	1–11 50–51 93–99	529–580
2	Kirchhoff's Laws of Current and Voltage	47–48	11–14 373–377	649–659
3	Power and Energy	29–31	99–100	635–640
4	Circuit Calculations		128–129 137–146	
5	Resistance and Temperature		63–73 77–81	
6	Conduction of Electricity in Solids and Liquids	34–36	21–22 37–44	
7	Inductance and Capacitance in Direct-Current Circuits		201–218 225–235 253–269 273–275	614–622
8	Alternating-Current Circuits	101–164	283–327	783–793
9	Three-Phase Circuits		599–634	798–801
10	Magnetism	55–72	14–21 167–181 185–196	708–739 743–776 778–780
11	Alternating-Current Machinery	189–196 337–355 370–387	653–672 463–473	798–801

TO STANDARD TEXTBOOKS

See pages xv–xvii for complete titles.

Siskind	Skilling	Slurzberg & Osterheld	Timbie & Pike	Turner	Weber, White, & Manning
3–11 19–22 47–49 55–63 230–232	4–6 20–21	26–30 34–47	1–37 176–180	1–22 32–42 43–46	281–302 316–322
77–85 101 191–195	1–4 367–369	99–115	79–98 197–203	46–49	324–338
51–53	21–25	115–132	111–130	42–43	384–391
85–104			99–106		
18–38			176–197		
63–72		62–84	131–173	22–31 66–72	303–310
201–215 232–242 247–263	37–43 46–52	255–271 291–303 336–339		105–114 160–161	398–400 420–426
271–389	32–37, 43–45 52–69, 82–98 115–184 193–225 235–245	353–394 410–433		91–104 116–123 145–163	431–444
470–510 518–523	686–690 692–701 706–720	233–239		215–224	
115–168	10–15	143–176	38–54	73–86	344–359 372–383
420–435	690–692 701–705	244–249		167–172 182–186 199–211	404–406

1 ELECTRICAL FUNDAMENTALS

1-1. Electrostatics. Matter—whether in the gaseous, liquid, or solid state—is composed of molecules. Molecules are composed of atoms, which, in turn, are composed primarily of electrons surrounding a body called the nucleus.

The nucleus, although it contains many bodies such as electrons, positrons, protons, and neutrons, is the smallest body in the universe. The nucleus is so small that if it were enlarged to the size of a pinhead and the pinhead were enlarged at the same time, the pinhead would, by comparison, be a sphere with a diameter of about 92,000,000 miles, or approximately the mean distance between the sun and the orbit of the earth.

When an electron is removed from an atom, the atom becomes positively charged and is known as a *positive ion*. When an electron is added to an atom, the atom becomes negatively charged and is called a *negative ion*. The process of adding or subtracting electrons is called *ionization*.

An electron which is not a part of the nucleus is about three million times the size of the hydrogen nucleus but is still exceedingly small. In the hydrogen atom, for example, an electron is only about 0.054 of one per cent of the mass of the hydrogen atom. Small as it is, however, the electron is capable of exerting a tremendous force—perhaps the greatest force known to man. It is estimated that if two grams of electrons could be collected into two equal spheres and these spheres were held a distance of one centimeter apart, they would repel each other with a force of 320 million, million, million, million (320,000,000,000,000,000,000,000,000) tons, a force greater than the weight of the water in all the oceans of the world.

The force between two electric charges in a vacuum or in air is given by the equation

$$F = k \frac{Q_1 Q_2}{r^2} \tag{1-1}$$

If mks (meter-kilogram-second) units are used, Q_1 and Q_2 are the charges in coulombs, r is the distance in meters between the two charges, and F is the total force (either attraction or repulsion) in newtons. The proportionality constant k is equal to 9×10^9 newton-meters squared per coulomb squared. This constant k is actually the product of two constants so that

$$k = \frac{1}{2\pi\, \epsilon_0} = 9 \times 10^9 \tag{1-2}$$

where ϵ_0 is equal to 8.85×10^{-12} coulombs squared per newton-meter squared. The newton has the equivalent unit of kilograms times meters per second squared and is equal to 0.22481 pound (about one-fourth pound).

Example 1-1. Two electrons, each with a charge of 1.6×10^{-19} coulomb, are placed 0.5 centimeter apart. Find the force of repulsion between them.

Solution. $0.5 \text{ cm} = 5 \times 10^{-3}$ meters

From equation (1-1),

$$F = k\,\frac{Q_1\,Q_2}{r^2} = \frac{(9 \times 10^9)\,(1.6 \times 10^{-19})^2}{(5 \times 10^{-3})^2}$$

$$= \frac{(9)\,(2.56)\,(10^9)\,(10^6)\,(10^{-38})}{25}$$

$$= 0.92 \times 10^{-20} = 9.2 \times 10^{-21} \text{ newtons}$$

1-2. The Electric Field. Whenever two electrically charged objects exist in space, an electric field is set up between them. These charged objects may be particles, such as electrons, or metallic plates. If these charged bodies are far enough apart, the force exerted by one body on the other may be neglected and one body may be considered to be at an infinite distance from the other.

If the field is generated by a point charge, the field spreads out in all directions like the radii of a sphere, the field intensity decreasing directly as the square of the distance from the point charge. If $\mathcal{E}$ is the electric field intensity, we may write

$$\mathcal{E} = k\,\frac{Q}{r^2} \tag{1-3}$$

The field intensity is in volts per meter. The other quantities have the significance and units previously assigned to them.

If more than one charged particle exists, the total field at a point may be found by determining the net effect of the field resulting from all charges. Equation (1-3) is used for every charge, one at a time, and the results are added by the principle of superposition.

Fig. 1-1 shows three charges, Q_1, Q_2, and Q_3. Let it be required to find the intensity at point a. The distances from point a to Q_1, Q_2, and Q_3 are r_1, r_2, and r_3, respectively. Then,

$$\mathcal{E}_a = k\left(\frac{Q_1}{r_1^2} + \frac{Q_2}{r_2^2} + \frac{Q_3}{r_3^2}\right) \tag{1-4}$$

If additional charges are present, their effect will be added in the same way. Electric fields are not vector quantities and do not involve angular directions. If forces are to be calculated, the resultant force is the vector sum of all the forces present.

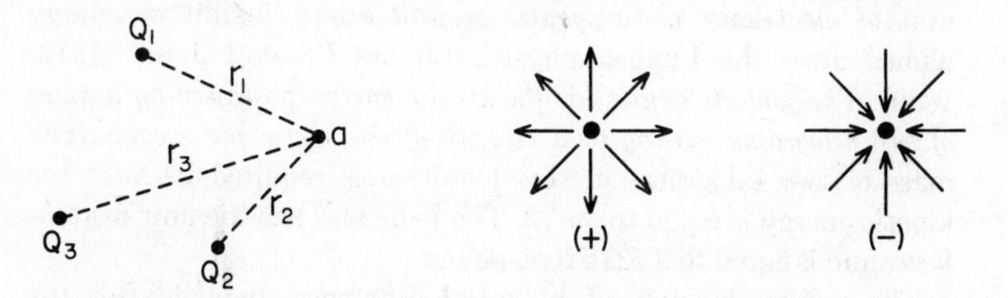

Fig. 1-1. Calculating an electric field.

Fig. 1-2. Direction of a field about an electric charge.

Equation (1-4) assumes that all charges are positive. If any negative charges exist, these charges are given negative signs in the equation. The directional characteristics of electric fields are indicated in Fig. 1-2. The direction of a field is considered to be away from a positive charge and toward a negative charge, as indicated.

From an engineering standpoint, difference in potential between a point charge Q_1 and a point a is important. This difference in potential is measured in volts, as

$$V_{a-1} = k\,\frac{Q}{r} \tag{1-5}$$

where V_{a-1} is the difference in potential in volts between Q_1 and point a. If all three charges in Fig. 1-1 are considered, then

$$V_a = k\left(\frac{Q_1}{r_1} + \frac{Q_2}{r_2} + \frac{Q_3}{r_3}\right) \tag{1-6}$$

where V_a is often considered as being the potential at point a, or the "potential of a." In equation (1-6), negative charges are preceded by a negative sign.

Example 1-2. Three point charges are placed as indicated in Fig. 1-1. $Q_1 = +3$ microcoulombs, $Q_2 = +4$ microcoulombs, and $Q_3 = -5$ microcoulombs. If $r_1 = 3$ cm, $r_2 = 5$ cm, and $r_3 = 8$ cm, find the potential of point a.

Solution. From equation (1-6),

$$V_a = k\left(\frac{Q_1}{r_1} + \frac{Q_2}{r_2} + \frac{Q_3}{r_3}\right) = 9 \times 10^9\left(\frac{3 \times 10^{-6}}{3 \times 10^{-2}} + \frac{4 \times 10^{-6}}{5 \times 10^{-2}} + \frac{5 \times 10^{-6}}{8 \times 10^{-2}}\right)$$

$$= 9 \times 10^9\,(1 \times 10^{-4} + 0.8 \times 10^{-4} - 0.625 \times 10^{-4})$$

$$= 9 \times 10^5\,(1.175) = 10.575 \times 10^5 \text{ or } 10.6 \times 10^5 \text{ volts}$$

1-3. Fundamental Concepts of Electricity. The basic unit of electricity is the *joule,* or *watt-second,* a unit of energy named after the English physicist James Prescott Joule (1818-1889). *The joule is defined as the kinetic energy possessed by a mass of two kilograms moving at a velocity of one meter per second.* The mass of two kilograms in the definition is required because the kinetic energy is equal to $mv^2/2$. The joule also has the unit *newton-meter* and is equal to 0.7376 foot-pound.

The *volt* is the unit of potential difference, named after the Italian physicist Alessandro Volta (1745-1827). *The potential at a point in an electrostatic field is one volt if one joule of work per coulomb is done against electrical forces when a charge is brought from infinity to the point.*

The volt also has the unit *joules per coulomb.* Potential can be referred to alternatively as *electromotive force* (abbreviated emf) and as *voltage.*

The unit of electric current, the *ampere,* is based on the *coulomb,* which contains 6.24×10^{18} electrons or electron charges. Both units were named after French physicists, André Marie Ampère (1775-1836) and Charles de Coulomb (1736-1806).

An ampere is defined as the rate of flow of electricity equal to one coulomb per second. It is analogous in hydraulics to gallons of water per minute. The ampere, therefore, is the rate of flow of a quantity of electricity and is not to be confused with a velocity, such as miles per hour or feet per second. It has been estimated that if we should attempt to count the electrons in a single ampere of current for one second, we would have to count 1000 electrons per second for 190 million years without stopping.

Currents may be classified by their characteristics, in the following manner:

Direct current is an electric current that flows in one direction.

Pulsating current is a direct current that changes in value because of characteristics of the source of the current. A current which changes in value because of changes in load is usually not considered to be a pulsating current.

Alternating current is an electric current that changes in direction at regular intervals of time. A 60-cycle alternating current changes direction 120 times every second, so that it has 60 positive and 60 negative alternations every second.

The unit of resistance is the *volt per ampere*, more commonly referred to as the *ohm. A circuit has a resistance of one ohm if one ampere of direct current flows when a difference of potential of one volt is connected across its terminals.*

The unit of conductance is the *mho* (ohm spelled backward). In a direct-current circuit, conductance is the reciprocal of resistance.

1-4. Ohm's Law. The definition of the ohm is the result of experiments performed in 1826 by George Simon Ohm. These experiments showed that when the voltage was increased, the current increased, and when the resistance was increased the current decreased. Because these changes in current were exactly proportional to the change in either voltage or resistance, we have the statement of Ohm's law, which is one of the most important concepts in electrical engineering:

The current in a direct-current circuit is directly proportional to the voltage and inversely proportional to the resistance.

The Ohm's law relationship is stated mathematically as

$$I = k\left(\frac{E}{R}\right)$$

where I is the symbol for current (from the French word "intensité," meaning current), E is voltage, R is the resistance, and k is the constant of proportionality. When I is in amperes, E is in volts, and R is in ohms, the constant k is unity (equal to 1), so that

$$I = \frac{E}{R} \tag{1-7}$$

The general practice is to use the letter E for the voltage of a source of emf and the letter V for the voltage drop in a circuit or in any part of a circuit, although there are no definite standards for either designation.

Ohm's law for alternating-current circuits requires a slightly different treatment from that indicated by equation (1-7). See Section 8-8.

Example 1-3. Find the current flowing in a circuit of 10 ohms resistance when an emf of 120 volts is impressed across it.

Solution. This problem is solved by direct substitution in equation (1-7). The voltage may be considered as either the potential across the voltage source (E) or the potential across the circuit (V), since these voltages are equal.

$$I = \frac{E}{R} = \frac{V}{R} = \frac{120}{10} = 12 \text{ amps}$$

Example 1-4. The current through a 5-ohm resistor is 3 amperes. Find the voltage across the resistance.

Solution. This problem requires that equation (1-7) be solved for V, the voltage drop across the resistor.

$$V = IR = (3)(5) = 15 \text{ volts}$$

Example 1-5. If the total voltage across the circuit of Example 1-4 is 150 volts, find the total resistance of the circuit.

Solution. $$R = \frac{E}{I} = \frac{150}{3} = 50 \text{ ohms}$$

1-5. Resistance. Since every current-carrying device has resistance, we should be able to determine in advance the resistance of the device. Careful studies have determined the electrical resistance of materials and have related this resistance to a standard conductor. There are three different sets of units of measurement of resistance in common use: the British Engineering System (BES), the centimeter-gram-second (cgs), and the mks, which has already been mentioned (Section 1-1).

The most commonly used system in the United States and Great Britain is the BES, which uses as its standard a conductor of circular cross-section with a diameter of 0.001 inch (called one mil) and a length of one foot. Such a wire is considered to have a cross-sectional area of one *circular mil* (abbreviated CM) and a volume of one *circular mil foot.* The resistance of this standard wire is called the *resistivity* of the material and is represented by the Greek letter ρ (rho). The resistivity of a circular mil foot (commonly called a mil foot) of annealed copper wire—which is the most commonly used conductor material—is 10.4 ohms at 20° Celsius (formerly called Centigrade*) or 68° Fahrenheit.

In the cgs system, the standard conductor is a cube with one centimeter along a side. The resistivity of this cube is called *ohms per cubic centimeter* or, simply, *ohm-centimeters* (abbreviated ohm-cm). This unit is also given in *microhms per cubic centimeter*. The relationship between the ohms per circular mil foot and the ohms per cubic centimeter units is given by the equation

$$\rho = \frac{R}{l}\,(6.02 \times 10^6) \qquad (1\text{-}8)$$

where ρ is the resistivity in ohms per mil foot, R is the resistance of a conductor in the cgs system, and l is the length in centimeters.† Consequently,

$$\frac{R}{l} = \frac{\rho}{6.02 \times 10^6} = \frac{\rho \times 10^{-6}}{6.02} \qquad (1\text{-}9)$$

If the resistivity in microhms per cubic centimeter is desired, equation (1-9) may be written

$$\frac{R}{l} = \frac{\rho}{6.02} \qquad (1\text{-}10)$$

The standard conductor in the mks system is a cube with one meter along a side. By Ohm's law, the increased area of the cube reduces the resistance and the increased length increases the resistance. If R/l is the resistivity of a conductor in the mks system, then

$$\rho = \frac{R}{l}\,(6.02 \times 10^8) \qquad (1\text{-}11)$$

Resistivity in the mks system is called *ohms per cubic meter* or, simply, *ohm-meters*.

---

* In 1948, the International Commission of Weights and Measures (CIPM) decided that the name "Centigrade" should be abandoned and the name "Celsius" be used instead. The United States Bureau of Standards ratified this action in January, 1949. This scale was originally suggested in 1742 by the Swedish astronomer, Anders Celsius (1701-1744).

† See "Converting Resistance Units from the Metric System" by Eugene George Key, *Power Plant Engineering*, Vol. 44 (August, 1940), p. 75.

Table 1-1. Resistivity of Electrical Conductors at 20° C (68° F)

Conductor	Ohms per circular mil foot	Ohms per cubic centimeter	Ohms per cubic meter
Aluminum	16.9	2.63×10^{-6}	2.63×10^{-8}
Brass	36.1 to 42.1	6 to 8×10^{-6}	6 to 8×10^{-8}
Carbon	21,000 to 42,000	3500 to 7000×10^{-6}	3500 to 7000×10^{-8}
Constantan (Cu 60%, Ni 40%)	295	49×10^{-6}	49×10^{-8}
Copper (commercially annealed)	10.4	1.72×10^{-6}	1.72×10^{-8}
Iron	60 to 84	10 to 14 $\times 10^{-6}$	10 to 14 $\times 10^{-8}$
Lead	132	22×10^{-6}	22×10^{-8}
Manganin (Cu 84%, Ni 4%, Mn 12%)	265	44×10^{-6}	44×10^{-8}
Mercury	566	94×10^{-6}	94×10^{-8}
Nichrome	602	100×10^{-6}	100×10^{-8}
Platinum	66.2	11×10^{-6}	11×10^{-8}
Silver	8.85	1.47×10^{-6}	1.47×10^{-8}
Tungsten	33.1	5.5×10^{-6}	5.5×10^{-8}
Zinc	36.7	6.1×10^{-6}	6.1×10^{-8}

Table 1-1 gives the resistivity for several materials in all three systems of units. All of the substances listed are used as conductors, but copper and aluminum are the most common. The information in Table 1-1 is from various sources.

When the resistance of a wire of known materials and dimensions is to be calculated, we use the formula

$$R = \frac{\rho l}{A} \tag{1-12}$$

where R is the resistance in ohms. If ρ is in ohms per circular mil foot, l is in feet and A is in circular mils. If ρ is in ohms per cubic centimeter, l is in centimeters and A is in square centimeters. If ρ

is in ohms per cubic meter, l is in meters and A is in square meters. In this book, the BES unit of measurement is used almost exclusively.

Example 1-6. A copper conductor 2000 feet long is to have less than one ohm resistance. What is the required area?

Solution. Equation (1-12) is solved for A.

$$A = \frac{\rho l}{R} = \frac{(10.4)\,(2000)}{1} = 20{,}800 \text{ CM}$$

The diameter of the wire is

$$d = \sqrt{20{,}800} = 144.3 \text{ mils} = 0.1443 \text{ in.}$$

The size thus calculated is the minimum size required. In actual practice a larger size would be used, since copper wire is not made with an area of 20,800 CM. Choice of actual wire sizes will be discussed in Chapter 5.

1-6. Series Circuits. A series circuit is a circuit in which a given current leaves the voltage source and flows through every part of an electrical device in a single path before it returns to the voltage source. Such a circuit is illustrated in Fig. 1-3 where E represents the voltage of the source—a battery in the diagram—and R_1 through R_6 represent several resistances connected in series as the load.

From the Ohm's law equation, we know that the voltage drop across any resistance, such as R_1, is IR_1, where I is the current in amperes and R_1 designates the resistance in ohms. If a voltmeter (a device for measuring the emf or potential of a circuit) is connected across points A and B, this voltmeter will measure the voltage not only across the voltage source but also across the remainder of the circuit. Therefore, the voltage E of the source is equal to the sum of the voltage drops across all of the resistors. Thus,

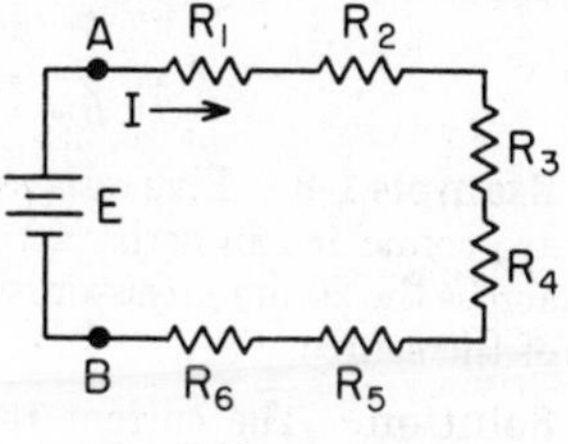

Fig. 1-3. A series circuit.

$$E = V_1 + V_2 + V_3 + V_4 + V_5 + V_6$$

where V_1 through V_6 are the voltage drops across the respective resistors. From Ohm's law,

$$E = IR_1 + IR_2 + IR_3 + IR_4 + IR_5 + IR_6$$

We may now let E equal the product of the current I and the total resistance R_T of the circuit. This gives the expression

$$IR_T = I(R_1 + R_2 + R_3 + R_4 + R_5 + R_6)$$

Dividing by I gives the relationship

$$R_T = R_1 + R_2 + R_3 + R_4 + R_5 + R_6$$

If a similar analysis is made for a series circuit with any number of resistances and the last resistance is designated R_N, we obtain the general equation for the resistance of a series circuit:

$$R_T = R_1 + R_2 + R_3 + \cdots + R_N \qquad (1\text{-}13)$$

In other words, the total resistance of a circuit is equal to the sum of the resistances of all parts of the circuit, including the resistance of the connecting leads. (Usually, in a series circuit, the resistance of these leads is so low that it is ignored. For example, 1000 feet of the wire most often used in wiring lights in homes has a resistance of less than 3 ohms, or about 0.0026 ohm per foot.)

Example 1-7. A series circuit consists of eight resistances of 3, 5, 8, 9, 12, 15, 20, and 25 ohms, respectively. If an emf of 150 volts is connected across this circuit, find the total resistance and the total current.

Solution. Equation (1-13) gives the resistance.

$$R_T = 3 + 5 + 8 + 9 + 12 + 15 + 20 + 25 = 97 \text{ ohms}$$

Equation (1-7) gives the total current.

$$I = \frac{E}{R_T} = \frac{150}{97} = 1.55 \text{ amps} \quad \text{(nearly)}$$

Example 1-8. Five resistances of 5, 10, 15, 20, and 25 ohms, respectively, are connected in series across an unknown source. If the voltage drop across the 20-ohm resistor is 35 volts, find the total current and the voltage of the source.

Solution. The current through the 20-ohm resistor flows through all parts of the series circuit. Equation (1-7) gives this current.

$$I = \frac{V}{R} = \frac{35}{20} = 1.75 \text{ amps}$$

The total resistance of the circuit is found from equation (1-13).

$$R_T = 5 + 10 + 15 + 20 + 25 = 75 \text{ ohms}$$

The total voltage across the circuit equals the voltage of the source. Solving equation (1-7) for the voltage E gives

$$E = IR_T = (1.75)(75) = 131.25 \text{ or } 131 \text{ volts}$$

1-7. Parallel Circuits. A parallel circuit is illustrated in Fig. 1-4. When a current I_T leaves the voltage source E, part of this current will flow through resistor R_1, part will flow through R_2, and the remainder through R_3. Obviously, these branch currents, which are designated in Fig. 1-4 as I_1, I_2, and I_3, may not be equal.

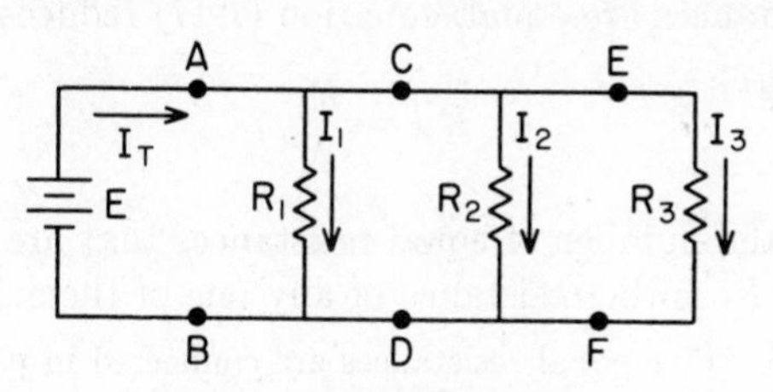

Fig. 1-4. A parallel circuit.

On the other hand, if a voltmeter is connected across points A and B, C and D, and E and F, voltages across these points will be exactly equal if the resistances of the connecting leads are neglected. Therefore,

$$E = V_1 = V_2 = V_3 \tag{A}$$

where V_1, V_2, and V_3 are the voltages across the designated resistors. Since the total current I_T is equal to the sum of all branch currents,

$$I_T = I_1 + I_2 + I_3$$

If there are N parallel circuits, then

$$I_T = I_1 + I_2 + I_3 + \cdots + I_N \tag{1-14}$$

But Ohm's law (equation (1-7)) gives the relationships

$$I_T = \frac{E}{R_T}, \quad I_1 = \frac{V_1}{R_1}, \quad \ldots, \quad I_N = \frac{V_N}{R_N}$$

Since, from equation (A), the voltages across the parallel circuits are equal,

$$I_T = \frac{E}{R_T} \tag{1-15}$$

Equation (1-14) may then be written

$$\frac{E}{R_T} = \frac{E}{R_1} + \frac{E}{R_2} + \frac{E}{R_3} + \cdots + \frac{E}{R_N} \tag{1-16}$$

Dividing by E gives the equation

$$\frac{1}{R_T} = \frac{1}{R_1} + \frac{1}{R_2} + \frac{1}{R_3} + \cdots + \frac{1}{R_N} \tag{1-17}$$

Equation (1-17) should be used in the form given here. Other forms of this equation seem simple when printed in a book but may be extremely difficult to handle mathematically.

If all resistances are equal, equation (1-17) reduces to

$$R_T = \frac{R_1}{N} \tag{1-18}$$

where N is the number of equal resistances that are connected in parallel and R_1 is the resistance of any one of them.

Example 1-9. Five equal resistances are connected in parallel across a 150-volt source. If the resistances are 10 ohms for every path, find the total resistance and the total current.

Solution. From equation (1-18) we find R_T.

$$R_T = \frac{R_1}{N} = \frac{10}{5} = 2 \text{ ohms}$$

The total current is found from equation (1-7).

$$I_T = \frac{E}{R_T} = \frac{150}{2} = 75 \text{ amps}$$

Example 1-10. A circuit consists of the following resistances in parallel: 25, 75, 100, 60, and 50 ohms. Find the total resistance, the total current, and the current in every circuit (or path, as it is sometimes called) if the emf is 120 volts.

Solution. Equation (1-17) will give the total resistance.

$$\frac{1}{R_T} = \frac{1}{25} + \frac{1}{75} + \frac{1}{100} + \frac{1}{60} + \frac{1}{50}$$

$$= 0.0400 + 0.0133 + 0.0100 + 0.0167 + 0.0200$$

$$= 0.1 \text{ mho}$$

$$R_T = \frac{1}{0.1} = 10 \text{ ohms}$$

The total current is found from equation (1-7).

$$I_T = \frac{E}{R_T} = \frac{120}{10} = 12 \text{ amps}$$

The current in every circuit or branch may be found from equation (1-7).

$$I_1 = \frac{V_1}{R_1} = \frac{120}{25} = 4.8 \text{ amps}$$

$$I_2 = \frac{V_1}{R_2} = \frac{120}{75} = 1.6 \text{ amps}$$

$$I_3 = \frac{V_1}{R_3} = \frac{120}{100} = 1.2 \text{ amps}$$

$$I_4 = \frac{V_1}{R_4} = \frac{120}{60} = 2.0 \text{ amps}$$

$$I_5 = \frac{V_1}{R_5} = \frac{120}{50} = 2.4 \text{ amps}$$

As a check, these currents may be added, as indicated by equation (1-14), to equal I_T.

$$I_T = 4.8 + 1.6 + 1.2 + 2.0 + 2.4 = 12 \text{ amps}$$

Example 1-11. The following resistors are connected in parallel: 15, 20, 15, 25, 40, and 15 ohms, respectively. Find the total resistance.

Solution. Since three of these resistances are equal (15 ohms), the equivalent circuit for these resistances may be found and then combined with the unequal circuits. From equation (1-18) we obtain

$$R_X = \frac{15}{3} = 5 \text{ ohms}$$

From equation (1-17) we now obtain

$$\frac{1}{R_T} = \frac{1}{5} + \frac{1}{20} + \frac{1}{25} + \frac{1}{40}$$

$$= 0.200 + 0.050 + 0.040 + 0.025 = 0.315 \text{ mho}$$

$$R_T = \frac{1}{0.315} = 3.17 \text{ ohms}$$

1-8. Series-Parallel Circuits. The most common circuits are a combination of series and parallel circuits. These combination circuits are called series-parallel circuits; a simple example is shown in Fig. 1-5. (The circuits are sometimes mistakenly called "parallel-series"; a parallel-series circuit consists of two or more series circuits connected in parallel, as shown in Fig. 1-6.)

There are no general formulas for the solution of series-parallel circuits, as there are an infinite variety of these circuits. The

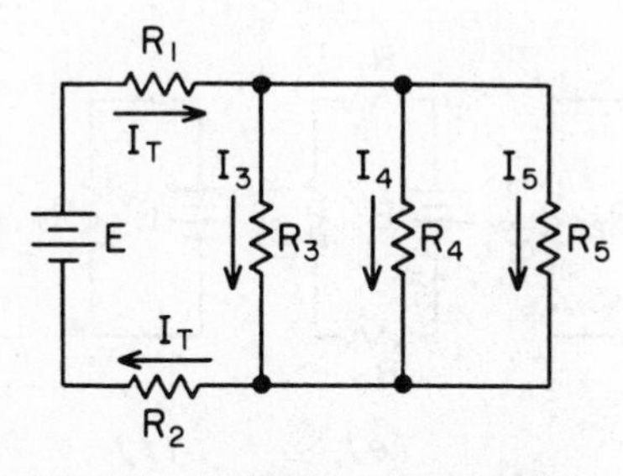

Fig. 1-5. A simple series-parallel circuit.

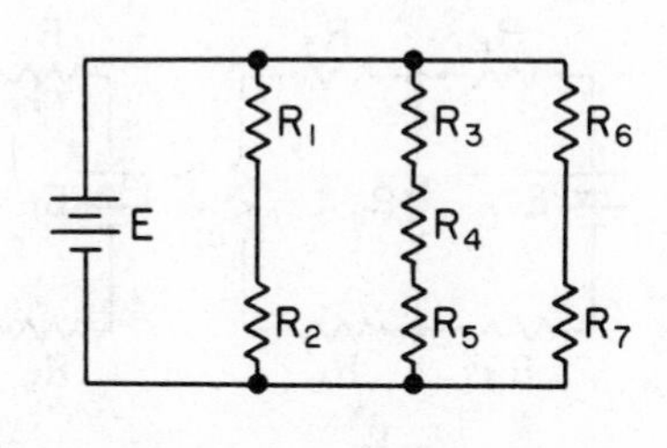

Fig. 1-6. A parallel-series circuit.

circuit shown in Fig. 1-5 can best be solved by considering that R_3, R_4, and R_5 comprise a parallel circuit and that the equivalent circuit is in series with R_1 and R_2.

From equation (1-17) we obtain

$$\frac{1}{R_P} = \frac{1}{R_3} + \frac{1}{R_4} + \frac{1}{R_5} \tag{B}$$

where R_P is the equivalent resistance of the parallel circuit. This equivalent resistance is now inserted in equation (1-13) to give the relationship

$$R_T = R_1 + R_P + R_2 \tag{C}$$

A more common type of series-parallel circuit is shown in Fig. 1-7*a*. This circuit can be solved by successively reducing the actual resistances to equivalent resistances as indicated in Fig. 1-7*b* through *f*. The method is best illustrated by an example. Constant reference must be made to Fig. 1-7*a* through *f* during study of this example.

Example 1-12. Resistances are connected in series-parallel as shown in Fig. 1-7*a*. Let R_1, R_3, R_5, R_7, R_8, and R_9 be line resistances, every one of which has a value of 0.5 ohm. $R_2 = 5$ ohms, $R_4 = 8$ ohms, and $R_6 = 10$ ohms. Find the total resistance of the circuit.

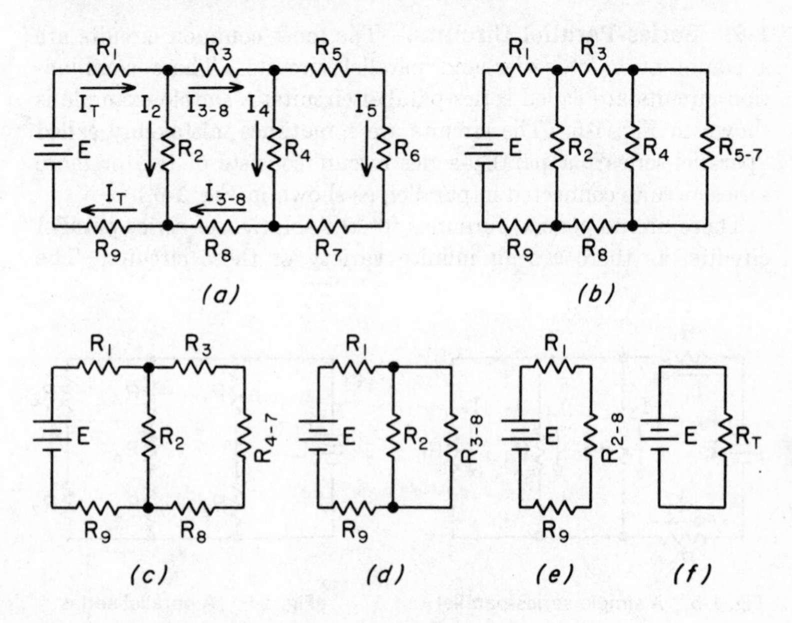

Fig. 1-7. Solution of a series-parallel circuit.

Solution. Let the equivalent resistance of R_5, R_6, and R_7 be designated as R_{5-7}. Then, from equation (1-13),

$$R_{5-7} = R_5 + R_6 + R_7 = 0.5 + 10 + 0.5 = 11 \text{ ohms}$$

R_4 and R_{5-7} form a parallel circuit whose resistance may be designated as R_{4-7}. From equation (1-17) we obtain

$$\frac{1}{R_{4-7}} = \frac{1}{R_4} + \frac{1}{R_{5-7}} = \frac{1}{8} + \frac{1}{11}$$
$$= 0.125 + 0.0909 = 0.2159 \text{ mho}$$
$$R_{4-7} = \frac{1}{0.2159} = 4.63 \text{ ohms}$$

R_{4-7} now forms a series circuit with R_3 and R_8. From equation (1-13) we find

$$R_{3-8} = R_{4-7} + R_3 + R_8 = 4.63 + 0.5 + 0.5 = 5.63 \text{ ohms}$$

R_{3-8} now forms a parallel circuit with R_2. Using equation (1-17), we obtain R_{2-8}.

$$\frac{1}{R_{2-8}} = \frac{1}{R_{3-8}} + \frac{1}{R_2} = \frac{1}{5.63} + \frac{1}{5} = 0.178 + 0.200 = 0.378 \text{ mho}$$
$$R_{2-8} = \frac{1}{0.378} = 2.64 \text{ ohms}$$

R_{2-8} forms a series circuit with R_1 and R_9 as shown in Fig. 1-7*e*. From equation (1-13) we find the equivalent or total resistance R_T, as indicated in Fig. 1-7*f*.

$$R_T = R_1 + R_{2-8} + R_9 = 0.5 + 2.64 + 0.5 = 3.64 \text{ ohms}$$

The fact that the total circuit resistance continues to decrease for every parallel circuit (from 11 to 3.64 ohms in Example 1-12) indicates that the resistance of the connecting leads may be important in a series-parallel circuit. The importance of this resistance will be discussed in Chapter 5 when voltage drops in line wires are determined.

In this example, the current in every resistance may be found by reversing the process of calculation. This is indicated by Example 1-13.

Example 1-13. Find the currents in the resistors of Example 1-12 if 120 volts are impressed on the circuit.

Solution. The total current is found from Ohm's law (equation (1-7)).

$$I_T = \frac{E}{R_T} = \frac{120}{3.64} = 33 \text{ amps}$$

This is the current in R_1 and R_9. The voltage across R_{2-8} is, therefore,

$$V_{2-8} = I_{2-8}\, R_{2-8} = (33)\,(2.64) = 87.1 \text{ volts}$$

This is the voltage across R_2 and R_{3-8}. The current in R_2 is

$$I_2 = \frac{V_2}{R_2} = \frac{87.1}{5} = 17.4 \text{ amps}$$

The current in the equivalent resistance R_{3-8} may be found in either of two ways. (Note that because some answers were "rounded off," the results will not check exactly, although the difference is very small.) One method is to subtract 17.4 from 33 amperes. The other method is to use the voltage drop across R_{3-8} and its equivalent resistance.

Method 1: $I_{3-8} = 33 - 17.4 = 15.6 \text{ amps}$

Method 2: $I_{3-8} = \dfrac{V_{2-8}}{R_{3-8}} = \dfrac{87.1}{5.63} = 15.5 \text{ amps}$

This is the current through R_3 and R_8 and the equivalent resistance R_{4-7}. The voltage across resistance R_4 and the equivalent resistance R_{4-7} is equal to

$$V_{4-7} = I_{3-8}\, R_{4-7} = (15.5)\ (4.63) = 71.8 \text{ volts}$$

The current through R_4 is equal to

$$I_4 = \frac{V_{4-7}}{R_4} = \frac{71.8}{8} = 8.96 \text{ amps}$$

The current through the equivalent resistance R_{5-7} may also be found by two methods (see solution of I_{3-8}).

$$I_{5-7} = 15.5 - 8.96 = 6.54 \text{ amps}$$

or

$$I_{5-7} = \frac{V_{4-7}}{R_{5-7}} = \frac{71.8}{11} = 6.52 \text{ amps}$$

1-9. Electric Energy. The purpose of using electric circuits is to transmit electric energy from a voltage source to a load. The load then converts the energy into power, heat, or light.

By definition, power in a direct-current circuit is found by the formula

$$W = EI \tag{1-19}$$

where W is the energy in watts. If the value of I is substituted from equation (1-7), we obtain the relationship

$$W = \frac{E^2}{R} \tag{1-20}$$

Since, from equation (1-7), $E = IR$, we may also write

$$W = I^2R \tag{1-21}$$

Equation (1-21) is the general power equation which applies to

Table 1-2. Conversion Factors

Multiply	by	to obtain
watts	seconds	joules
horsepower	746	watts
kilowatt-hours	3413	Btu
kilowatt-hours	2.655×10^6	foot-pounds
kilowatt-hours	1.341	horsepower-hours

alternating and direct-current circuits, except those supplying motors.

In a distribution or larger power system, the watt is too small a unit to use. The kilowatt (equal to 1000 watts) is more convenient; the symbol of abbreviation is kw. One thousand watts for one hour is a kilowatt-hour, abbreviated kwh. In even larger systems, the megawatt (MW), equal to one million watts, is the unit used.

The conversion of these electrical units to mechanical equivalents is sometimes necessary. Some of these conversions are given in Table 1-2.

If a motor is connected in the circuit, the power required to run the motor is found by the equation

$$W = \frac{746 \times \text{hp}}{\text{eff}} \tag{1-22}$$

where hp is the horsepower of the motor and eff is the efficiency, expressed as a decimal. In direct current, the current required for a voltage V is

$$I = \frac{746 \times \text{hp}}{V \times \text{eff}} \tag{1-23}$$

Equation (1-23) is obtained by substituting the value for W in equation (1-19) in equation (1-22) and then solving for the current.

Example 1-14. Find the energy dissipated in the entire circuit and in the 15-ohm resistor in Example 1-7.

Solution. In Example 1-7, the resistance is 97 ohms, the voltage is 150 volts, and the current is 1.55 amperes. By use of equation (1-19) we obtain

$$W = EI = (150)\,(1.55) = 232.5 \text{ watts}$$

From equation (1-20) we obtain

$$W = \frac{E^2}{R} = \frac{(150)^2}{97} = 232.8 \text{ watts}$$

Equation (1-21) gives

$$W = I^2R = (1.55)^2\,(97) = 233 \text{ watts}$$

The energy dissipated in the 15-ohm resistor is

$$W = I^2R = (1.55)^2(15) = 36 \text{ watts}$$

Example 1-15. A 5-horsepower motor with an efficiency of 80 per cent drives a mechanical load. Find the power in watts. Find the current when an emf of 240 volts is applied to the motor terminals.

Solution. The wattage is found from equation (1-22).

$$W = \frac{746 \times \text{hp}}{\text{eff}} = \frac{(746)\,(5)}{0.8} = 4660 \text{ watts or } 4.66 \text{ kw}$$

The current is found from either equation (1-19) or equation (1-23). Equations (1-20) and (1-21) cannot be used for motor circuits.

$$I = \frac{W}{E} = \frac{4660}{240} = 19.4 \text{ amps}$$

$$I = \frac{746 \times \text{hp}}{V \times \text{eff}} = \frac{(746)\,(5)}{(240)\,(0.8)} = 19.4 \text{ amps}$$

Problems Based on Chapter 1

P1-1. How many electrons per second will flow through a 100-watt, 120-volt lamp when the voltage at its terminals is 110 volts? (Hint: Find the resistance on the basis of full-rated voltage first.)
Ans. 4.8×10^{18} electrons.

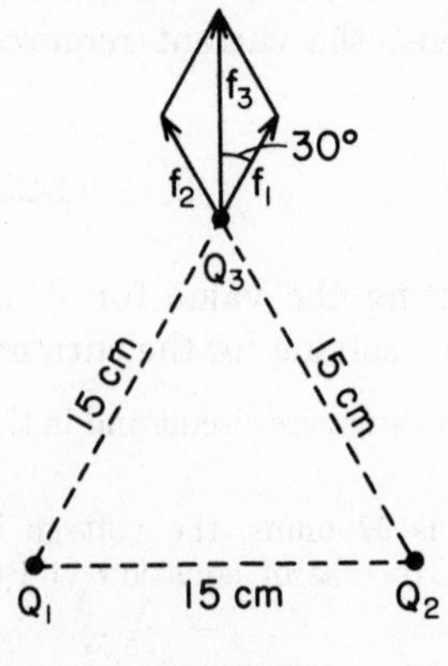

Fig. P1-2.

P1-2. In Fig. P1-2, three charges are placed as shown. $Q_1 = Q_2 = +3 \times 10^{-6}$ coulomb and $Q_3 = +5 \times 10^{-6}$ coulomb. Find the resultant force, f_3, on Q_3 as the result of Q_1 and Q_2. (Note: f_1 and f_2 are forces exerted by Q_1 and Q_2, respectively, on Q_3.)
Ans. 10.4 newtons directed vertically upward.

P1-3. In Fig. P1-2, assume that $Q_3 = 0$. Find the potential at point Q_3 as the result of the presence of charges Q_1 and Q_2.
Ans. $V_3 = 360{,}000$ volts.

P1-4. What is the area in circular mils of a copper wire if the resistance is to be not more than 0.641 ohm in 1000 ft? What is this area in the mks system? (One foot equals 0.3048 meter.)

Ans. 16,200 CM. 0.818×10^{-5} square meters.

P1-5. If the conductor of problem P1-4 were aluminum, what would be its area in CM?

Ans. 26,400 CM.

P1-6. If a conductor were listed with a resistivity of 700 ohms per CM ft, what would be its resistivity in ohms per cubic meter?

Ans. 116.3×10^{-8} ohms per cubic meter.

P1-7. If 240 volts are impressed on a circuit, what value of resistance is required to hold the current at 5 amps?

Ans. 48 ohms.

P1-8. If 10 amps of current flow in a circuit of 52 ohms, what is the voltage?

Ans. 520 volts.

P1-9. Three resistors of 10, 7, and 8 ohms, respectively, are connected in series across a 550-volt source. If the maximum safe voltage across the 8-ohm resistor is 160 volts, what additional resistance is required? What is the total circuit resistance after this resistor is added?

Ans. 2.5 ohms. 27.5 ohms.

P1-10. Five resistors are connected in series across a 120-volt source. If the values of the resistors are 2, 5, 7, 8, and 10 ohms, what is the current?

Ans. 3.75 amps.

P1-11. Three lamps, designed to operate at 120 volts, are rated at 50, 75, and 100 watts, respectively. If they are connected in series across a 360-volt source, what is the actual voltage across each lamp?

Ans. Since $I = 0.58$ amp, $V = 166.5$, 111.0, and 82.5 volts. (The 50-watt lamp would probably explode because of the high voltage across its terminals.)

P1-12. A 20,000-ohm voltmeter and a 30,000-ohm voltmeter are connected in series across a 500-volt line. What will each meter indicate?

Ans. 200 volts and 300 volts, respectively.

P1-13. In Fig. P1-13, $R_1 = 5$ ohms, $R_2 = 15$ ohms, and $R_3 = 20$ ohms. What is the total equivalent resistance?

Ans. 10 ohms.

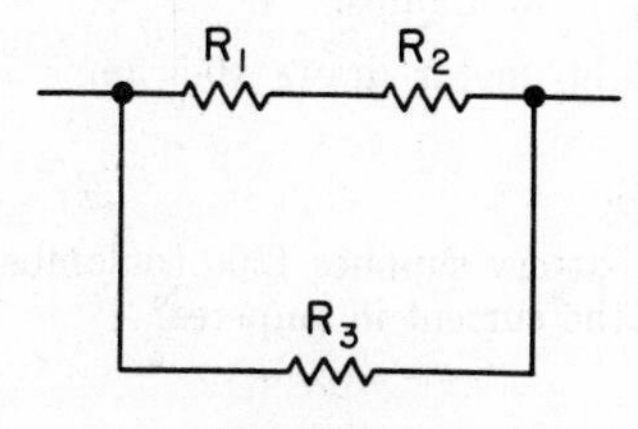

Fig. P1-13.

P1-14. In Fig. P1-14, $R_1 = 6$ ohms, $R_2 = 4$ ohms, $R_3 = 8$ ohms, $R_4 = 10$ ohms. Find the equivalent resistance.

Ans. 2.86 ohms.

P1-15. If a potential of 250 volts is connected across the resistors of problem P1-14, what is the total power dissipated in the circuit? Check this value by adding the power in the three branch circuits.

Ans. 21.9 kw, 10.4 kw, 5.2 kw, 6.25 kw.

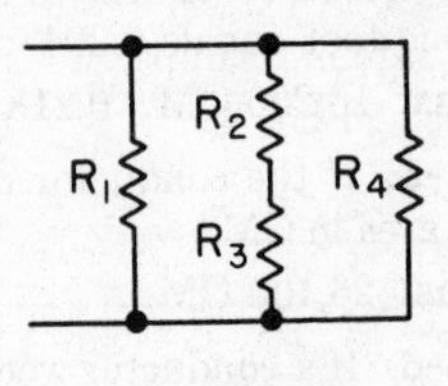

Fig. P1-14.

P1-16. In Fig. P1-16, $R_1 = 8$ ohms, $R_2 = 5$ ohms, $R_3 = 12$ ohms, $R_4 = 20$ ohms, and $R_5 = 15$ ohms. What is the total equivalent resistance of the circuit?

Ans. 10.5 ohms.

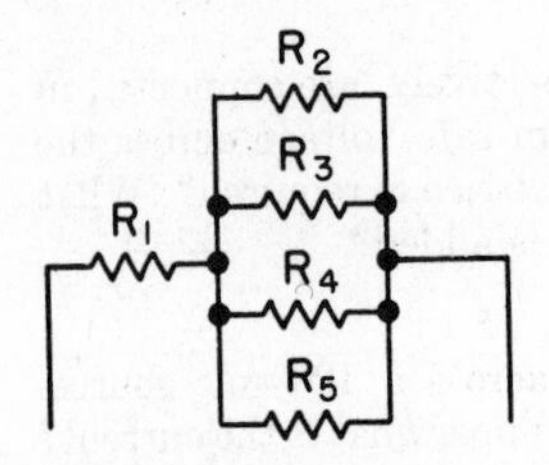

Fig. P1-16.

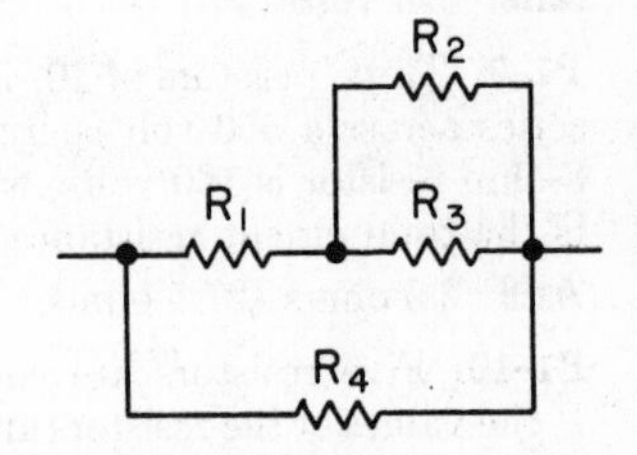

Fig. P1-18.

P1-17. In problem P1-16, what is the current in the five resistors if 120 volts are impressed across the circuit terminals?

Ans. 11.42 amps (total). 5.73, 2.38, 1.44, and 1.9 amps.

P1-18. In Fig. P1-18, $R_1 = 20$ ohms, $R_2 = 15$ ohms, $R_3 = 30$ ohms, and $R_4 = 30$ ohms. Find the total resistance of the circuit. What is the power dissipated in the resistances if an emf of 300 volts is connected across the circuit?

Ans. 15 ohms. 2 kw, 0.67 kw, 0.33 kw, and 3 kw. Total 6 kw.

P1-19. A 10-hp motor draws 9.35 kw from the line. What is its efficiency? At 250 volts, what is the current?

Ans. 0.798 or 79.8%. 37.4 amps.

P1-20. A 500-volt 5-hp motor draws 10.5 amps current. What is its efficiency?

Ans. 0.711 or 71.1%.

P1-21. If a storage battery supplies 1200 coulombs in five minutes to a steady load, what is the current in amperes?

Ans. 4 amps.

P1-22. A battery requires 864,000 coulombs for full charge. If the charging rate is 10 amps, how long is the battery on charge?

Ans. 24 hours.

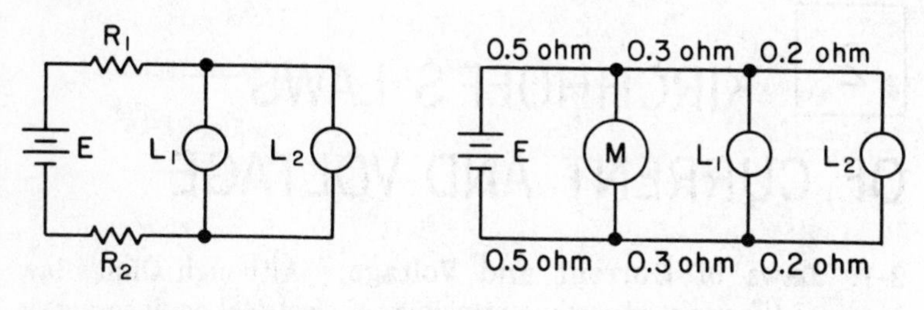

Fig. P1-23. Fig. P1-24.

P1-23. The lamps L_1 and L_2 in Fig. P1-23 take 3 amps each. If the voltage E is 120 volts, find the voltage drop in the line wires and the voltage across the lamps if the line resistances, R_1 and R_2, are 0.6 ohm each.

Ans. 7.2 volts in line. 112.8 volts across lamps.

P1-24. The resistances of the line wires in Fig. P1-24 are shown on the diagram. The motor requires 5 amps at 120 volts. If the resistances of lamps L_1 and L_2 are equal to 300 ohms for each lamp, find the voltage across each lamp and at the battery.

Ans. 125.8 volts at battery (0.399 amp to each lamp). Voltages at lamps are 119.52 and 119.36 volts.

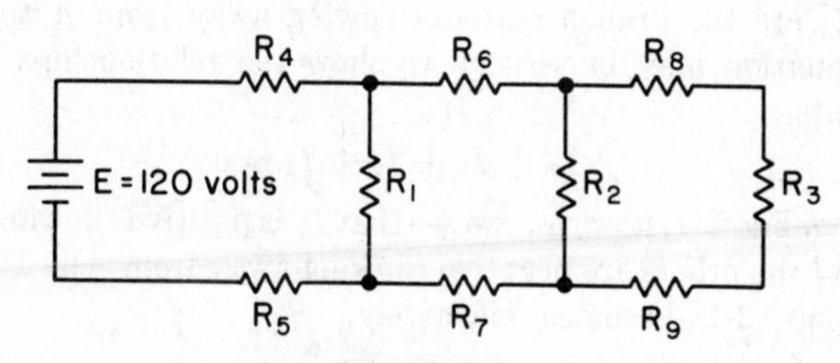

Fig. P1-25.

P1-25. Nine resistances are connected as shown in Fig. P1-25. $R_1 = 10$ ohms, $R_2 = 20$ ohms, $R_3 = 30$ ohms, $R_4 = R_5 = R_6 = R_7 = R_8 = R_9 =$ 1 ohm. Find the total resistance and the current in all resistors if the voltage at the source is 120 volts.

Ans. $R_T = 7.92$ ohms. $I_T = 15.15$ amps in R_4 and R_5. $I_1 = 8.97$ amps in R_1, $I_6 = I_7 = 6.18$ amps, $I_2 = 3.87$ amps, $I_8 = I_3 = I_9 = 2.31$ amps.

2 KIRCHHOFF'S LAWS OF CURRENT AND VOLTAGE

2-1. Laws of Current and Voltage. Although Ohm's law is one of the most important principles of electrical engineering, it cannot be used in its fundamental form to solve complex circuits. Kirchhoff's laws were devised for the purpose of extending the use of Ohm's law to the solution of these complex circuits.

Kirchhoff's laws present nothing new but are essentially restatements of concepts already learned.

First law (current or nodal law): the current flowing toward a junction (or node, as it is also called) in a circuit is equal to zero.

In applying this law, we consider that currents flowing away from a node are negative and currents flowing toward the node are positive. This relationship is shown in Fig. 2-1, where I_T is the current flowing toward junction A and away from B, and I_1, I_2, and I_3 are the branch currents flowing away from A toward B. An equation may be written to show the relationships of these currents.

$$I_T + I_1 + I_2 + I_3 = 0 \qquad (2\text{-}1)$$

From Fig. 2-1, however, we see that I_T is positive (flowing toward A) and the others are negative (flowing away from A). Therefore, equation (2-1) becomes, effectively,

$$I_T - I_1 - I_2 - I_3 = 0$$

for the circuit of Fig. 2-1. The number of independent nodal equations that can be written is equal to half the number of nodes. In Fig. 2-1, A and B are nodes, so that one current equation is possible.

Second law (voltage or loop law): the voltage around any closed path is equal to zero.

In applying this law, we consider that a voltage rise is positive and a voltage drop is negative. Therefore, we may restate the loop law by saying simply that the voltage rises equal the voltage drops.

Fig. 2-2 illustrates the loop or voltage law. The battery terminals are marked plus (+) and minus (−) to indicate the direction of current flow. In other than electronic circuits, the current is always assumed to flow from positive to negative, although the flow of electrons is from negative to positive because electrons are negative. However, about 200 years ago, Benjamin Franklin had to choose a convention for the direction of current flow. He picked the wrong one and, to avoid confusion, we are forced to keep it, since laws for circuits, motors, and generators have all been worked out in terms of Franklin's choice. As a means of getting around the difficulty, we say that electric current flows from positive to negative but electron flow is from negative to positive.

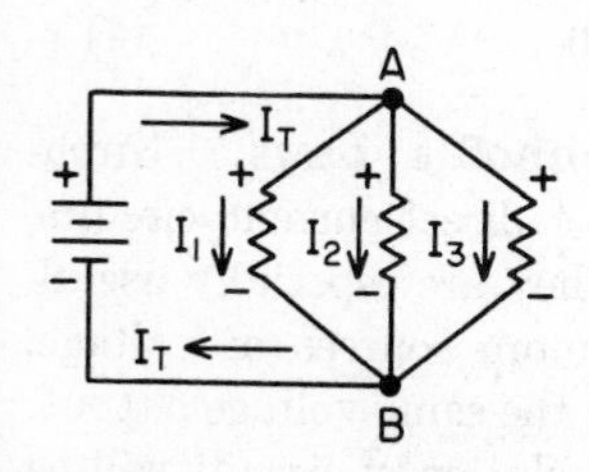

Fig. 2-1. The current law.

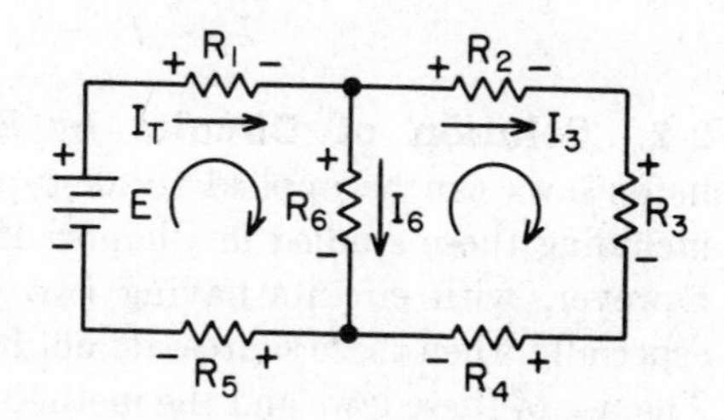

Fig. 2-2. The voltage law.

The positive terminals of all loads are connected to or toward the positive terminal of the voltage source, and these terminals should be marked as indicated in Fig. 2-2. With these terminals marked to indicate the polarity of every load—including the resistances of the line wires—we can adopt a system for writing voltage rises and voltage drops for our loop equations.

1. If we go through a part of the circuit from − to +, we have a voltage rise and the voltage for that part of the circuit is positive in the equation.

2. If we go through a part of the circuit from + to −, we have a voltage drop and the voltage for that part of the circuit is negative in the equation.

In Fig. 2-2, we have three possible loops, two of which are marked with a looped arrow. These three loops are

1. Battery, R_1, R_6, and R_5.
2. R_6, R_2, R_3, and R_4.
3. Battery, R_1, R_2, R_3, R_4, and R_5.

Experience has shown that any two of these loops will produce usable equations, but the third loop is merely the sum of or the difference between the other two and cannot be used. The number of usable voltage or loop equations that can be obtained from any circuit, then, is one less than the number of loops present in the circuit. In Fig. 2-2 the three voltage equations are

$$E - I_T R_1 - I_6 R_6 - I_T R_5 = 0 \qquad (1)$$

$$I_6 R_6 - I_3 R_2 - I_3 R_3 - I_3 R_4 = 0 \qquad (2)$$

$$E - I_T R_1 - I_3 R_2 - I_3 R_3 - I_3 R_4 - I_T R_5 = 0 \qquad (3)$$

Any two of these equations would then be solved simultaneously with the one current equation to determine the currents and voltages in the circuit. The current equation is

$$I_T - I_3 - I_6 = 0 \qquad (4)$$

2-2. Solution of Circuits by Kirchhoff's Laws. Kirchhoff's laws can be applied to all types of direct-current circuits, including those studied in Chapter 1. They are especially useful, however, with circuits having two or more sources of voltage, especially when these sources do not have the same voltage output. The use of these laws and the method of solution of circuits will be explained in the following examples.

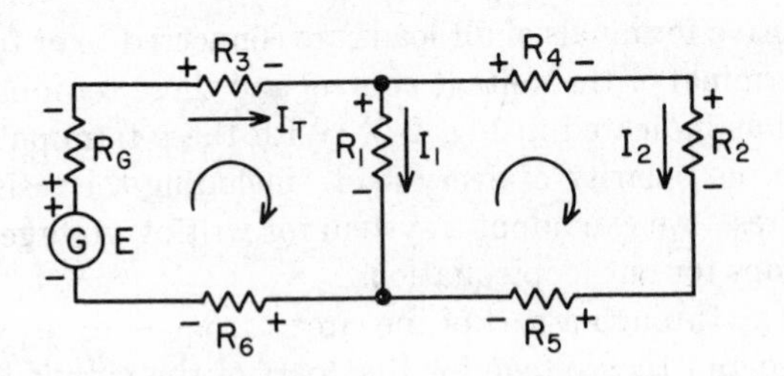

Fig. 2-3. A solution by Kirchhoff's laws.

Example 2-1. In Fig. 2-3, the source voltage E is 170 volts, the internal resistance of the generator R_G is 1 ohm, $R_3 = R_4 = R_5 = R_6 = 0.5$ ohm, $R_1 = 8$ ohms, and $R_2 = 11$ ohms. Find all the currents and the voltage drops in the circuit.

Solution. The first step is to indicate the polarities of the generator and of all resistances, including R_G, the internal resistance of the generator. The internal resistance of the voltage source acts as a load on the voltage source. Consequently, it is shown as a load in Fig. 2-3 and is identified on the drawing.

The one nodal equation, and two of the loop equations, may now be written.

$$I_T - I_1 - I_2 = 0 \quad (1)$$
$$170 - 1I_T - 0.5I_T - 8I_1 - 0.5I_T = 0 \quad (2)$$
$$8I_1 - 0.5I_2 - 11I_2 - 0.5I_2 = 0 \quad (3)$$

By solving equation (1) for I_T, we obtain

$$I_T = I_1 + I_2 \quad (1a)$$

Substituting equation (1a) in equation (2) and collecting terms, we get

$$170 - I_1 - I_2 - 0.5I_1 - 0.5I_2 - 8I_1 - 0.5I_1 - 0.5I_2 = 0$$
$$170 - 10I_1 - 2I_2 = 0 \quad (2a)$$

If we collect terms in equation (3), we get the following equation:

$$8I_1 - 12I_2 = 0 \quad (3a)$$

Equations (2a) and (3a) may be further simplified, since all terms in equation (2a) are divisible by 2 and those in equation (3a) are divisible by 4.

$$85 - 5I_1 - I_2 = 0 \quad (2b)$$
$$2I_1 - 3I_2 = 0 \quad (3b)$$

If we solve these two equations simultaneously, we get the value for I_1:

$$I_1 = 15 \text{ amps}$$

Substituting this value in equation (3b) gives

$$I_2 = 10 \text{ amps}$$

From equation (1a) we may now obtain I_T.

$$I_T = I_1 + I_2 = 15 + 10 = 25 \text{ amps}$$

The voltage drops in all the resistors are

$$I_T R_G = (25)(1) = 25 \text{ volts}$$
$$I_T R_3 = (25)(0.5) = 12.5 \text{ volts}$$
$$I_T R_6 = (25)(0.5) = 12.5 \text{ volts}$$
$$I_1 R_1 = (15)(8) = 120 \text{ volts}$$
$$I_2 R_4 = (10)(0.5) = 5 \text{ volts}$$
$$I_2 R_2 = (10)(11) = 110 \text{ volts}$$
$$I_2 R_5 = (10)(0.5) = 5 \text{ volts}$$

Solutions of circuits by Kirchhoff's laws must always be checked against the original circuit and not against the equations. There are many ways for errors to creep into a calculation of this kind, and these errors can be detected only by comparing the results with the circuit. Checking against the equations would not uncover a possible error in the writing of the equations, but checking against the circuit would.

Check: The first loop consists of $I_T R_G$, $I_T R_3$, $I_1 R_1$, and $I_T R_6$. These drops should equal the voltage source of 170 volts.

$$I_T R_G + I_T R_3 + I_1 R_1 + I_T R_6 = E$$
$$25 + 12.5 + 120 + 12.5 = 170$$

The second loop consists of I_2R_4, I_2R_2 and I_2R_5. These drops should equal I_1R_1, or 120 volts.

$$I_2R_4 + I_2R_2 + I_2R_5 = I_1R_1$$
$$5 + 110 + 5 = 120$$

Example 2-2. In Fig. 2-4, G_A and G_B are generators and R_L is the load resistance. R_A and R_B are the internal resistances of the generators, and R_1 and R_2 are voltage dropping resistors. $E_A = 180$ volts, $E_B = 150$ volts, $R_A = R_B = 0.8$ ohm, $R_1 = R_2 = 1$ ohm, and $R_L = 50$ ohms. Find the currents in the three parts of the circuit.

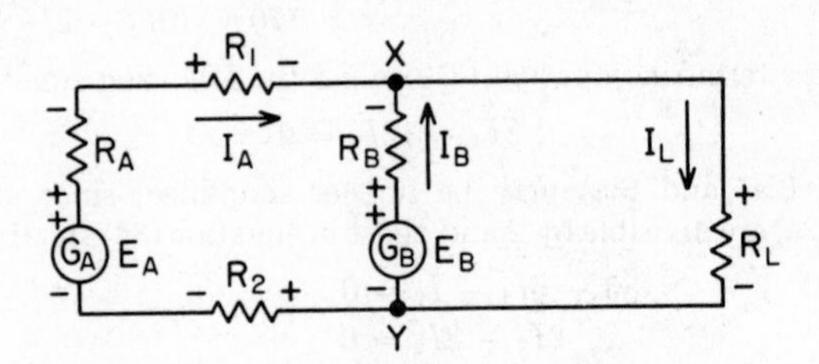

Fig. 2-4. Application of Kirchhoff's laws.

Solution. The polarity (+ and −) signs and the assumed direction of current flow are marked on Fig. 2-4. The current or nodal equation is

$$I_A + I_B - I_L = 0 \tag{1}$$

or

$$I_L = I_A + I_B$$

One of the voltage or loop equations can be around the circuit which contains both generators. In writing this equation, we must remember that a voltage rise is from − to + and a voltage drop is from + to −, even though a generator is involved.

$$180 - 0.8I_A - 1I_A + 0.8I_B - 150 - 1I_A = 0$$

or

$$30 - 2.8I_A + 0.8I_B = 0 \tag{2}$$

The second loop equation can be

$$180 - 0.8I_A - 1I_A - 50I_L - 1I_A = 0$$

or

$$180 - 2.8I_A - 50I_L = 0 \tag{3}$$

When these equations are solved simultaneously according to any of the methods described in books on algebra,* the currents are found to be

$$I_A = 9 \text{ amps}$$
$$I_B = -5.9 \text{ amps}$$
$$I_L = 3.1 \text{ amps}$$

The negative sign for I_B indicates that the current through generator

* See *Algebra* by Gerald E. Moore, in the College Outline Series, published by Barnes & Noble.

G_B is in the reverse direction, and this generator is therefore acting as a load on generator A. Further analysis of the connections shown in Fig. 2-4 would show that if R_L has a very low value of resistance, both generators would supply current to the load. At some intermediate value, generator B would "float" on the line. That is, generator B would neither draw current from the line nor supply current to the load. The value of R_L for this condition would be found by letting R_L be the unknown and $I_B = 0$.

The results obtained for the circuit in this example can be checked by finding the voltage between points X and Y for all three branches.

Generator A branch: $-(9)(1) + 180 - (9)(0.8) - (9)(1) = 154.8$ volts
Generator B branch: $150 + (5.9)(0.8) = 154.7$ volts
Load branch: $(3.1)(50) = 155$ volts

2-3. The Three-Wire System. An economical circuit often used with either direct current or single-phase alternating current is the *three-wire system*, sometimes known as the *Edison three-wire system.*†

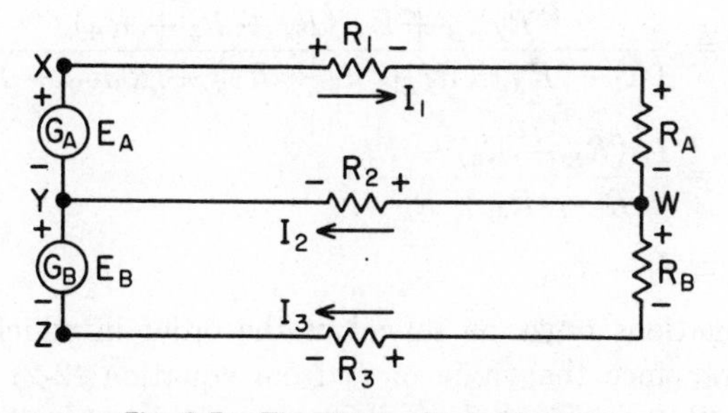

Fig. 2-5. The three-wire system.

A three-wire system is illustrated in Fig. 2-5. G_A and G_B are direct-current generators whose output voltages are E_A and E_B as shown. (In alternating current, G_A and G_B would be the secondary winding of a transformer with a center tap at Y.) R_1, R_2, and R_3 are the resistances of the line wires between the generators and the load, and R_A and R_B are the load resistances. I_1, I_2, and I_3 are the currents in the line wires.

† The three-wire system sometimes causes confusion to uninformed personnel who think that three wires always mean three phase. The information in this section is based on the article "Calculations on the Three-Wire System" by Eugene George Key, in *Power Plant Engineering*, Vol. 44 (June, 1940), pp. 63-65.

I_1 and I_3, if they exist, will always flow in the direction indicated by the arrows. I_2, on the other hand, may flow in the direction from W to Y as indicated, or from Y to W, or may not exist at all (may equal zero). As a general rule, I_2 should always be assumed to flow as indicated in Fig. 2-5. The actual direction of flow will be determined by the sign of I_2 in the solution. A plus sign for I_2 in the answer means that the current actually flows in the direction shown in the figure. A minus sign means that the current flow is in the reverse direction.

The Kirchhoff's law equations for the circuit in Fig. 2-5 are:

$$I_1 - I_2 - I_3 = 0 \qquad (1)$$

$$I_3 = I_1 - I_2 \qquad (1a)$$

$$E_A - I_1R_1 - I_1R_A - I_2R_2 = 0 \qquad (2)$$

$$E_B + I_2R_2 - I_3R_B - I_3R_3 = 0 \qquad (3)$$

If we solve equations (1a), (2), and (3) simultaneously, we obtain the general solution of the three-wire system.

$$I_1 = \frac{R_2E_B + E_A\,(R_2 + R_3 + R_B)}{(R_1 + R_A)\,(R_2 + R_3 + R_B) + R_2R_B + R_2R_3} \qquad (2\text{-}2)$$

$$I_2 = \frac{I_1\,(R_B + R_3) - E_B}{R_2 + R_3 + R_B} \qquad (2\text{-}3)$$

$$I_3 = I_1 - I_2 \qquad (2\text{-}4)$$

These equations must be solved in the order in which they are listed here, since the value of I_1 from equation (2-2) is used in equation (2-3) and both I_1 and I_2 appear in equation (2-4).

If the three wires are equal in size—as they usually are—their resistances are equal. The three-wire equations may be simplified by letting $R = R_1 = R_2 = R_3$.

$$I_1 = \frac{RE_B + E_A\,(2R + R_B)}{(R + R_A)\,(2R + R_B) + R(R_B + R)} \qquad (2\text{-}5)$$

$$I_2 = \frac{I_1\,(R_B + R) - E_B}{2R + R_B} \qquad (2\text{-}6)$$

Equation (2-4) remains the same.

If V_A and V_B are the voltages across loads R_A and R_B, respectively, then, by Kirchhoff's voltage law,

$$V_A + V_B = E_A + E_B - I_1R_1 - I_3R_3 \qquad (2\text{-}7)$$

Equation (2-7) shows that the total voltage across the two loads combined is independent of whatever conditions exist in the central (or neutral) wire. However, the values of V_A and V_B, taken separately, depend very much on the conditions in the neutral wire. If the current flows as indicated in Fig. 2-5,

$$V_A = E_A - I_1R_1 - I_2R_2 = E_A - (I_1R_1 + I_2R_2) \quad \text{(A)}$$

$$V_B = E_B + I_2R_2 - I_3R_3 = E_B - (I_3R_3 - I_2R_2) \quad \text{(B)}$$

If the current flows from Y to W in the neutral wire in Fig. 2-5, however,

$$V_A = E_A - I_1R_1 + I_2R_2 = E_A - (I_1R_1 - I_2R_2) \quad \text{(C)}$$

$$V_B = E_B - I_2R_2 - I_3R_3 = E_B - (I_3R_3 + I_2R_2) \quad \text{(D)}$$

If we compare equation (A) with equation (C) and equation (B) with equation (D), we find that the voltages have the following relationships:

$$V_A = E_A - (I_1R_1 \pm I_2R_2) \qquad \text{(2-8)}$$

$$V_B = E_B - (I_3R_3 \mp I_2R_2) \qquad \text{(2-9)}$$

In the brackets in these equations, when I_2R_2 is positive in equation (2-8), it is negative in equation (2-9), and vice versa.

Line voltage drops are much lower in the three-wire system than in the two-wire system, so that the voltage across the load is higher. However, one precaution must always be followed in using the three-wire system: the neutral wire must never contain a fuse for protection of the circuit. The reason for this warning will be evident from Example 2-4.

Example 2-3. A three-wire circuit has line resistances of 0.5 ohm per line, and load resistors R_A = 10 ohms and R_B = 5 ohms. If E_A and E_B are 136 volts each, find the currents and voltages at the loads.

Solution. Substitution in equations (2-5), (2-6), and (2-4) will give the required currents.

$$I_1 = \frac{(0.5)\,(136) + 136(1 + 5)}{(0.5 + 10)\,(1 + 5) + 0.5(5 + 0.5)} = 13.5 \text{ amps}$$

$$I_2 = \frac{13.5(5 + 0.5) - 136}{1 + 5} = -10.3 \text{ amps}$$

$$I_3 = 13.5 + 10.3 = 23.8 \text{ amps}$$

The voltages across the loads may be obtained from either Ohm's law or equations (2-8) and (2-9). The better practice is to use both, thereby obtaining a check on the accuracy of the currents.

$$V_A = I_1R_A = (13.5)(10) = 135 \text{ volts}$$
$$V_A = E_A - (I_1R_1 - I_2R_2) = 136 - 6.2 + 5.2 = 135 \text{ volts}$$
$$V_B = I_3R_B = (23.8)(5) = 119 \text{ volts}$$
$$V_B = E_B - (I_3R_3 + I_2R_2) = 136 - 11.9 - 5.2 = 119 \text{ volts}$$

If the two loads were connected across a two-wire system such as those previously studied, the voltage across the load would be only 104 volts.

Example 2-4. Assume that the three lines in Example 2-3 are all fused and that the fuse in the neutral line is blown, opening the neutral line (or "leg" as it is often called). What are the voltages across the two loads?

Solution. The connection is now reduced to a two-wire circuit. Only one equation is now needed as there is only one current. By use of Kirchhoff's laws, we obtain

$$136 + 136 - 0.5I - 10I - 5I - 0.5I = 0$$
$$I = 17 \text{ amps}$$
$$V_A = (17)(10) = 170 \text{ volts}$$
$$V_B = (17)(5) = 85 \text{ volts}$$

The high voltage across R_A could destroy the equipment connected at that point in the circuit. If the loads were lights, the light bulbs on this section of the circuit would probably explode. For this reason, the three-wire system is always used with a "solid" or unfused neutral.

2-4. Loop Currents. A modification and simplification of Kirchhoff's laws is a method that makes use of *loop currents* or *mesh currents*. This method eliminates most of the current equations.

A loop current is assumed to flow clockwise around a single loop in a circuit, as shown in Fig. 2-6. A current I_1 is assumed to flow through generator G_A and its internal resistance R_A, then through R_B (the internal resistance of G_B) and generator G_B. Another current I_2 is assumed to flow clockwise through G_B, R_B, R_2, and R_L.

In any circuit with three or more branches, there will be at least one branch through which two different loop currents are assumed to flow. In Fig. 2-6, the branch that contains generator G_B is the one that contains the two loop currents.

The method of marking polarities on resistances is somewhat different from the one used for Kirchhoff's laws. Since all currents are assumed to flow clockwise, *the polarities of the resistances are marked so that the current from the left enters the positive terminals of the resistances*. Even R_B, the internal resistance of generator G_B, has its positive terminal located on the side toward G_A rather than toward G_B, as far as the current I is concerned. The current $I_1 - I_2$ in this branch is therefore assumed to flow downward in its branch, and R_B is a voltage drop for this current when the

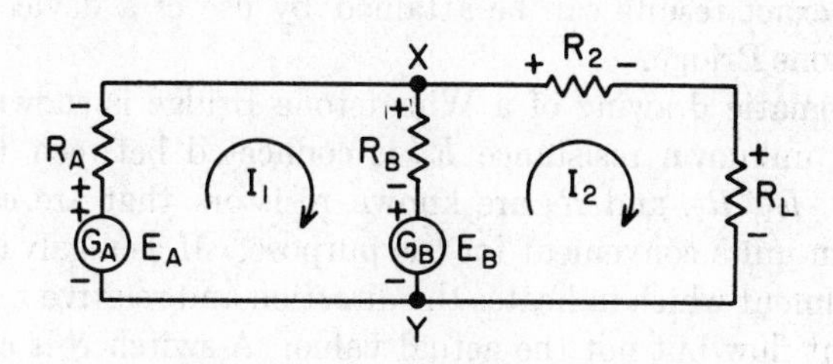

Fig. 2-6. Solution by loop currents.

loop to the left of G_B is concerned. In tracing the circuit containing I_2, we trace it in a direction opposite to $I_1 - I_2$, and $R_B\ (I_1 - I_2)$ is a voltage rise. The two equations that are written for the circuit in Fig. 2-6 are, therefore,

$$E_A - I_1R_A - (I_1 - I_2)\ R_B - E_B = 0$$
$$E_B + (I_1 - I_2)\ R_B - I_2R_2 - I_2R_L = 0$$

In collecting the final results, I_1 is the actual current from terminal Y to terminal X through G_A, I_2 is the actual current from X to Y through R_L, and $I_1 - I_2$ is the actual current from Y to X through G_B.

Example 2-5. In Fig. 2-6, $E_A = 100$ volts, $R_A = R_B = 1$ ohm, $E_B = 115$ volts, $R_2 = 1$ ohm, and $R_L = 60$ ohms. The loop equations are

$$100 - 1I_1 - 1\ (I_1 - I_2) - 115 = 0$$
$$115 + 1\ (I_1 - I_2) - 1I_2 - 60I_2 = 0$$

When we collect terms, these equations become

$$-15 - 2I_1 + I_2 = 0$$
$$115 + I_1 - 62I_2 = 0$$

When these two equations are solved simultaneously, we find the currents.

$$I_2 = 1.75 \text{ amps}$$
$$I_1 = -\ 6.63 \text{ amps}$$
$$I_2 - I_1 = 1.75 + 6.63 = 8.38 \text{ amps}$$

The voltage drops check with the current values obtained.

G_A branch:	$100 + 6.63 = 106.63$ volts
G_B branch:	$115 - 8.38 = 106.62$ volts
Load branch:	$1.75 + 105 = 106.75$ volts

2-5. The Wheatstone Bridge. The values of unknown resistances can be approximated by using a voltmeter and an ammeter and applying Ohm's law. Even the best meters, however, may not be accurate enough to give precise results.

More exact results can be attained by use of a device called a Wheatstone Bridge.

A schematic drawing of a Wheatstone Bridge is shown in Fig. 2-7. An unknown resistance R_x is connected between terminals *a* and *b*. R_1, R_2, and R_3 are known resistors that are calibrated to read in units convenient for the purpose. *M* is a galvanometer, an instrument which indicates the direction and relative magnitude of current flow but not the actual value. A switch *S* is connected as shown so that the galvanometer reading can be obtained when desired. A battery is used to supply voltage to the circuit.

The value of R_x is determined when no current flows through the meter when the switch is closed. The bridge is then said to be "balanced." R_1 and R_3 will then have a current I_1, and R_x and R_2 will have a current I_x. With no current through the galvanometer, there is no difference in potential between points *c* and *d*. The voltage drop across R_1 is then equal to the voltage drop across R_x. Similarly, the drop across R_3 equals the drop across R_2. In equation form, therefore,

$$I_1R_1 = I_xR_x \tag{A}$$

$$I_1R_3 = I_xR_2 \tag{B}$$

Dividing equation (A) by equation (B) gives the relationship

$$\frac{I_1R_1}{I_1R_3} = \frac{I_xR_x}{I_xR_2}$$

or

$$\frac{R_1}{R_3} = \frac{R_x}{R_2} \tag{C}$$

Solving equation (C) for R_x gives the equation

$$R_x = R_1 \frac{R_2}{R_3} \tag{2-10}$$

In the commercial Wheatstone Bridge, all parts of the circuit except the unknown resistance are placed in a single box. R_1 is adjusted by a series of knobs which indicate the value of this resistance for every adjustment. The values of R_2 and R_3 are not given directly, but are calibrated to read as a ratio, such as 1 to 1,

1 to 10, 1 to 100, etc., or 10 to 1, 100 to 1, etc. The battery voltage is not known, as its value is not needed in the calculations. The only requirement of the battery voltage is that it be steady (not pulsating).

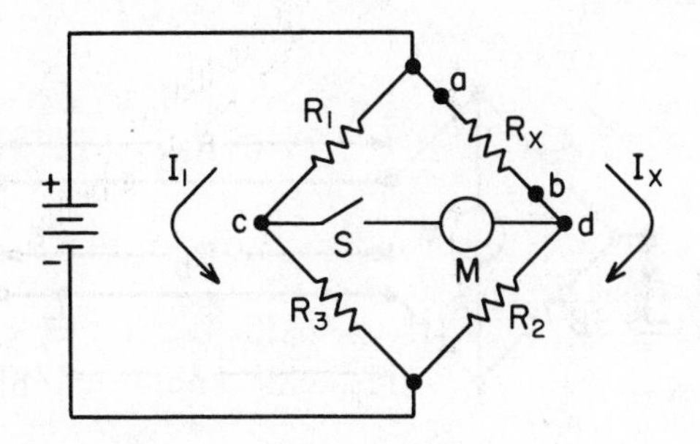

Fig. 2-7. The Wheatstone Bridge.

Wheatstone Bridges can be made up by use of slide wires, resistance boxes, and the like. Reasonable accuracy can be obtained by their use. The computation for the unknown resistance is the same as given above.

Example 2-6. An unknown resistance is to be checked. The Wheatstone Bridge shows R_1 to be equal to 1352 and the ratio R_2/R_3 to be equal to 10. What is the value of the unknown resistance?

Solution. The result is obtained by direct substitution in equation (2-10).

$$R_x = (1352)\,(10) = 13{,}520 \text{ ohms}$$

In using a Wheatstone Bridge, the student should realize that the most accurate results are obtained when the ratio is 1 to 1, as the value of R_1 is then exactly equal to R_x. When the bridge can be balanced with more than one value of the ratio, use the value nearest to 1 to 1. A reading taken with a ratio of 1,000,000 to 1, or 1 to 1,000,000, may be necessary, but the actual value of such a resistance may be considerably different from the value obtained by the bridge.

2-6. The Varley Loop. When underground power lines become short-circuited or grounded, the location of the "fault" is determined by use of one of several adaptations or variations of the Wheatstone Bridge connection. One of these, called the Varley Loop, is shown in Fig. 2-8.

The battery is connected in the ground lead. The underground line is indicated as R_b and R_g in the figure and the fault is the distance X_a from the Varley Loop connection. X_b is the distance from the fault to the end of the line which is being checked. M is a galvanometer.

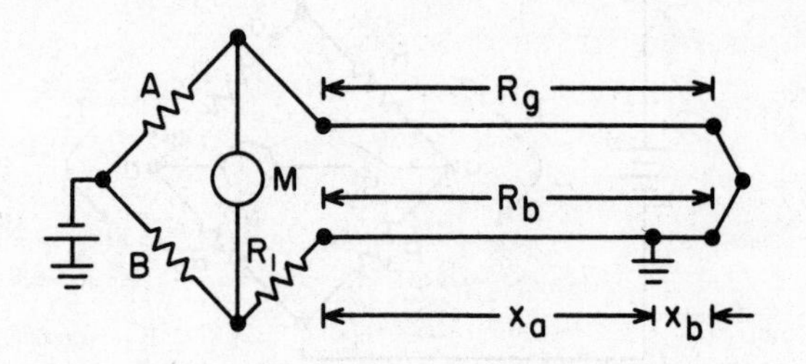

Fig. 2-8. The Varley Loop.

Since the potential difference across the galvanometer is zero, the voltage across A equals the voltage across B. If I_A is the current in A and I_B is the current in B,

$$I_A A = I_B B \tag{1}$$

$$I_A (R_g + X_b) = I_B (R_1 + X_a) \tag{2}$$

Dividing equation (1) by equation (2), we obtain

$$\frac{A}{R_g + X_b} = \frac{B}{R_1 + X_a} \tag{3}$$

Dividing both sides of this equation by B and multiplying both sides by $(R_g + X_b)$, we have

$$\frac{A}{B} = \frac{R_g + X_b}{R_1 + X_a} \tag{4}$$

Equation (4) has two unknowns, X_b and X_a, but $X_b = R_b - X_a$. Therefore,

$$\frac{A}{B} = \frac{R_g + R_b - X_a}{R_1 + X_a} \tag{2-11}$$

The ratio A/B should be as low as possible for accurate determinations of X_a. Solving equation (2-11) for X_a, we find

$$X_a = \frac{B(R_g + R_b) - AR_1}{A + B} \tag{2-12}$$

In an actual line, R_g will usually—though not always—equal R_b.

When it does, equation (2-12) reduces to

$$X_a = \frac{2R_gB - AR_1}{A + B} \tag{2-13}$$

Equation (2-12) or (2-13) will yield results sufficiently accurate to locate a fault as being between two manholes. A more accurate determination would be needless, since the faulted section would have to be removed and replaced. It cannot be repaired.

Example 2-7. A line 20 miles long has a resistance of 0.102 ohm per 1000 feet. When the line becomes grounded, a test is made with a Varley Loop. The test line R_g has a resistance of 0.410 ohm per 1000 feet, $A = B = 1000$, and $R_1 = 50.2$ ohms. How far is the fault from the point where the Varley Loop test is made?

Solution. The line has a total resistance in one leg of

$$R_b = (5.28)\,(0.102)\,(20) = 10.7712 \text{ ohms}$$

The test line R_g has a total resistance of

$$R_g = (5.28)\,(0.410)\,(20) = 43.296 \text{ ohms}$$

The problem can now be solved by use of equation (2-12).

$$X_a = \frac{1000(43.296 + 10.7712) - (1000)\,(50.2)}{1000 + 1000} = 1.9335$$

The required distance is

$$\text{distance} = \frac{1.9335(20)}{10.7712} = 3.59 \text{ miles} = 18{,}950 \text{ ft}$$

or

$$d = \frac{1.9335 \text{ ohms}}{0.102 \text{ ohms}/1000 \text{ ft}} = 18{,}950 \text{ ft}$$

Ordinarily, slide rule calculations are not sufficiently accurate for Varley Loop calculations. Assume that manholes are 200 feet apart in the approximate location of the fault. An error of only 0.02 ohm in this problem would mean a difference of 200 feet in the apparent location of the fault, since the cable has a resistance of 0.02 ohm in 200 feet. This distance might result in considerable delay in finding the actual faulted section. In actual practice, power companies have charts showing cable resistances between manholes, so that the actual distance can be found without any calculation after X_a is determined.

2-7. The Murray Loop. Another method for locating faults is the use of the Murray Loop, shown in Fig. 2-9. The return leg of the loop—including $r - x_a$ in the diagram—is an unfaulted conductor of the line. The resistance of one leg of the line (one conductor) is $r/2$ so that r is the resistance of two conductors. A and R are resistances in the Wheatstone Bridge used for test.

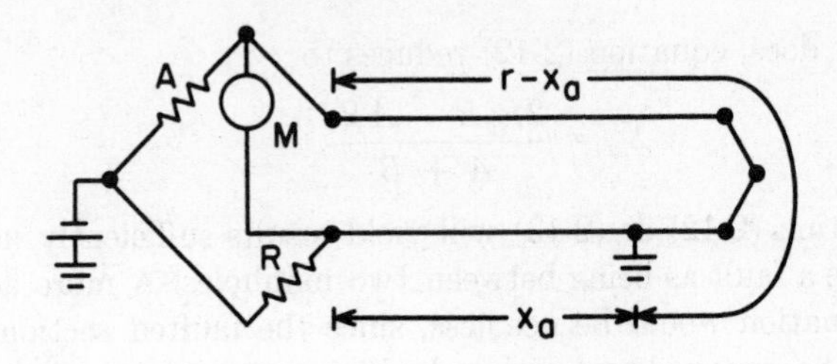

Fig. 2-9. The Murray Loop.

Since the potential difference across the meter is zero when the bridge is balanced,

$$AI_A = RI_R \quad (1)$$

$$I_A(r - x_a) = I_R x_a \quad (2)$$

Dividing equation (2) by equation (1) gives the relationship

$$\frac{A}{r - x_a} = \frac{R}{x_a} \quad (3)$$

Equation (3) is now solved for x_a.

$$x_a A = Rr - Rx_a$$

$$x_a(A + R) = Rr$$

$$x_a = \frac{Rr}{A + R} \quad (2\text{-}14)$$

The Murray Loop is particularly useful in locating faults in relatively low resistance loops.

Example 2-8. A faulted cable has a resistance of 0.26875 ohm per mile and the normal one-way length of the line is 11 miles. When a Murray Loop test is balanced, R = 500 ohms and A = 1500 ohms. Find the distance to the fault.

Solution. From equation (2-14) we obtain x_a.

$$x_a = \frac{(500)(0.26875)(22)}{1500 + 500} = \frac{2956.25}{2000} = 1.4781 \text{ ohms}$$

$$d = \frac{1.4781 \text{ ohms}}{0.26875 \text{ ohms/mile}} = 5.4999 \text{ miles}$$

$$d = (5.4999)(5{,}280) = 29{,}038 \text{ ft}$$

Problems Based on Chapter 2

P2-1. Find the voltage E in the circuit of Fig. P2-1. What is the value of R_2 and of the current I?

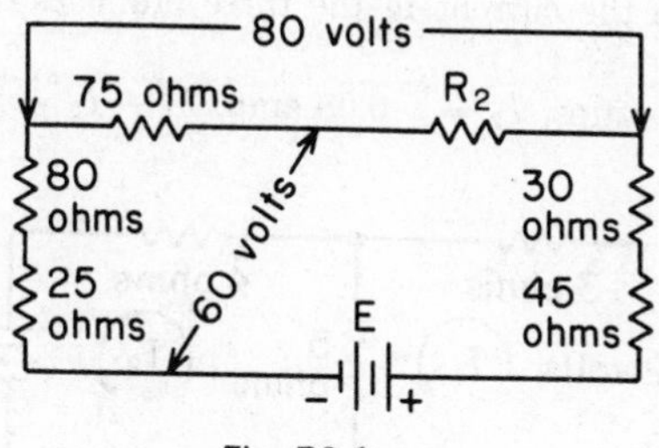

Fig. P2-1.

Ans. E = 140 volts. R_2 = 165 ohms. I = 1/3 amp.

P2-2. In Fig. 2-4 (p. 26), E_A = 180 volts, E_B = 150 volts, $R_A = R_B$ = 0.8 ohm, $R_1 = R_2$ = 1 ohm. What is the value of R_L if the current through generator G_B is to be zero?

Ans. 14 ohms.

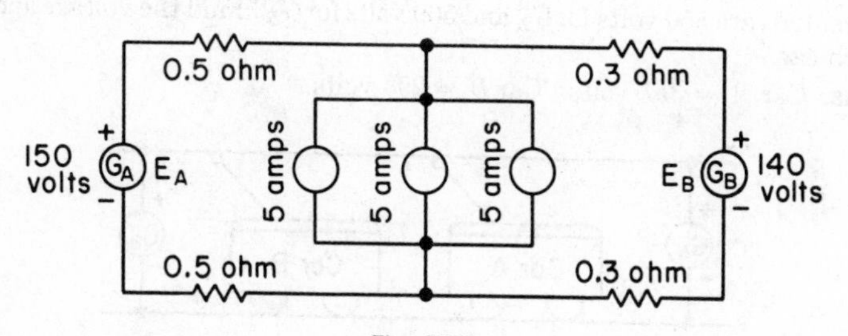

Fig. P2-3.

P2-3. In Fig. P2-3, find I_A and I_B and their direction of flow.

Ans. I_B = 3.12 amps, I_A = 11.88 amps, both feeding the load.

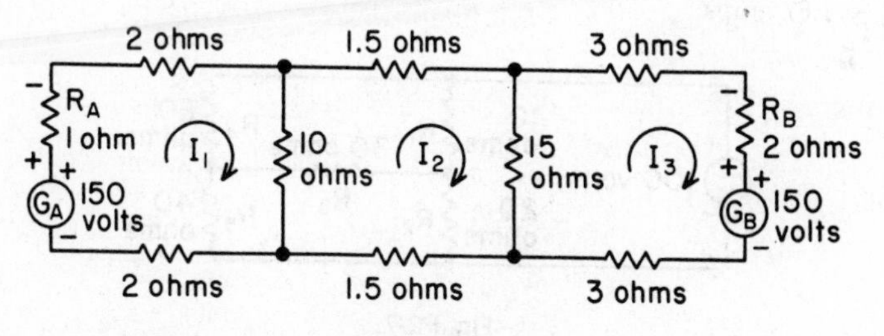

Fig. P2-4.

P2-4. Find the currents in the circuit in Fig. P2-4.

Ans. I_1 = 10.16 amps, I_2 = 0.24 amp, I_3 = − 6.3 amps, $I_1 - I_2$ = 9.92 amps, $I_2 - I_3$ = − 6.1 amps.

P2-5. Calculate the current in the three branches of the circuit shown in Fig. P2-5.

Ans. $I_1 = 1.45$ amps, $I_2 = -0.08$ amp, $I_1 - I_2 = 1.53$ amps.

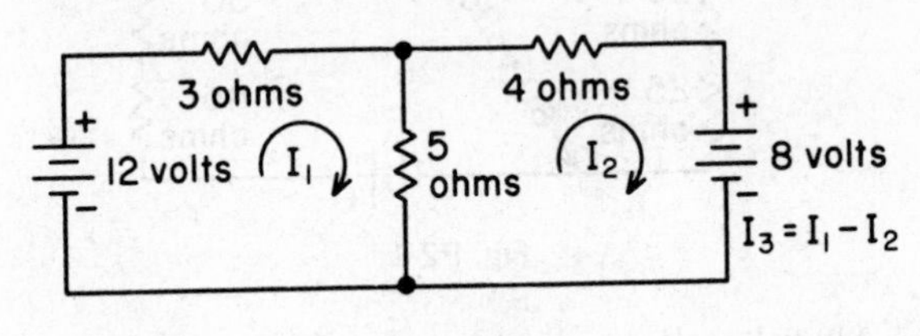

Fig. P2-5.

P2-6. In Fig. P2-6, car A draws 200 amps and car B draws 100 amps. Car A is 2 miles from generator G_A and 10 miles from car B. Car B is 4 miles from generator G_B. The resistance of the trolley wire is 0.265 ohm per mile and resistance of the track is 0.187 ohm per mile. The generator potentials are 550 volts for G_A and 500 volts for G_B. Find the voltage across each car.

Ans. Car A = 357 volts. Car B = 293 volts.

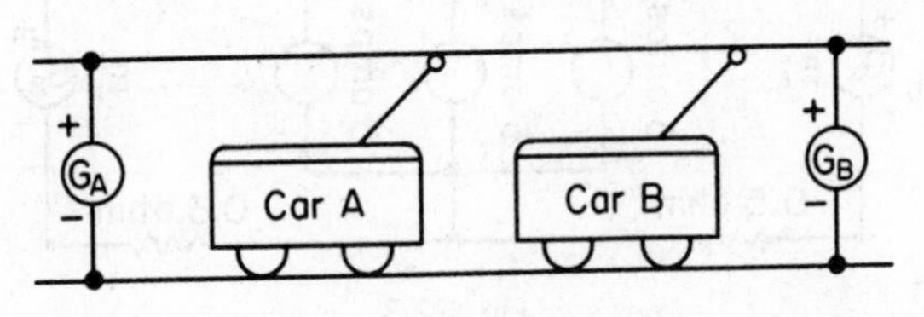

Fig. P2-6.

P2-7. In Fig. P2-7, find the current in the five resistors.

Ans. $I_1 = 3.33$ amps, $I_2 = 3.33$ amps, $I_3 = 0$ amp, $I_4 = 1.67$ amps, $I_5 = 1.67$ amps.

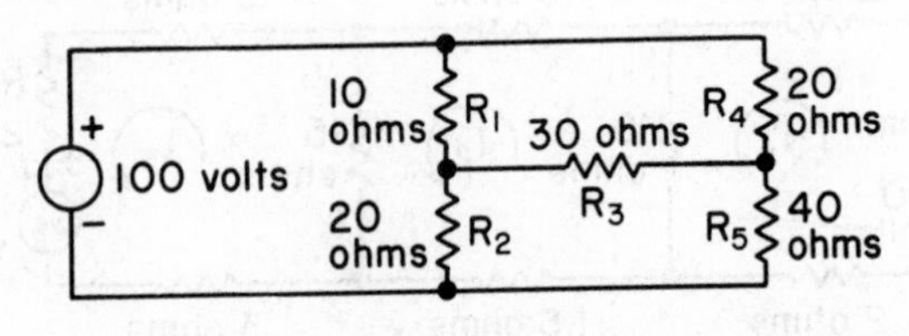

Fig. P2-7.

P2-8. In Fig. P2-8, $R_1 = 1$ ohm, $R_2 = 2$ ohms, $R_3 = 3$ ohms, $R_4 = 4$ ohms, and $R_5 = 5$ ohms. Find the current in every resistor.

Ans. $I_1 = 6.84$ amps, $I_2 = 6.59$ amps, $I_3 = 0.25$ amp, $I_4 = 2.71$ amps, $I_5 = 2.96$ amps.

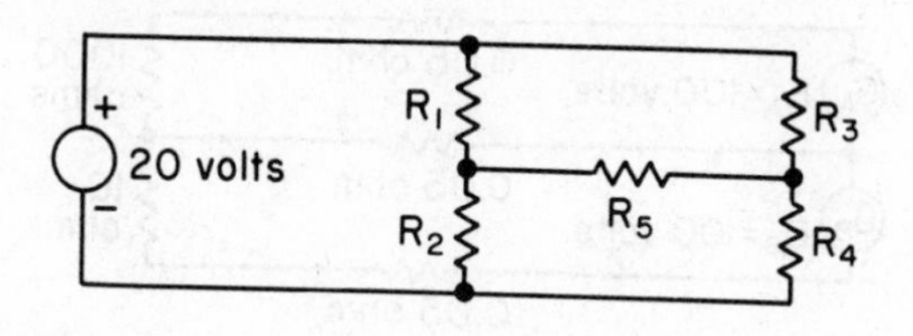

Fig. P2-8.

P2-9. In Fig. P2-9, VR-150-30 is a regulator tube which has a constant potential of 150 volts across its terminals when the current is between 5 milliamperes (ma) and 30 ma. Find the voltage E of the source and the voltage across the 2000-ohm resistance when the regulator current is (a) 30 ma and (b) 5 ma.

Ans. (a) 364.2 and 153 volts. (b) 245.7 and 150.5 volts.

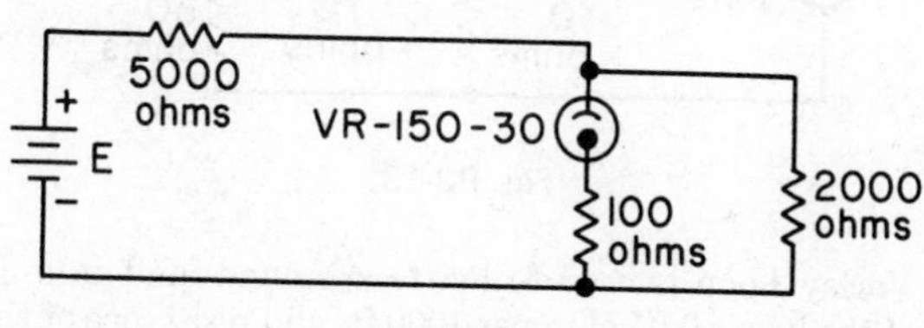

Fig. P2-9.

P2-10. In Fig. P2-10, find the currents in the five branches. (Hint: Find the equivalent resistance of the three parallel resistances.)

Ans. 10-volt battery, 2.2 amps. 12-volt battery, 2.15 amps. $I_5 = 1.11$ amps. $I_3 = 1.85$ amps. $I_4 = 1.39$ amps.

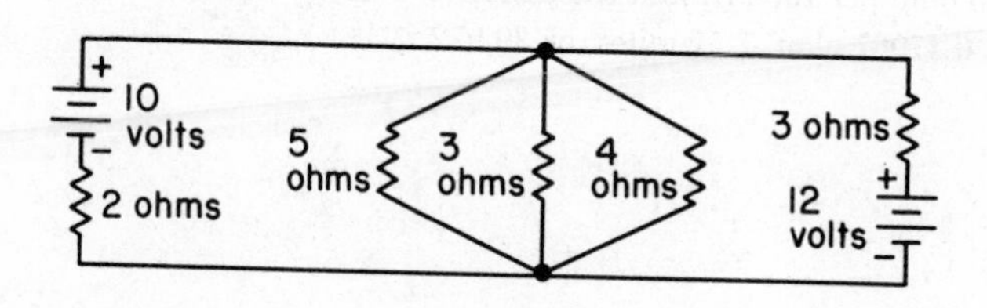

Fig. P2-10.

P2-11. In Fig. P2-11, find the currents in the three lines.

Ans. $I_1 = 0.10$ amp. $I_2 = 9.8$ amps. $I_3 = 9.9$ amps.

P2-12. Assume that the neutral leg in Fig. P2-11 is broken at point X, possibly by a blown fuse. Find the current and the voltages across the loads.

Ans. $I = 0.198$ amp. $V_1 = 198$ volts. $V_2 = 1.98$ volts.

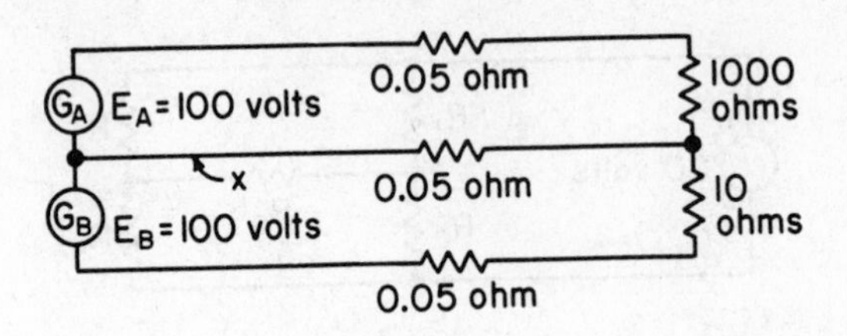

Fig. P2-11.

P2-13. In Fig. P2-13, find the current in the 70-ohm resistance.
Ans. 0.078 amp.

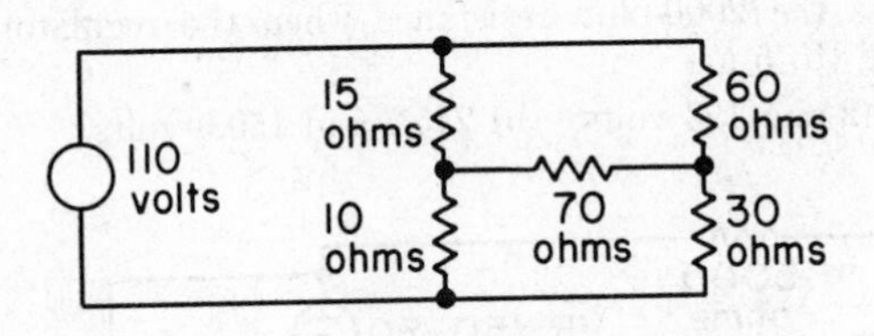

Fig. P2-13.

P2-14. A Varley Loop is used to locate a ground fault in a cable. The resistance of the line is 0.05 ohm per 1000 ft, and resistance of the test lead is 1.018 ohms per 1000 ft. If $A = B = 500$ ohms, $R_1 = 52.12$ ohms, and the line is 10 miles long, find the distance to the fault.
Ans. 2.135 ohms, 8.087 miles, or 42,699 ft.

P2-15. A Murray Loop is used to locate a ground fault in a cable. The normal one-way length of the line is 8 miles. When the bridge is balanced, $R = 900$ ohms and $A = 1000$ ohms. If the cable has a resistance of 0.0120 ohm per 1000 ft, find the distance to the fault.
Ans. 0.47967 ohm, 7.57 miles, or 39,972 ft.

3 POWER AND ENERGY

3-1. The Equation for Electric Power. In direct current, the power developed or utilized in any section *ab* of a circuit is

$$P_{ab} = V_{ab} I_{ab} \tag{3-1}$$

where P_{ab} is in watts, V_{ab} is the potential difference in volts between points *a* and *b* of the section, and I_{ab} is the current in amperes. Where large amounts of power are used, power is more conveniently expressed in kilowatts, so that equation (3-1) is written

$$P_{ab} = \frac{V_{ab} I_{ab}}{1000} \tag{3-2}$$

Where extremely large amounts of power are involved, the unit for P_{ab} may be the megawatt (millions of watts). The power equation would then be written

$$P_{ab} = \frac{V_{ab} I_{ab}}{1,000,000} \tag{3-3}$$

In alternating current, the voltage may be expressed in kilovolts (KV) which equal volts divided by 1000. The kilovolt is almost never encountered in direct current except in high tension testing equipment.

The watts lost in a line are usually found from the current and resistance of the line:

$$P_{\text{line}} = I_{\text{line}}^2 R_{\text{line}} \tag{3-4}$$

Since the efficiency of any device is found by dividing output by input, the efficiency of a transmission or feeder line is found by the equation

$$\text{Efficiency} = \frac{P_{ab} - P_{\text{line}}}{P_{ab}} \tag{3-5}$$

Example 3-1. A generator is delivering 400 amperes into a line at a potential of 300 volts across the generator. If the potential at the receiving end is 250 volts, find (a) the power delivered by the generator, (b) the power at the receiving end of the line, (c) the power lost in the line, and (d) the efficiency of the line. (e) Derive an expression (equation) for the efficiency of the line, using only the potentials at both ends of the line.

Solution. (a) From equation (3-1) or equation (3-2) we obtain the power generated.

$$P_{\text{gen}} = (300)\,(400) = 120{,}000 \text{ watts}$$

$$P_{\text{gen}} = \frac{(300)\,(400)}{1000} = 120 \text{ kw}$$

(b) The power at the receiving end is found by use of the same equations.

$$P_{\text{load}} = (250)\,(400) = 100{,}000 \text{ watts}$$

$$P_{\text{load}} = \frac{(250)\,(400)}{1000} = 100 \text{ kw}$$

(c) The power lost in the line is the difference between the power into the line and the power at the receiving end.

$$P_{\text{line}} = 120{,}000 - 100{,}000 = 20{,}000 \text{ watts or } 20 \text{ kw}$$

The power lost may also be found from the voltage drop.

$$P_{\text{line}} = (300 - 250)\,(400) = 20{,}000 \text{ watts}$$

(d) The efficiency of the line may be found from equation (3-5).

$$\text{Efficiency} = \frac{120 - 20}{120} = \frac{100}{120} = 0.833 \text{ or } 83.3\%$$

(e) The current in the line is the same as that generated. Therefore,

$$P_{\text{line}} = \frac{(V_{\text{gen}} - V_{\text{line}})}{V_{\text{gen}}\,I_{\text{line}}}\,(I_{\text{line}}) = \frac{V_{\text{gen}} - V_{\text{line}}}{V_{\text{gen}}}$$

or

$$P_{\text{line}} = \frac{V_{\text{load}}}{V_{\text{gen}}}$$

In this equation, V_{line} is the voltage drop in the line.

3-2. The Equation for Electric Energy.

Power and energy are so closely related that the terms are sometimes used interchangeably. Power is the rate of doing work. Energy exists whether or not work is done. The amount of energy that is converted into work is an important consideration in electrical engineering, and this energy is equal to the product of power and time.

If the power is steady over a period of time, the energy W is equal to

$$W = Pt \tag{3-6}$$

If P is in watts and t is in seconds, W is in joules or watt-seconds. If P is in watts and t is in hours, W is in watt-hours. If P is in kilowatts (kw) and t is in hours, W is in kilowatt-hours (kwh).

If the power is not steady, the power is integrated over the specified period of time to determine the energy. This concept is expressed by the equation

$$W = \int_{T_1}^{T_2} P dt \tag{3-7}$$

where the period between T_1 and T_2 is the period under consideration. From a practical standpoint, equation (3-7) can never be evaluated except by an integrating meter, called a kilowatt-hour-meter, such as power companies use to measure the use of energy by their customers.

3-3. Heat Loss in Resistance. Energy may be intentionally or unintentionally converted into heat. The power loss in transmission lines is an example of the unintentional conversion of energy to heat. As shown in Chapter 1, the power—or energy—lost or converted into heat in a resistance is given by the equation

$$W = I^2 Rt \tag{3-8}$$

where P, the power lost, is equal to I^2R. The heat thus formed has four undesirable effects: (1) It increases the resistance of the conductor, thereby causing an increase in the I^2R loss. (2) It causes heating of adjacent conductors, thereby increasing the I^2R loss in those conductors. (3) Since $V = IR$, the heat causes a voltage drop that may become large enough to put circuits or parts of circuits partly or entirely out of operation. (4) If the I^2R loss occurs in lines on the consumer's side of the meter, the consumer is forced to pay for energy he is not using in his lighting or other energy-converting devices. If the I^2R loss occurs on the power company's side of the meter, the power company adjusts its rates so that the consumer is forced to pay for that loss, too, on the theory that the consumer causes the loss.

A further study of the effects of this heat loss in the lines will be made in Chapter 5.

Example 3-2. The resistance of a feeder line is 0.0432 ohm. If the line carries a current of 400 amperes, find the voltage drop and the watts lost. If this load continues steadily for one hour, how many kilowatt-hours does this loss represent? Express this value in Btu.

Solution. The voltage drop is found from Ohm's law.

$$V = IR = (400)(0.0432) = 17.28 \text{ volts}$$

$$P = I^2R = (400)^2 (0.0432) = (400)(17.28) = 6912 \text{ watts} = 6.912 \text{ kw}$$

In one hour, this loss amounts to 6.912 kwh. Since one kwh equals 3413 Btu,

$$(6.912)(3413) = 23{,}590 \text{ Btu}$$

A gallon of water weighs 8.34 lbs; therefore, this heat loss represents enough heat to raise the temperature of 28 gallons of water 100° F.

3-4. Power Conversion. Electric energy in a transmission line actually comes into being by the conversion of mechanical energy into electric energy in a generator. At the point of use, electric energy is converted into heat—as in a range or furnace—or into light, or back to mechanical energy as in a motor. Some energy is lost as undesirable heat even during the conversion to desirable work.

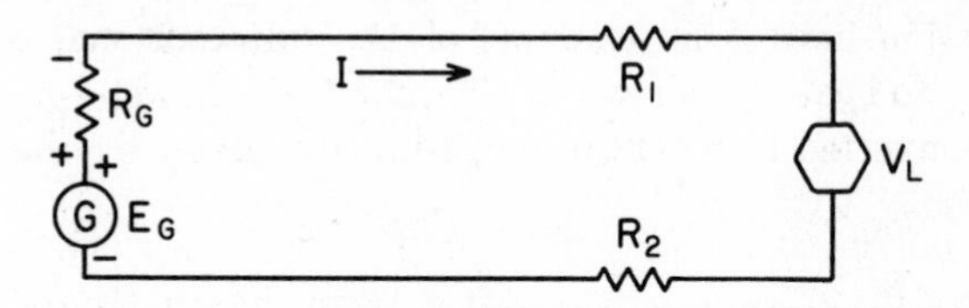

Fig. 3-1. Conversion of energy to power.

Fig. 3-1 is a circuit which illustrates these energy conversions. G is a generator which converts mechanical energy—supplied by gas, steam, water, or other fuel—into electric energy at a voltage E_G. This voltage represents the actual voltage generated but neglects any IR loss in the generator windings. Even though the terminal voltage changes as the current load increases, E_G does not change unless some adjustment is made by a human operator or an automatic voltage regulator. The terminal voltage depends on the current output and the resistance of the generator windings. If E_o is the generator output voltage and R_G is the resistance of the generator windings, then

$$E_o = E_G - IR_G \tag{3-9}$$

By Kirchhoff's laws, the voltage or loop equation for the circuit in Fig. 3-1 is

$$E_G - IR_G - IR_1 - V_L - IR_2 = 0 \tag{A}$$

If equation (A) is multiplied by the current I we obtain

$$IE_A - I^2R_G - I^2R_1 - IV_L - I^2R_2 = 0 \qquad \text{(B)}$$

Equation (B) shows that the total power around a circuit is—like the voltage—equal to zero. In other words, power cannot be stored in a warehouse, but must be used the instant it is produced.*

The load voltage in Fig. 3-1 may be the voltage across a heating coil, a lamp, a motor, or any other load.

Example 3-3. In Fig. 3-1, the voltage across the load is 220 volts and the current is 50 amperes. If the line resistance $R_1 = R_2 = 0.5$ ohm and the generator resistance R_G is 1.5 ohms, what is the generated voltage? What is the terminal voltage of the generator? What is the total power produced by the generator?

Solution. The generated voltage may be found from equation (A).

$$E_A = (50)\,(1.5) + (50)\,(0.5) + 220 + (50)\,(0.5)$$
$$= 220 + (50)\,(2.5) = 345 \text{ volts}$$

The terminal voltage of the generator is found from equation (3-9).

$$E_o = E_G - IR_G = 345 - (50)\,(1.5) = 270 \text{ volts}$$

The power in the load is found by multiplying the current by the voltage.

$$P_L = (50)\,(220) = 11{,}000 \text{ watts} = 11 \text{ kw}$$

The loss in the line is

$$P_W = (50)^2\,(0.5) + (50)^2\,(0.5) = 2500 \text{ watts} = 2.5 \text{ kw}$$

The loss in the generator is

$$P_G = (50)^2\,(1.5) = 3750 \text{ watts} = 3.75 \text{ kw}$$

The sum of these values is the total generated power.

$$P_T = 11{,}000 + 2500 + 3750 = 17{,}250 \text{ watts} = 17.25 \text{ kw}$$

This value should check against the power found by multiplying the current by the total generated voltage.

$$P_T = (50)\,(345) = 17{,}250 \text{ watts} = 17.25 \text{ kw}$$

3-5. Measurement of Power. Since power in a direct-current circuit is calculated from voltage and current, the logical way to measure power is to use a voltmeter and an ammeter.

* Power can be stored in a capacitor or in a coil, but this is not storage in the way we think of keeping coal, food, or other commodities for future use. Storage of electricity, from a practical viewpoint, can be accomplished for only a matter of a few seconds, and then only in extremely small quantities.

These meters may be connected in a circuit in two ways, as shown in Fig. 3-2.

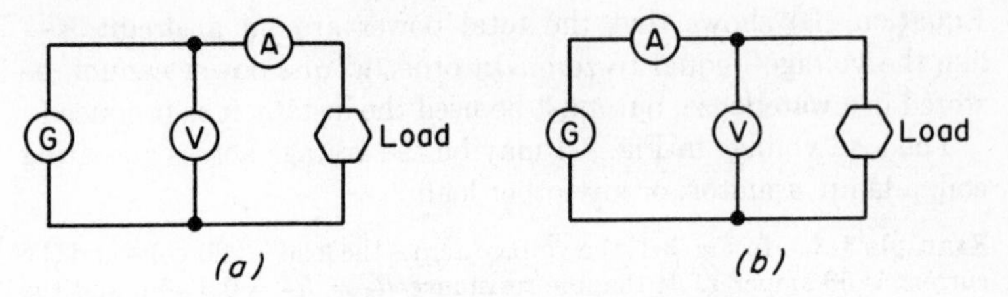

Fig. 3-2. Voltmeter and ammeter connections.

In Fig. 3-2*a*, the voltmeter is connected so that it reads the voltage across both the load and the ammeter. In order to determine the actual power in the load, the power absorbed by the ammeter would have to be subtracted from the product of the meter readings.

$$P_L = VI - I^2R_A \tag{3-10}$$

In equation (3-10), P_L is the power of the load in watts, V is the reading of the voltmeter in volts, I is the reading of the ammeter in amperes, and R_A is the resistance of the ammeter in ohms.

The connection shown in Fig. 3-2*b* gives the actual voltage across the load, but the reading of the ammeter includes the current in the voltmeter. The actual power delivered to the load is given by the equation

$$P_L = VI - \frac{V^2}{R_V} \tag{3-11}$$

where R_V is the resistance of the voltmeter in ohms.

From a practical viewpoint, the corrections shown in equations (3-10) and (3-11) are extremely small. The resistance of an ammeter is usually about 0.001 or 0.002 ohm, and that of a voltmeter, 15,000 ohms or more. Therefore, the correction factors are seldom used except in electronic circuits where the quantity of power is very small.

Power may also be measured by a wattmeter, which contains both a current coil and a voltage coil, connected by the method of either Fig. 3-2*a* or 3-2*b*. In more accurate instruments, the scale of the meter is calibrated to read only the power supplied to the load. If power or energy over a period of time is to be measured, a timing device is included in the wattmeter and the scale is calibrated to read directly in watt-hours or kilowatt-hours. These meters are read to determine the amount of energy delivered over a period of time, and a reading is taken at both the beginning and the end of the period. The energy is, therefore, the difference between the two readings.

Example 3-4. The power delivered to a motor is to be determined. The meters, when connected as shown in Fig. 3-2*a*, show readings of 10 amperes and 230 volts. What is the actual power to the motor? The ammeter has a resistance of 0.002 ohm.

Solution. Using equation (3-10), we obtain

$$P_L = (230)(10) - (10)^2(0.002) = 2300 - 0.2 = 2299.8 \text{ watts}$$

Obviously, this result is accurate beyond the realm of common sense, since meters cannot be read that accurately.

3-6. Regulation of Transmission Lines. Power lines and other electrical equipment are rated in two ways: by their efficiency and by their regulation. Efficiency is always the output divided by the input, as indicated by equation (3-5).

The regulation of a transmission line (also of a generator or of a battery) is defined as the per cent rise in voltage from the no-load condition to the full-load condition. In equation form, this definition is

$$\%V \text{ Reg} = \frac{V_{NL} - V_{FL}}{V_{FL}} \times 100 \qquad (3\text{-}12)$$

From a practical standpoint, the no-load voltage V_{NL} is the voltage at the sending end of the line regardless of the load, if the voltage drop in the generator is neglected, since the terminal voltage of the generator is adjusted either manually or automatically when the load changes. Equation (3-12) shows that the regulation of the line is an indication of the loss in the line, so that the larger the losses in the line, the larger is the figure representing the regulation.

Example 3-5. A load of 300 amperes is to be supplied by a transmission line. If the line has a total resistance of 0.25 ohm and the receiving end voltage is 250 volts, find the regulation and the voltage at the sending or generator end. If the resistance is reduced to 0.15 ohm, what are the regulation and the voltage at the generator end of the line for the same receiving end voltage?

Solution. The voltage drop in the line is

$$(300)(0.25) = 75 \text{ volts}$$

The sending end voltage is, therefore,

$$E_S = 250 + 75 = 325 \text{ volts} = V_{NL}$$

where E_S is the symbol for the sending end voltage.

The regulation, from equation (3-12), is

$$\%V \text{ Reg} = \frac{325 - 250}{250} = \frac{75}{250} = 0.3 = 30\%$$

If the resistance is reduced to 0.15 ohm, the line loss is

$$(300)\,(0.15) = 45 \text{ volts}$$

The sending end voltage is then equal to

$$E_S = 250 + 45 = 295 = V_{NL}$$

The regulation for this condition is

$$\%V \text{ Reg} = \frac{295 - 250}{250} = \frac{45}{250} = 0.18 = 18\%$$

3-7. Attenuators. In communications circuits, one type of measuring instrument used in the laboratory is called the *attenuator*. The attenuator is a device for changing the power to a load by a known amount without changing the power output of an electronic stage.

Such an attenuator is illustrated in Fig. 3-3. The box at the left represents an amplifier or other electronic circuit. For maximum transfer of power to the load, the output impedance of this stage must equal the load impedance R_L. When the attenuator is connected into the circuit, the combined impedance of the load and the attenuator must equal R_L.

Since R_2 and R_L are in parallel, their equivalent resistance R_P is found from Ohm's law.

$$\frac{1}{R_P} = \frac{1}{R_2} + \frac{1}{R_L} = \frac{R_L}{R_2 R_L} + \frac{R_2}{R_2 R_L} \tag{3-13}$$

Solving this equation for R_P gives

$$R_P = \frac{R_2 R_L}{R_2 + R_L}$$

The total impedance of R_L plus the attenuator must equal R_L. Therefore we have the equation

$$R_L = R_1 + \frac{R_2 R_L}{R_2 + R_L} \tag{3-14}$$

Equation (3-14) can now be solved for R_1.

$$R_1 = R_L - \frac{R_2 R_L}{R_2 + R_L}$$

If we now choose a value for R_2, we can find a value for R_1 which will satisfy the relationship of equation (3-14). The power absorbed by R_L is

$$P_L = I_L^2 R_L \quad (3\text{-}15)$$

where P_L is the power in the load, I_L is the current, and R_L is the load resistance. R_L is in ohms. Usually, I_L is in milliamperes (thousandths of an ampere) and P_L is in milliwatts (thousandths of a watt), since power in an electronic device is generally extremely small.

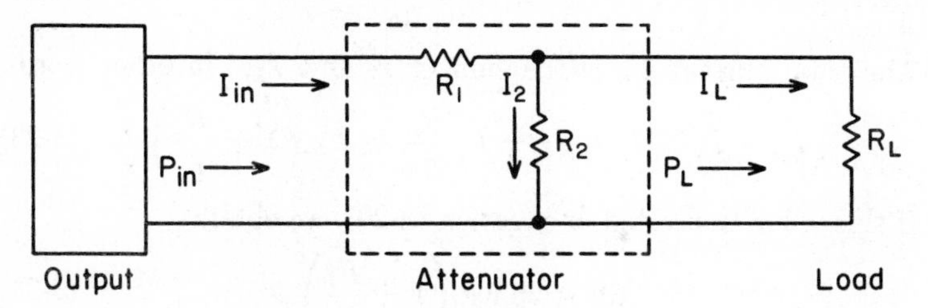

Fig. 3-3. An attenuator circuit.

The power input P_{in} to the attenuator is expressed by the equation

$$P_{in} = I_{in}^2 R_{in} = I_{in}^2 R_L \quad (3\text{-}16)$$

The ratio of these two amounts of power is found by dividing equation (3-16) by equation (3-15).

$$\frac{P_{in}}{P_L} = \frac{I_{in}^2 R_L}{I_L^2 R_L} = \left(\frac{I_{in}}{I_L}\right)^2 \quad (3\text{-}17)$$

The relationship of power dissipated in a circuit is conveniently measured in decibels (db). The decibel is defined so that

$$\text{number of db} = 10 \log \frac{P_{in}}{P_{out}} \quad (3\text{-}18)$$

In equation (3-17), P_{out} is equal to P_L, the power in R_L. Consequently, equation (3-18) is written

$$\text{db} = 10 \log \frac{P_{in}}{P_L} = 10 \log \left(\frac{I_{in}}{I_L}\right)^2 \quad (3\text{-}19)$$

In these equations, the abbreviation "log" refers to logarithms to the base 10. By the rules of logarithms, which are given in almost any good text on algebra or trigonometry,† we may convert equation (3-19) to the form

$$\mathrm{db} = 20 \log \frac{I_{\mathrm{in}}}{I_L} \tag{3-20}$$

We may now find the relationship between I_2 and I_L in terms of the resistances in the circuit. From Fig. 3-3 and Ohm's law,

$$I_2R_2 = I_LR_L \tag{3-21}$$

and the current in R_2 is, therefore,

$$I_2 = I_L \frac{R_L}{R_2} \tag{3-22}$$

The total current I_{in} is the sum of I_2 and I_L. In other words,

$$I_{\mathrm{in}} = I_L + I_2 = I_L + I_L \frac{R_L}{R_2} = I_L \left(1 + \frac{R_L}{R_2}\right) \tag{3-23}$$

If this value is inserted in equation (3-20), we obtain

$$\mathrm{db} = 20 \log \left(1 + \frac{R_L}{R_2}\right) \tag{3-24}$$

In a laboratory, equation (3-24) would be changed into a form which would allow R_2 to be computed for a desired range of decibels. This form is

$$R_2 = \frac{R_L}{10^x - 1} \tag{3-25}$$

where x, the exponent of 10, is equal to the number of db divided by 20, or

$$x = \frac{\mathrm{db}}{20} \tag{3-26}$$

The value of R_1 is then computed from equation (3-14). Several values of R_2 and R_1 are computed and the attenuator is adjusted to these values. The output of the previous stage is not affected because the impedance of the attenuator and of the stage under test remains constant. The output of the stage represented by R_L is then tested for its response at several values of power input.

---

† See *Algebra* by Gerald E. Moore, or *Plane and Spherical Trigonometry* by Kaj L. Nielsen and John H. Vanlonkhuyzen, in the College Outline Series, published by Barnes & Noble.

Example 3-6. A fixed attenuator is to give a loss of 25 db between a source and a load resistance of 500 ohms. Find the attenuator resistances and check the results.

Solution. Equation (3-25) will give

$$R_2 = \frac{500}{10^{25/20} - 1} = \frac{500}{10^{1.25} - 1} = 30 \text{ ohms}$$

From equation (3-14) we get

$$R_1 = 500 - \frac{(30)\,(500)}{30 + 500} = 471.7 \text{ ohms}$$

R_{in} can be checked by use of equation (3-14) where the R_L to the left of the equal sign is R_{in}.

$$R_{in} = 471.7 + \frac{(30)\,(500)}{30 + 500} = 500 \text{ ohms}$$

The db loss can be checked by equation (3-24).

$$\text{db loss} = 20 \log \left(1 + \frac{500}{30}\right) = 20 \log 17.7 = (20)\,(1.25) = 25 \text{ db}$$

Tables of logarithms are readily available in many books.‡ Values of 10^x can be found by use of a slide rule and by the definition of a logarithm:

$$x = \log \left(1 + \frac{R_L}{R_2}\right) \tag{3-27}$$

Problems Based on Chapter 3

P3-1. In Fig. P3-1, (a) What is the voltage across load L? (b) What is the current through load L? (c) What is the power delivered by the generator? (d) What is the efficiency of transmission? (e) What is the regulation of the line?

Ans. (a) 220 volts. (b) 100 amps. (c) 37,500 watts. (d) 85.3%. (e) 20%.

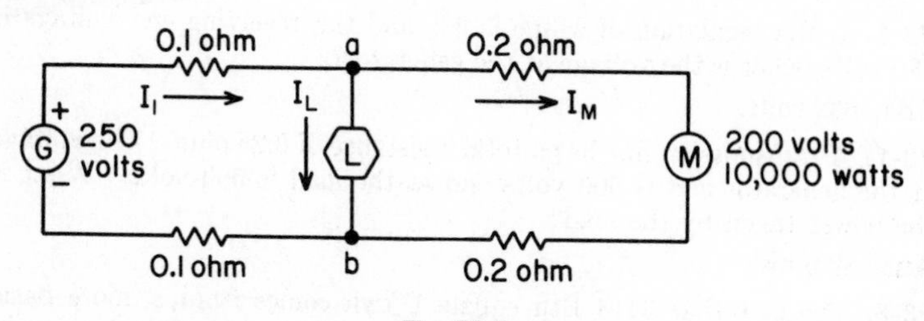

Fig. P3-1.

‡ See *Logarithmic and Other Trigonometric Tables* by Kaj L. Nielsen, in the College Outline Series, published by Barnes & Noble.

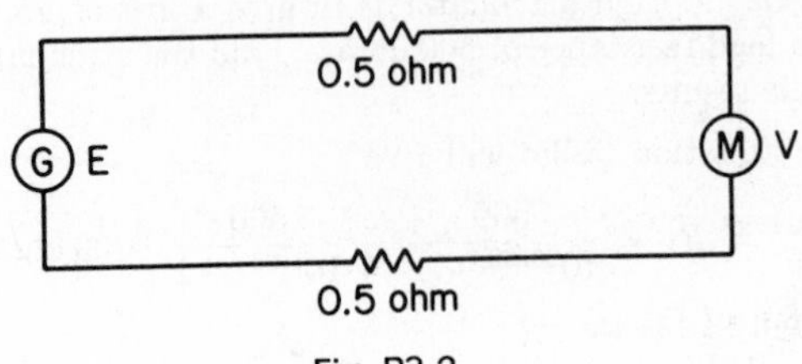

Fig. P3-2.

P3-2. A direct current motor will draw 11.5% more current at 90% of its rated voltage than it will at full rated voltage. In Fig. P3-2, M is a 10-hp motor which is 85% efficient at its rated 220 volts. If the actual voltage V is 90% of rated voltage, find (a) the power delivered to the motor at reduced voltage, (b) the regulation of the transmission line, (c) the efficiency of the transmission line. (d) If the motor output decreases 16% at reduced voltage, what is the efficiency of the motor?

Ans. (a) Normal current is 39.9 amps. Current at reduced voltage is 44.5 amps. $P = 8800$ watts or 11.8 hp. (b) 22.5%. (c) 81.5%. (d) 71.2%.

P3-3. What electric power is required to drive a pump which must raise water 150 ft at the rate of 2000 gallons per hour if the driving motor is 90% efficient? One gallon of water weighs 8.34 lbs and one horsepower equals 33,000 ft-lb per minute.

Ans. 1.27 hp output. 1.40 hp or 10.5 kw input.

P3-4. A 20-hp motor operates at full load for 10 minutes, three-fourths load for 15 minutes, half load for 30 minutes, and full load for 20 minutes more. How many kwh of energy are consumed during the time if the motor is 88% efficient at all loads?

Ans. 15.8 kwh.

P3-5. A generator delivers 2500 amps at 600 volts into a line whose resistance is 0.01 ohm. What is the voltage at the receiving end and what is the efficiency of the line?

Ans. 550 volts. 91.8%.

P3-6. If the regulation of a line is 9% and the receiving end voltage is 580 volts, what is the voltage at the generator?

Ans. 632 volts.

P3-7. A transmission line has a total resistance of 0.25 ohm. The voltage at the generator end is 600 volts and at the load is 560 volts. What is the power taken by the load?

Ans. 89.6 kw.

P3-8. The fact that 3413 Btu equals 1 kwh comes from a more basic equation called Joule's law, of the form $H = JEIT$, where H is the heat in Btu, J is Joule's mechanical equivalent of heat, EI is the power in watts, and T is the time in minutes. What is the value of J?

Ans. $H = 0.0568\ EIT$ or $H = 0.057\ EIT$.

P3-9. Using the value of J found in problem P3-8, find the amount of heat produced in a heater whose resistance is 100 ohms if 5 amps flow through it for 10 minutes.

Ans. 1425 Btu.

P3-10. A series of measurements is taken on a radio tube with the following readings:

volts	0	25	50	75
milliamperes	0	4	8	12.5

The voltmeter which was connected as shown in Fig. 3-2b (p. 46) has a resistance of 50 ohms per volt and was used on the 150-volt scale. What were the actual values of current and voltage?

Ans.

volts	0	25	50	75
milliamperes	0	0.667	1.34	2.51

P3-11. If the voltmeter resistance was 1000 ohms per volt on the 150-volt scale, would a correction have been necessary? Use the readings given in problem P3-10.

Ans.

volts	0	25	50	75
milliamperes	0	3.83	7.68	12

The readings are more accurate but the correction is still necessary, as there is an error of about 4% in some of the readings.

P3-12. The ammeter in problem P3-10 has a resistance of 1.5 ohms for the scale used. If the test was made with the meters connected as shown in Fig. 3-2a (p. 46), what corrections would have to be made?

Ans.

volts	0	24.994	49.983	75
milliamperes	0	4	8	12.5

No correction is needed.

P3-13. Show that R_1 in equation (3-14) is also equal to $\dfrac{R_L^2}{R_2 + R_L}$.

P3-14. The power received at an antenna is 0.1 microwatt. In the receiver, this signal is amplified to 3 watts to operate a speaker. What is the gain in decibels?

Ans. 74.77 db.

P3-15. An attenuator is to be used with a load resistance of 1000 ohms. Determine the values of R_1 and R_2 if the loss in the attenuator is to be 20 and 40 db for two of the settings.

Ans. R_1 = 900 and 990 ohms. R_2 = 111 and 10.1 ohms.

4 CIRCUIT CALCULATIONS

4-1. Equivalent Circuits. Some complex circuits or networks can be solved quite readily by converting them to more simple circuits which present the same resistance to the generator as the original circuit. These simple or equivalent circuits can then be used to solve the original circuit. An elementary approach to the use of equivalent circuits was given in Sections 1-6, 1-7, and 1-8.

The use of equivalent circuits simplifies network calculations, but only when handled with extreme care. Every step of the simplification must be accompanied by accurately labeled diagrams to prevent confusion in the solution of the circuits.

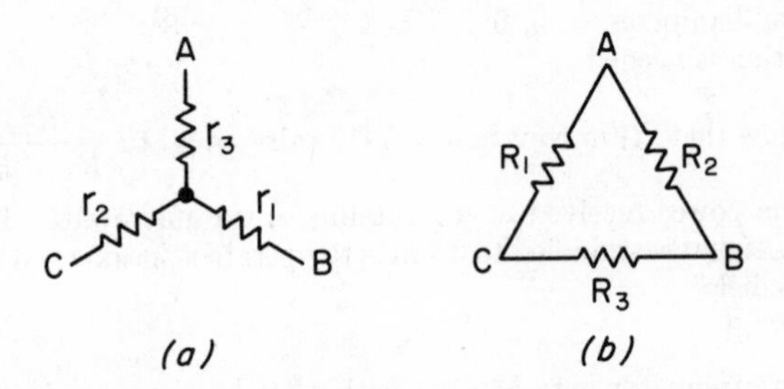

Fig. 4-1. Equivalent wye and delta connections.

4-2. Equivalent Wye and Delta Connections. Some networks can be converted by what is called a wye-delta transformation. The wye (or "Y," sometimes called a "star," especially if more than three paths are involved) is shown in Fig. 4-1*a*. The delta connection, shown in Fig. 4-1*b*, is so named because of its resemblance to the triangular shape of the Greek letter "delta," or Δ. The wye-delta transformation can be used for the solution of three-terminal networks.

The wye-delta transformation formulas are as follows:*

wye to delta

$$R_1 = \frac{r_1 r_2 + r_2 r_3 + r_3 r_1}{r_1} \tag{4-1}$$

$$R_2 = \frac{r_1 r_2 + r_2 r_3 + r_3 r_1}{r_2} \tag{4-2}$$

$$R_3 = \frac{r_1 r_2 + r_2 r_3 + r_3 r_1}{r_3} \tag{4-3}$$

delta to wye

$$r_1 = \frac{R_2 R_3}{R_1 + R_2 + R_3} \tag{4-4}$$

$$r_2 = \frac{R_1 R_3}{R_1 + R_2 + R_3} \tag{4-5}$$

$$r_3 = \frac{R_1 R_2}{R_1 + R_2 + R_3} \tag{4-6}$$

The relationship between these sets of formulas can be seen more clearly in Fig. 4-2. The corresponding resistances, as shown in this drawing, are "opposite" to each other. For example, R_1 of the delta connects from A to C, but r_1 of the wye connects to B. In the wye to delta transformation, the three numerators are identical, but the denominators are the wye resistances corresponding to delta resistance being sought. In the delta to wye, the denominators are identical and the numerators are the products of the delta resistors that do not correspond with the wye resistance. For example, in equation (4-4), R_1 does not appear in the numerator for the solution of r_1.

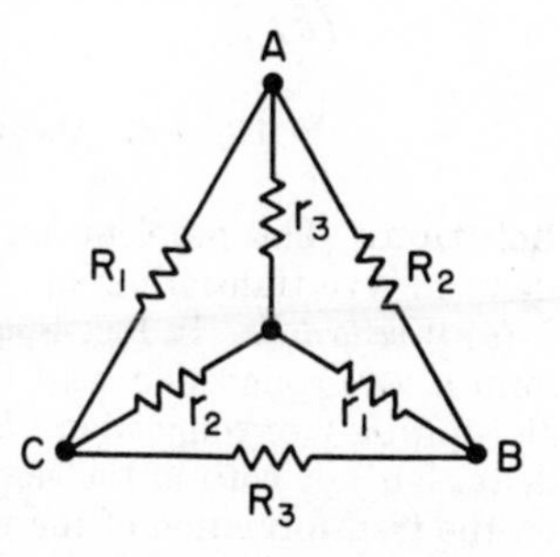

Fig. 4-2. Relationship between wye and delta transformer connections.

---

* The derivation of these formulas is explained in textbooks such as *Principles of Electrical Engineering* by William H. Timbie and Vannevar Bush, assisted by George B. Hoadley (4th ed.; New York: John Wiley & Sons, Inc., 1951).

Example 4-1. In Fig. 4-3*a*, R_A = 5 ohms, R_B = 30 ohms, R_C = 100 ohms, R_D = 10 ohms, and R_E = 20 ohms. If the voltage E of the generator is 150 volts, find the current in all five resistors.

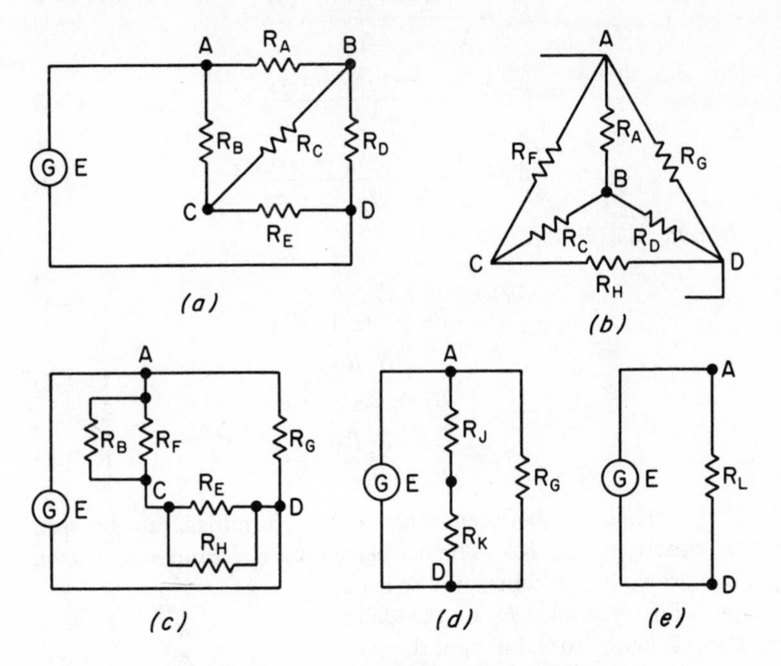

Fig. 4-3. Use of wye-delta transformation.

Solution. This problem can be solved by either the wye to delta or the delta to wye transformation. Both methods will be illustrated.

(a) *Wye to delta.* In Fig. 4-3*a*, the three resistors connected to terminal B form a wye connection, and the three that are connected to terminal C also form a wye connection. Either of these sets can be converted to the delta, but not both in the same solution. The following solution is based on the transformation of the wye at terminal B.

R_A, R_C, and R_D are shown in the wye form in Fig. 4-3*b*. The equivalent delta resistances are R_F, R_G, and R_H. The letters A, C, and D are the terminals to which the original resistors are connected. The equivalent delta resistors must be shown connected to these terminals. The new circuit to be solved is shown in Fig. 4-3*c*.

From Fig. 4-3*c*, we can determine that R_F is connected between terminals A and C; R_G, between A and D; and R_H, between C and D. In addition, R_B is connected from A to C, in parallel with R_F, and R_E is connected from C to D, in parallel with R_H. Since R_B and R_E were not in the transformed connection, they remain in the circuit.

R_B and R_F are now to be replaced by an equivalent resistor, R_J.

R_E and R_H are also to be replaced by an equivalent resistor, R_K. R_J and R_K are then in series as shown in Fig. 4-3*d*, and these resistors are in parallel with R_G. The final step is to determine the resistance R_L, which is equal to $R_J + R_K$ and R_G in parallel. R_L presents the same resistance between terminals A and D as the original five resistors.

The numerical solution follows the steps already described. Both the figures and the explanation should be checked during the study of the solution.

$$R_F = \frac{R_D R_C + R_C R_A + R_A R_D}{R_D}$$

$$= \frac{(10)\,(100) + (100)\,(5) + (5)\,(10)}{10}$$

$$= \frac{1550}{10} = 155 \text{ ohms}$$

$$R_G = \frac{R_D R_C + R_C R_A + R_A R_D}{R_C} = \frac{1550}{100} = 15.5 \text{ ohms}$$

$$R_H = \frac{R_D R_C + R_C R_A + R_A R_D}{R_A} = \frac{1550}{5} = 310 \text{ ohms}$$

$$\frac{1}{R_J} = \frac{1}{R_B} + \frac{1}{R_F} = \frac{1}{30} + \frac{1}{155}$$

$$= 0.03333 + 0.00645 = 0.03978 \text{ mho}$$

$$R_J = 25.1 \text{ ohms}$$

$$\frac{1}{R_K} = \frac{1}{R_E} + \frac{1}{R_H} = \frac{1}{20} + \frac{1}{310} = 0.05 + 0.00322 = 0.05322 \text{ mho}$$

$$R_K = 18.8 \text{ ohms}$$

$$R_J + R_K = 25.1 + 18.8 = 43.9 \text{ ohms}$$

$$\frac{1}{R_L} = \frac{1}{R_J + R_K} + \frac{1}{R_G} = \frac{1}{43.9} + \frac{1}{15.5} = 0.02278 + 0.06451$$

$$= 0.08729 \text{ mho}$$

$$R_L = 11.5 \text{ ohms}$$

The total current I_L is

$$I_L = \frac{\mathrm{E}}{R_L} = \frac{150}{11.5} = 13.05 \text{ amps}$$

The currents in R_G and in $R_J + R_K$ are

$$I_G = \frac{E}{R_G} = \frac{150}{15.5} = 9.67 \text{ amps}$$

$$I_J + I_K = \frac{E}{R_J + R_K} = \frac{150}{43.9} = 3.42 \text{ amps}$$

The voltages across R_J and R_K are

$$V_J = (I_J + I_K)\, R_J = (3.42)\,(25.1) = 86 \text{ volts}$$

$$V_K = (I_J + I_K)\, R_K = (3.42)\,(18.8) = 64.3 \text{ volts}$$

V_J is the voltage across R_B and R_F. V_K is the voltage across R_E and R_H.

$$I_B = \frac{V_J}{R_B} = \frac{86}{30} = 2.86 \text{ amps}$$

$$I_F = \frac{V_J}{R_F} = \frac{86}{155} = 0.56 \text{ amps}$$

$$I_E = \frac{V_K}{R_E} = \frac{64.3}{20} = 3.21 \text{ amps}$$

$$I_H = \frac{V_K}{R_H} = \frac{64.3}{310} = 0.21 \text{ amp}$$

I_B and I_E are currents in the resistors R_B and R_E in the original connection shown in Fig. 4-3*a*.

$$I_C = I_E - I_B = 3.21 - 2.86 = 0.35 \text{ amp from } B \text{ to } C$$

From Kirchhoff's laws, we know

$$V_A + V_C = V_B$$

$$I_A R_A + I_C R_C = I_B R_B$$

$$I_A = \frac{I_B R_B - I_C R_C}{R_A} = \frac{(2.86)\,(30) - (0.35)\,(100)}{5}$$

$$= 10.2 \text{ amps}$$

$$I_D = I_A - I_C = 10.2 - 0.35 = 9.85 \text{ amps}$$

(b) *Delta to wye.* The circuit of Fig. 4-3*a* is redrawn in Fig. 4-4*a* with the equivalent wye resistances R_F, R_G, and R_H added. The new equivalent circuit is shown in Fig. 4-4*b*. Resistors R_H and R_E now form a parallel circuit with R_G and R_D. If $R_J = R_H + R_E$ and $R_K = R_G + R_D$, we can then draw the equivalent circuits of Fig. 4-4*c*. If R_M is the effective resistance of R_J and R_K in parallel, we have the circuit of Fig. 4-4*d*. The effective or equivalent resistance R_L is then shown in Fig. 4-4*e*. This is the same equivalent circuit obtained by the wye-delta transformation shown in Fig. 4-3*e*.

The successive calculations are as follows:

$$R_F = \frac{R_A R_B}{R_A + R_B + R_C} = \frac{(5)\,(30)}{135} = \frac{150}{135} = 1.11 \text{ ohms}$$

$$R_G = \frac{R_A R_C}{R_A + R_B + R_C} = \frac{(5)\,(100)}{135} = \frac{500}{135} = 3.7 \text{ ohms}$$

$$R_H = \frac{R_B R_C}{R_A + R_B + R_C} = \frac{(30)\,(100)}{135} = \frac{3000}{135} = 22.2 \text{ ohms}$$

$$R_J = R_H + R_E = 22.2 + 20 = 42.2 \text{ ohms}$$

$$R_K = R_G + R_D = 3.7 + 10 = 13.7 \text{ ohms}$$

$$\frac{1}{R_M} = \frac{1}{R_J} + \frac{1}{R_K} = \frac{1}{42.2} + \frac{1}{13.7} = 0.0237 + 0.0730 = 0.0967 \text{ mho}$$

$$R_M = 10.35 \text{ ohms}$$

$$R_L = R_F + R_M = 1.11 + 10.35 = 11.46 \text{ ohms}$$

The value of R_L obtained by the wye-delta transformation was 11.5. The currents can now be found by a method similar to that used in Example 4-1(a). These results are obtained without the need for solving several equations simultaneously, as with the previously discussed methods.

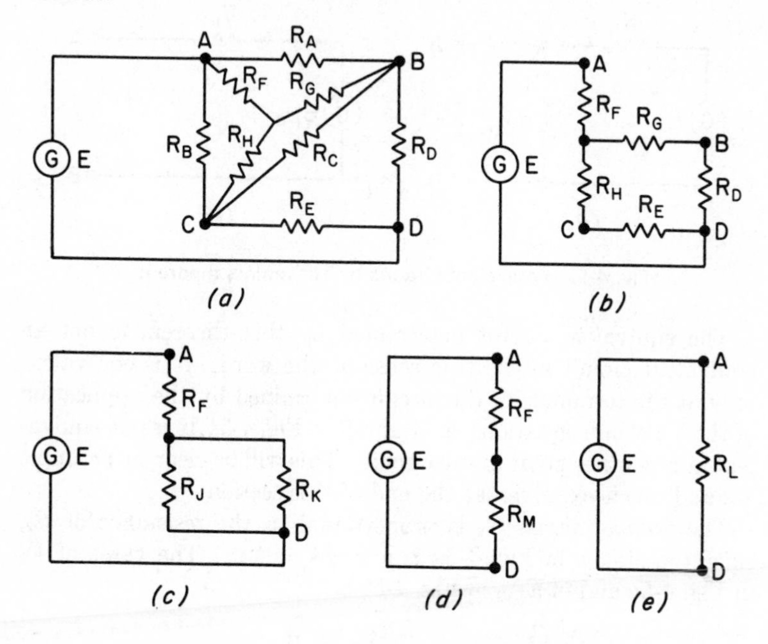

Fig. 4-4. Use of delta-wye transformation.

Note that there is no relationship between the wye and delta connections used for solving direct-current or single-phase alternating-current circuits and the three-phase connections of the same name and similar schematic appearance. The three-phase connections will be discussed in Chapter 9.

4-3. Thévenin's Theorem. Thévenin's theorem is a process by which a circuit is reduced, starting from the generator instead of from the load. It has been called the constant voltage source method and finds its principal application in the electronics and communications fields.

The Thévenin conversion requires two steps. One step is to find the voltage drop across a resistor such as R_2 in Fig. 4-5*a*. The other step is to find a series resistor that can replace both R_1 and R_2 and still have the same output voltage across terminals *A* and *B* as the original resistors. The equivalent circuit is shown in Fig. 4-5*b*.

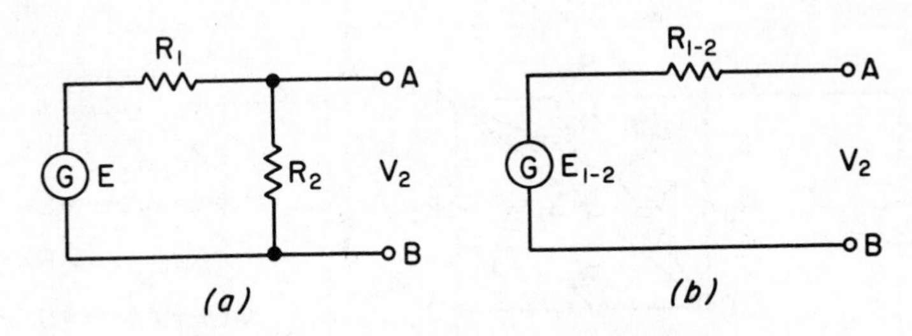

Fig. 4-5. Equivalent circuits by Thévenin's theorem.

The equivalent circuit determined by this theorem is not an equivalent circuit in the true sense of the word. It is equivalent only at the terminals of the circuit determined by the application of the Thévenin equations, as *A* and *B* in Fig. 4-5. It is not equivalent at any other point in the circuit. This will be clear in Example 4-2 and its check, given at the end of this section.

The voltage across R_2 is proportional to the resistance of R_2, since the circuit in Fig. 4-5*a* is a series circuit. The value of V_2 in Fig. 4-5*a* and of E_{1-2} in Fig. 4-5*b* is

$$V_2 = \frac{ER_2}{R_1 + R_2} = E_{1-2} \tag{4-7}$$

Now consider that the voltage source is zero, so that R_1 and R_2 are in parallel. Their equivalent resistance R_{1-2} is found, therefore, by the parallel resistance formula. An entire circuit can be reduced by successive steps in this manner.

Example 4-2. Find the current in R_6 in the circuit shown in Fig. 4-6*a*.

Solution. The first step is to find the equivalent voltage and the equivalent resistance of the circuit at the left of the dotted line 1-1 in Fig. 4-6*a*.

$$E_{1-1} = \frac{(150)\,(10)}{5 + 10} = 100 \text{ volts}$$

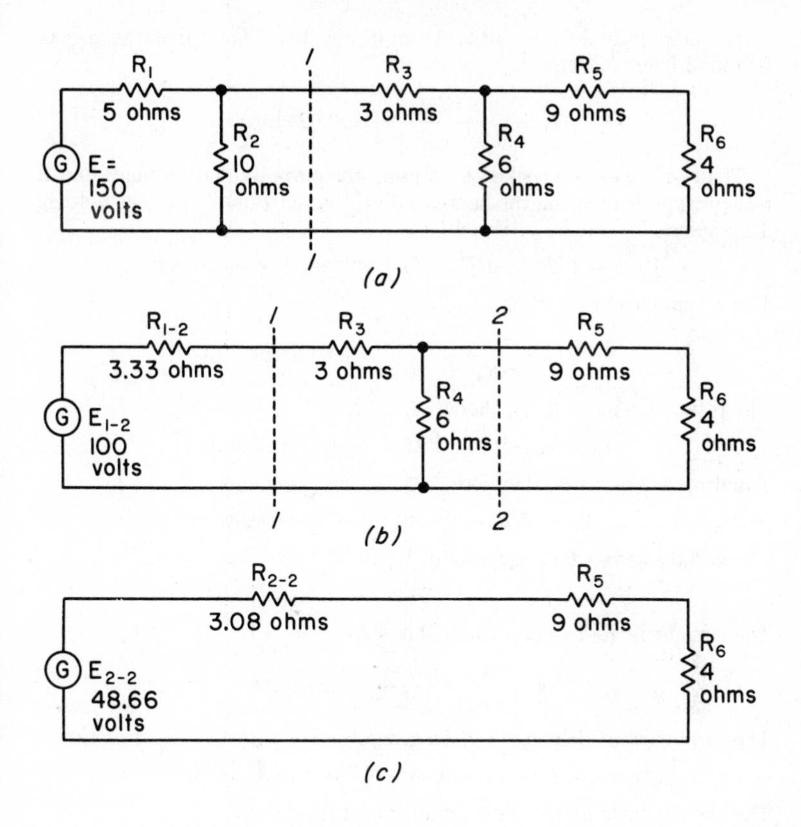

Fig. 4-6. Application of Thévenin's theorem.

The equivalent resistance is

$$\frac{1}{R_{1-1}} = \frac{1}{R_1} + \frac{1}{R_2} = \frac{1}{5} + \frac{1}{10} = 0.2 + 0.1 = 0.3 \text{ mho}$$

$$R_{1-1} = \frac{1}{0.3} = 3.33 \text{ ohms}$$

This equivalent circuit has been drawn in Fig. 4-6*b* with the rest of the circuit connected. We now find the equivalent circuit for everything to the left of the dotted line 2-2.

$$V_{2-2} = \frac{(100)\,(6)}{3.33 + 3 + 6} = 48.66 \text{ volts}$$

$$\frac{1}{R_{2-2}} = \frac{1}{R_{1-1} + R_3} + \frac{1}{R_4} = \frac{1}{3.33 + 3} + \frac{1}{6} = 0.325 \text{ mho}$$

$$R_{2-2} = 3.08 \text{ ohms}$$

The new equivalent circuit is shown in Fig. 4-6*c*. The current in R_6 can be found from this circuit.

$$I_6 = \frac{48.66}{3.08 + 9 + 4} = 3.02 \text{ amps}$$

The result can be checked by finding the currents and voltages for all resistors and comparing the figures with the given value of E. The voltage drop across R_5 and R_6 in Fig. 4-6*a* is

$$V_{5-6} = I(R_5 + R_6) = (3.02)\,(9 + 4) = 39.26 \text{ volts}$$

The actual current in R_4 is

$$I_4 = \frac{V_{4-5}}{R_4} = \frac{39.26}{6} = 6.54 \text{ amps}$$

The total current in R_3 is, therefore,

$$I_3 = I_6 + I_4 = 3.02 + 6.54 = 9.56 \text{ amps}$$

The drop across R_3 is, therefore,

$$V_3 = I_3R_3 = (9.56)\,(3) = 28.68 \text{ volts}$$

The voltage across R_2 is the sum of V_{5-6} and V_3.

$$V_2 = V_{5-6} + V_3 = 39.26 + 28.68 = 67.94 \text{ volts}$$

The current in R_2 is found from Ohm's law.

$$I_2 = \frac{V_2}{R_2} = \frac{67.94}{10} = 6.79 \text{ amps}$$

The total current delivered by the generator is

$$I_G = I_3 + I_2 = 9.56 + 6.79 = 16.35 \text{ amps}$$

The voltage drop across R_1 is found from this current.

$$V_1 = I_GR_1 = (16.35)\,(5) = 81.75 \text{ volts}$$

The voltage at the generator is, therefore,

$$E = V_1 + V_2 = 81.75 + 67.94 = 149.69 \text{ volts}$$

Since the voltage given for E was 150 volts, the check indicates that the results are reasonably correct. The degree of accuracy attained depends on how many decimal places are desired in every computation.

4-4. Norton's Theorem. The principle of Norton's theorem is to reduce the circuit to a constant current source and a conductance rather than to a constant voltage source and a resistance. Fig. 4-7*a* shows a voltage source G with a constant voltage output E and a current I_t. The voltage V_t at the terminals A-B is equal to the voltage output of the generator E minus the voltage drop in R_1. In equation form, this is

$$V_t = E - I_tR$$

The Norton equivalent is shown in Fig. 4-7*b*, with a constant current source and a conductance. The symbols used in Fig. 4-7*b* are the ones most commonly used by authors and engineers in the absence of any generally accepted standards.

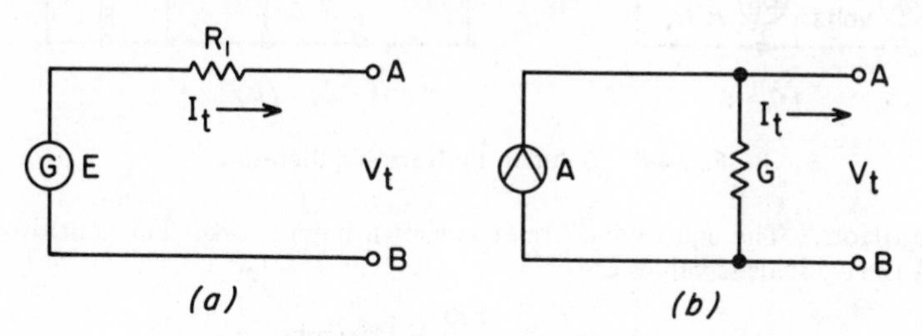

Fig. 4-7. Equivalent circuits by Norton's theorem.

The symbol G in direct current is the reciprocal of the resistance, or $1/R$. Since $I = V/R = VG$, the current at terminals A-B in the Norton circuit is

$$I_t = A - V_t G$$

where A is the constant current output of the equivalent generator. If this equation is solved for V_t, we obtain the relationship

$$V_t = \frac{A - I_t}{G} = \frac{A}{G} - \frac{I_t}{G}$$

The constant term A/G is independent of the terminal current and therefore represents the constant voltage of the generator E.

$$E = \frac{A}{G} = AR \tag{4-8}$$

From equation (4-8) we find the values of A and G.

$$A = EG = \frac{E}{R} \tag{4-9}$$

$$G = \frac{1}{R} \tag{4-10}$$

Equations (4-9) and (4-10) are the ones used for the Norton conversion. Norton's theorem is widely used in the solution of circuits that have more than one voltage source. (See also Section 4-7, Millman's Theorem.)

Example 4-3. Find the current in the 10-ohm resistor and in the two generators in Fig. 4-8*a*.

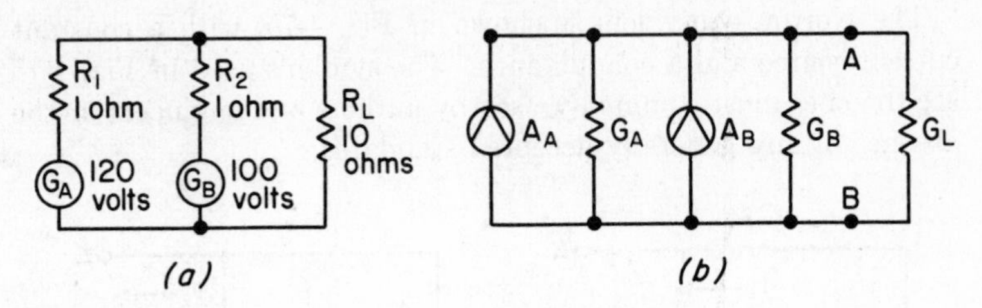

Fig. 4-8. Solution by Norton's theorem.

Solution. The equivalent circuit is shown in Fig. 4-8*b*. For generator G_A the equivalent values are

$$A_A = \frac{E_A}{R_1} = \frac{120}{1} = 120 \text{ amps}$$

$$G_1 = \frac{1}{1} = 1 \text{ mho}$$

$$A_B = \frac{E_B}{R_2} = \frac{100}{1} = 100 \text{ amps}$$

$$G_2 = \frac{1}{1} = 1 \text{ mho}$$

The conductance of R_L is

$$G_L = \frac{1}{10} = 0.1 \text{ mho}$$

The total conductance is the sum of all the conductances.

$$G_T = G_1 + G_2 + G_L = 1 + 1 + 0.1 = 2.1 \text{ mhos}$$

The total current A_T is

$$A_T = A_A + A_B = 120 + 100 = 220 \text{ amps}$$

The voltage across R_L is the voltage across terminals *A-B*.

$$V_{A-B} = A_T R_T = \frac{A_T}{G_T} = \frac{220}{2.1} = 104.76 \text{ volts}$$

The current through R_L is found from Ohm's law.

$$I_L = \frac{V_{A-B}}{R_L} = \frac{104.76}{10} = 10.48 \text{ amps}$$

The current supplied by each generator is found from the voltage across terminals *A-B* which is also the voltage across the generator terminals, or 104.76 volts.

$$120 - 1I_A = 104.76$$

$$I_A = 120 - 104.76 = 15.24 \text{ amps}$$

$$100 - 1I_B = 104.76$$

$$I_B = 100 - 104.76 = -4.76 \text{ amps}$$

This result indicates that generator G_B is a load on the circuit and that the current flows downward through this generator. As a check, we find that

$$I_A + I_B = I_L$$

$$15.24 - 4.76 = 10.48 \text{ amps}$$

The accuracy achieved in this solution is not necessary in most engineering problems but is used here merely to indicate the accuracy of the results possible by use of Norton's theorem. From a practical standpoint, the results could be

$$V_{A-B} = 105 \text{ volts}$$
$$I_L = 10.5 \text{ amps}$$
$$I_A = 15.2 \text{ amps}$$
$$I_B = -4.8 \text{ amps}$$

4-5. The Superposition Theorem. The superposition theorem is a time-saving device for finding the current in a particular current path when two or more voltage sources are present. No formulas are possible and none are needed in the solution.

In Fig. 4-9*a* is shown the circuit used in Example 4-3. The first step in applying the superposition theorem is to assume that generator G_B is short-circuited but that its internal resistance and all other resistances are still in the circuit. The current contributed by generator G_A under those circumstances is then determined. From this value of current, the voltage drop is determined across terminals *A-B* in Fig. 4-9*b* and the current is then found through the load resistor.

Generator G_B is now put back in the circuit and G_A is short-

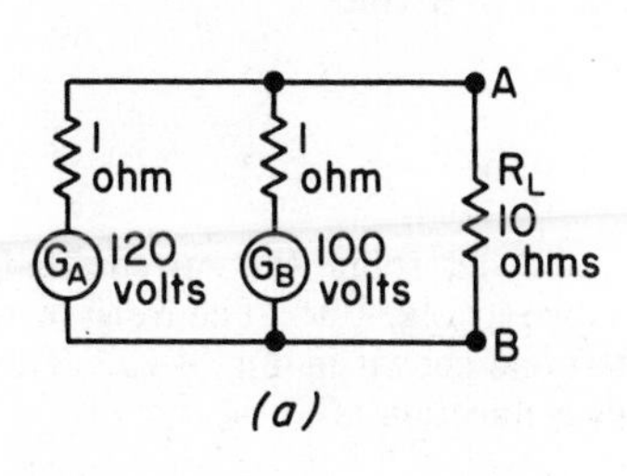

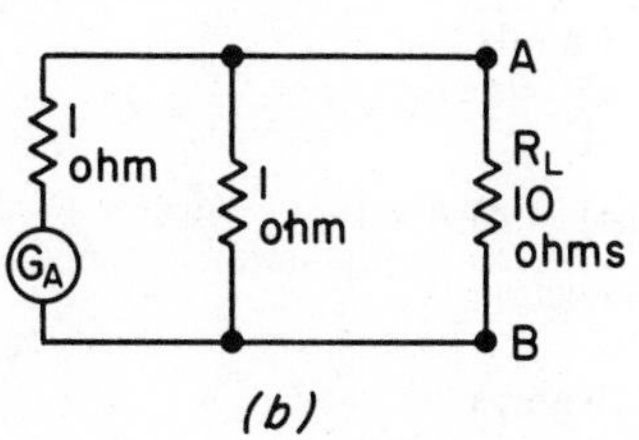

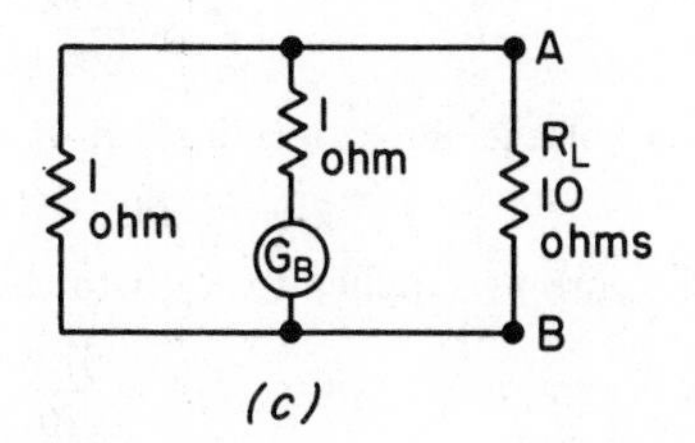

Fig. 4-9. The superposition theorem.

circuited as shown in Fig. 4-9*c*. The calculations are then repeated for this circuit and the current in R_L is found. The actual current in R_L is the algebraic sum of the two currents obtained from the solution of the calculations based on Fig. 4-9*b* and *c*.

The currents found by this method are not the actual currents flowing anywhere in the circuit other than in the resistance R_L. Currents actually delivered by G_A and G_B can be calculated from the values found.

Example 4-4. Solve Example 4-3 by the superposition theorem.

Solution. The first step is to solve the circuit as it appears in Fig. 4-9*b*, with G_A supplying the current. The resistance of the parallel circuit is found first.

$$\frac{1}{R_P} = \frac{1}{1} + \frac{1}{10} = 1 + 0.1 = 1.1 \text{ mhos}$$

$$R_P = 0.909 \text{ ohm}$$

The 1-ohm internal resistance of G_A is in series with R_P. The total resistance is, therefore,

$$R_T = 1 + 0.909 = 1.909 \text{ ohms}$$

The current in R_T for this circuit is

$$I_T' = \frac{120}{1.909} = 62.9 \text{ amps}$$

The voltage across terminals A–B is equal to the voltage of G_A minus the voltage drop across its internal resistance of one ohm.

$$V_{A\text{-}B} = 120 - (1)(62.9) = 57.1 \text{ volts}$$

The current I_L' with 57.1 volts across R_L is

$$I_L' = \frac{57.1}{10} = 5.71 \text{ amps}$$

The second step is to short-circuit G_A and determine the current that G_B alone would supply. This circuit is shown in Fig. 4-9*c*. The resistance for this connection is the same as for the one shown in Fig. 4-9*b*. The current in the total resistance R_T for this connection is

$$I_T'' = \frac{100}{1.909} = 52.4 \text{ amps}$$

The voltage across terminals A–B is

$$V_{A\text{-}B} = 100 - (1)(52.4) = 47.6 \text{ volts}$$

The current supplied to R_L with this connection is

$$I_L'' = \frac{47.6}{10} = 4.76 \text{ amps}$$

The actual current in the load is the sum of the two currents.

$$I_L = I_L' + I_L'' = 5.71 + 4.76 = 10.47 \text{ amps}$$

The currents actually supplied by the generators are found by finding the actual voltage across R_L from the actual current I_L.

$$V_L = (10.47)(10) = 104.7 \text{ volts}$$

The current supplied by G_A is

$$I_A = \frac{120 - 104.7}{1} = 15.3 \text{ amps}$$

The current supplied by G_B is

$$I_B = \frac{100 - 104.7}{1} = -4.7 \text{ amps}$$

4-6. The Ladder Method. The *ladder method* is a means of reducing the work required to solve circuits similar to that of Example 1-13 (see Fig. 1-7). This principle, like the superposition theorem, is an analytic process and cannot be solved by simplified formulas. Ohm's law is used throughout the solution.

The circuit of Fig. 1-7 is redrawn in Fig. 4-10 and labeled for the purpose of solution by the ladder method. The first step is to assume that a current I flows as indicated in the path *C-E-F-D* through R_5, R_6, and R_7. The voltage drop across these resistances

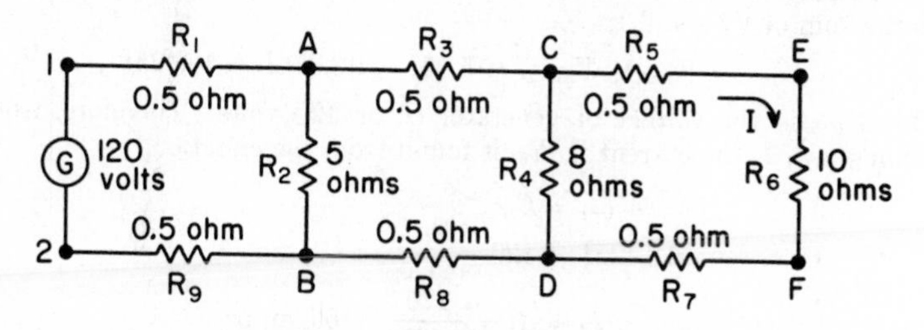

Fig. 4-10. The ladder method.

is equal to I times the total resistance of the path. Since this is also the voltage across R_4, the value of R_4 is divided into that voltage and the current through R_4 is then obtained in terms of I. The method is better illustrated by a study of Example 4-5.

Example 4-5. Find the currents flowing in resistances R_2, R_4, and R_6 of the network in Fig. 4-10.

Solution. If I is the current flowing through R_5, R_6, and R_7, the voltage drop across $C-D$ is found by Ohm's law.

$$V_{C-D} = I(R_5 + R_6 + R_7) = I(0.5 + 10 + 0.5) = 11I$$

Since V_{C-D} is the voltage drop across resistor R_4, the current in R_4 is found from Ohm's law.

$$I_4 = \frac{V_{C-D}}{R_4} = \frac{11I}{8} = 1.375I$$

The total current flowing through R_3 and R_8 is the sum of I and I_4.

$$I_3 = I_8 = I + 1.375I = 2.375I$$

The voltage drop across R_3 and R_8 is found by Ohm's law.

$$V_{3-8} = 2.375I\ (R_3 + R_8) = 2.375I\ (0.5 + 0.5) = 2.375I$$

The voltage across terminals $A-B$ is V_{3-8} plus the voltage drop across $C-D$.

$$V_{A-B} = V_{3-8} + V_{C-D} = 2.375I + 11I = 13.375I$$

Since V_{A-B} is the voltage across R_2, the current through this resistor is, by Ohm's law,

$$I_2 = \frac{V_{A-B}}{R_2} = \frac{13.375I}{5} = 2.675I$$

The current in R_1 and R_9 is the sum of I_2 and I_3.

$$I_1 = I_9 = I_2 + I_3 = 2.675I + 2.375I = 5.05I$$

The voltage drops across R_1 and R_9 are, from Ohm's law,

$$V_{1-9} = (5.05I)\ (R_1 + R_9) = (5.05I)\ (0.5 + 0.5) = 5.05I$$

The total voltage from terminal 1 to terminal 2 through *A-C-E-F-D-B* is the sum of V_{1-9} and V_{A-B}.

$$V_{1-2} = V_{1-9} + V_{A-B} = 5.05I + 13.375I = 18.425I$$

But V_{1-2} is the voltage of generator G, or 120 volts. Therefore, from Ohm's law, I, the current in R_6, is found from the equation

$$V_{1-2} = E_G$$

$$18.425I = 120$$

$$I_6 = I = \frac{120}{18.425} = 6.5 \text{ amps}$$

This is the value obtained in Example 1-13. Other currents are found from the value obtained in this example:

$$I_2 = 2.675I = (2.675)\ (6.5) = 17.4 \text{ amps}$$

$$I_4 = 1.375I = (1.375)\ (6.5) = 8.94 \text{ amps}$$

The line currents, if desired, can be found in the same way.

4-7. Millman's Theorem. Norton's constant current theorem actually deals with one voltage source. According to Millman's theorem, when there is more than one voltage source, the several sources can be combined into a single source. In other words, the currents may be added after they have been determined by the Norton equation.

The basic significance of the current A, determined from the Norton equations, is that it is the maximum current that can be obtained from the generator with its terminals short-circuited. Consequently, the number of short-circuit currents obtained from two or more voltage sources in parallel is the sum of the short-circuit currents of all the sources under consideration in the circuit. Millman's theorem can be used as a means of reducing a network of voltage sources and loads into a solvable form much more quickly than by the superposition theorem or Kirchhoff's laws.

Example 4-6. In the circuit shown in Fig. 4-11*a*, find the current in loads R_4 and R_5 and the current supplied by generators (voltage sources) S_1, S_2, and S_3.

Solution. S_1 and S_2 may be generators located at a power station some distance from generator S_3. The resistance R_x is the resistance of the transmission line between the two stations. The characteristics of S_1 and S_2 may be combined by Millman's theorem, using the Norton equations.

For S_1:

$$G_1 = \frac{1}{R_1} = \frac{1}{0.05} = 20 \text{ mhos}$$

$$A_1 = \frac{E_1}{R_1} = \frac{500}{0.05} = 10{,}000 \text{ amps}$$

For S_2:

$$G_2 = \frac{1}{R_2} = \frac{1}{0.1} = 10 \text{ mhos}$$

$$A_2 = \frac{E_2}{R_2} = \frac{520}{0.1} = 5200 \text{ amps}$$

These generators may now be combined by Millman's theorem.

$$G_{1-2} = G_1 + G_2 = 20 + 10 = 30 \text{ mhos}$$

$$A_{1-2} = A_1 + A_2 = 10{,}000 + 5200 = 15{,}200 \text{ amps}$$

Because of the resistance R_x between these generators and S_3, the three generators cannot be combined directly. The voltage and resistance of a composite generator must be found. This composite generator – which may be called S_{1-2} – has a voltage E_{1-2} and resistance R_{1-2}. These values are obtained by reversing the Norton equations.

$$R_{1-2} = \frac{1}{G_{1-2}} = \frac{1}{30} = 0.033 \text{ ohm}$$

$$E_{1-2} = A_{1-2}\,R_{1-2} = (15{,}200)\left(\frac{1}{30}\right) = 507 \text{ volts}$$

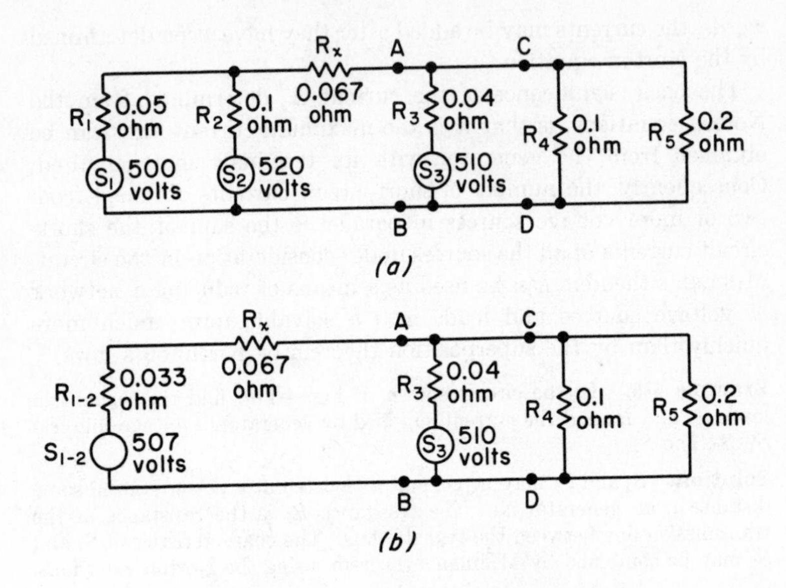

Fig. 4-11. Circuit for solution by Millman's theorem.

This combined voltage source is shown in Fig. 4-11*b*. S_{1-2} may now be considered as a new voltage source with a resistance equal to R_{1-2} plus R_x. The new characteristics are with respect to terminals $A-B$ in the figure.

$$R_{A-B} = R_{1-2} + R_x = 0.033 + 0.067 = 0.1 \text{ ohm}$$

$$G_{A-B} = \frac{1}{R_{A-B}} = \frac{1}{0.1} = 10 \text{ mhos}$$

$$A_{A-B} = \frac{E_{1-2}}{R_{A-B}} = \frac{507}{0.1} = 5070 \text{ amps}$$

The characteristics of S_3 are now to be determined.

$$G_3 = \frac{1}{R_3} = \frac{1}{0.04} = 25 \text{ mhos}$$

$$A_3 = \frac{E_3}{R_3} = \frac{510}{0.04} = 12{,}750 \text{ amps}$$

The load conductances are calculated.

$$G_4 = \frac{1}{R_4} = \frac{1}{0.1} = 10 \text{ mhos}$$

$$G_5 = \frac{1}{R_5} = \frac{1}{0.2} = 5 \text{ mhos}$$

The total Norton current and circuit conductance are found.

$$G_T = G_{A-B} + G_3 + G_4 + G_5 = 10 + 25 + 10 + 5 = 50 \text{ mhos}$$

$$A_T = A_{A-B} + A_3 = 5070 + 12{,}750 = 17{,}820 \text{ amps}$$

The voltage across terminals $C-D$, equal to the voltage across the load, is now determined. Since the current A_T flows through the total conductance G_T, the voltage is

$$V_{C-D} = \frac{A_T}{G_T} = \frac{17{,}820}{50} = 356.4 \text{ volts}$$

The load currents may now be calculated.

$$I_5 = \frac{V_{C-D}}{R_5} = \frac{356.4}{0.2} = 1782 \text{ amps}$$

$$I_4 = \frac{V_{C-D}}{R_4} = \frac{356.4}{0.1} = 3564 \text{ amps}$$

The total load current is 3564 + 1782, or 5346 amps.

The voltage across S_3 and its internal resistance is also V_{C-D}. The current supplied by S_3 is found by Ohm's law.

$$510 - 0.04I_3 = 356.4$$

$$I_3 = \frac{153.6}{0.04} = 3840 \text{ amps}$$

The current supplied by the composite generator S_{1-2} is determined in the same way.

$$507 - 0.1I_{1-2} = 356.4$$

$$I_{1-2} = \frac{150.6}{0.1} = 1506 \text{ amps}$$

The voltage drop in transmission resistance R_x is now found.

$$V_x = \frac{I_{1-2}}{G_x} = \frac{1506}{15} = 100.4 \text{ volts}$$

(Note that $G_x = \frac{1}{R_x} = \frac{1}{0.067} = 15$ mhos.)

V_x is added to V_{C-D} to determine the voltage across generators S_1 and S_2.

$$V_{C-D} + V_x = 356.4 + 100.4 = 456.8 \text{ volts}$$

The currents in S_1 and S_2 can now be found.

$$520 - 0.1I_2 = 456.8$$

$$I_2 = \frac{520 - 456.8}{0.1} = \frac{63.2}{0.1} = 632 \text{ amps}$$

$$500 - 0.05I_1 = 456.8$$

$$I_1 = \frac{43.2}{0.05} = 864 \text{ amps}$$

$I_1 + I_2 = 632 + 864 = 1496$ amperes, instead of 1506, the value found for I_{1-2}. An error of 10 amperes in 1500 is reasonable.

Problems Based on Chapter 4

P4-1. In Fig. P4-1, the resistance from A to B is 25 ohms, from B to C is 30 ohms, and from C to A is 35 ohms. (a) Find the value of r_1, r_2, and r_3. (b) Find the value of the resistors in the equivalent delta.

Ans. (a) $r_1 = 15$ ohms, $r_2 = 10$ ohms, $r_3 = 20$ ohms. (b) $R_1 = 43.3$ ohms, $R_2 = 65$ ohms, $R_3 = 32.5$ ohms.

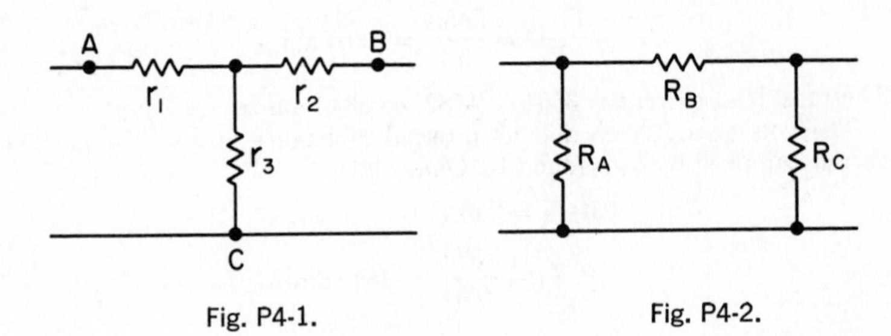

Fig. P4-1. Fig. P4-2.

P4-2. In Fig. P4-2, $R_A = 15$ ohms, $R_B = 22$ ohms, and $R_C = 28$ ohms. Find the equivalent wye resistances.

Ans. $r_a = 9.5$ ohms, $r_b = 6.45$ ohms, $r_c = 5.08$ ohms.

P4-3. In Fig. P4-3, $r_1 = 10$ ohms, $r_2 = 12$ ohms, $r_3 = 15$ ohms, $R_4 = 20$ ohms, $R_5 = 18$ ohms, and $R_6 = 22$ ohms. Find the equivalent resistance of the three-terminal network by either the wye to delta or the delta to wye transformation.

Ans. 8.9 ohms.

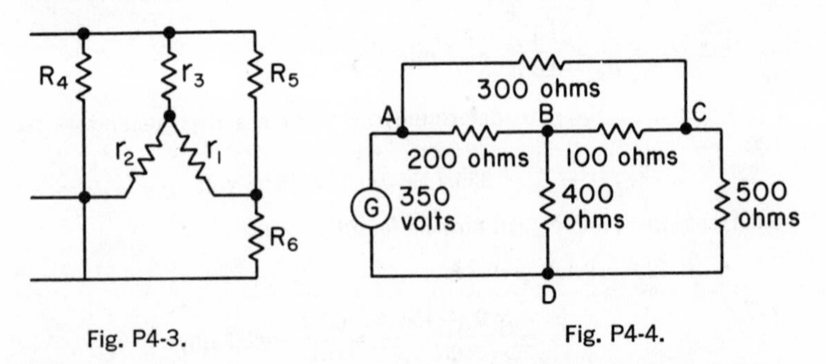

Fig. P4-3. Fig. P4-4.

P4-4. In Fig. P4-4, find (a) the current in the 300-ohm resistor, (b) the current from the generator, (c) the power in the 500-ohm resistor, and (d) the power delivered by the generator.

Ans. (a) 0.416 amp. (b) 1.02 amps. (c) 102 watts. (d) 356 watts.

P4-5. In Fig. P4-5, find (a) the current in $B-D$ and $C-E$, (b) the current in the 10-ohm resistor, (c) the current delivered by the generator.

Ans. (a) 9.6 amps, 5.8 amps. (b) 10 amps. (c) 15.4 amps.

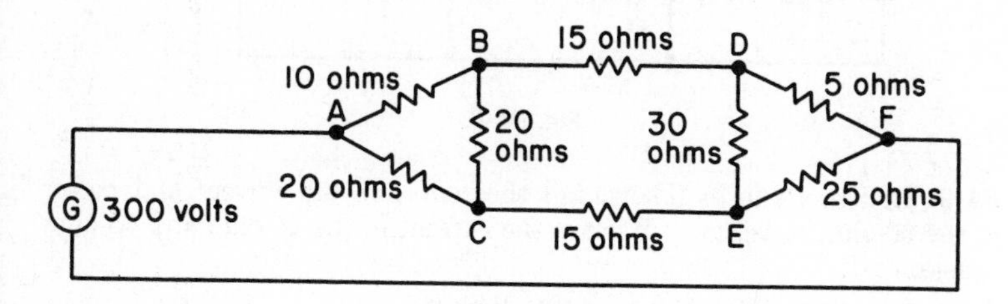

Fig. P4-5.

P4-6. In the circuit of Fig. P4-6, find the power in the 35-ohm load, using Thévenin's theorem.

Ans. $I = 5.85$ amps. $P = I^2R = 1200$ watts.

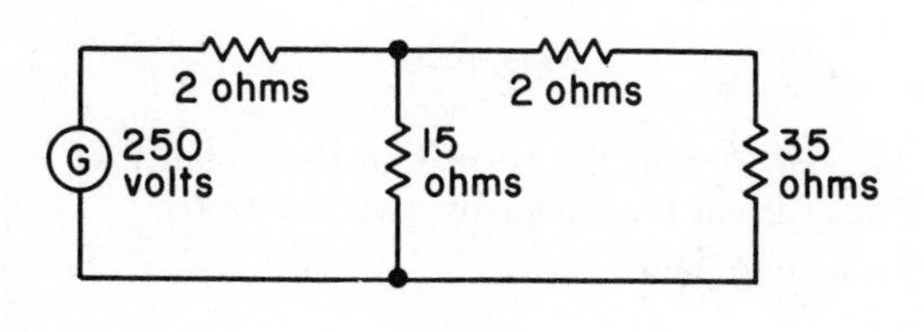

Fig. P4-6.

P4-7. Find the current in the 500-ohm resistor in Fig. P4-7 by using Thévenin's theorem.

Ans. 0.29 amp.

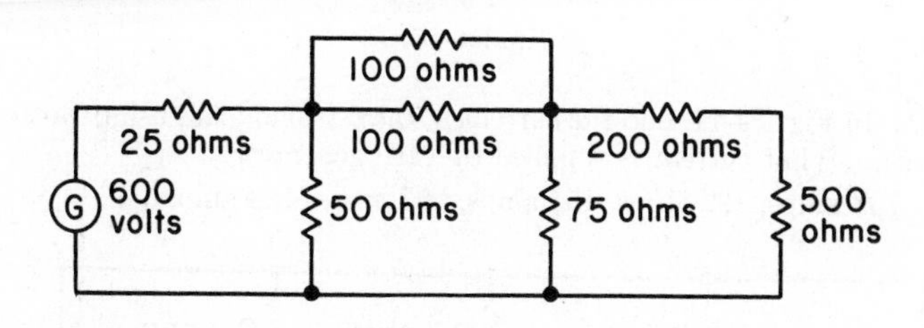

Fig. P4-7.

P4-8. Using Thévenin's theorem, find the current in the 50-ohm resistance in Fig. P4-8.

Ans. 4.7 amps.

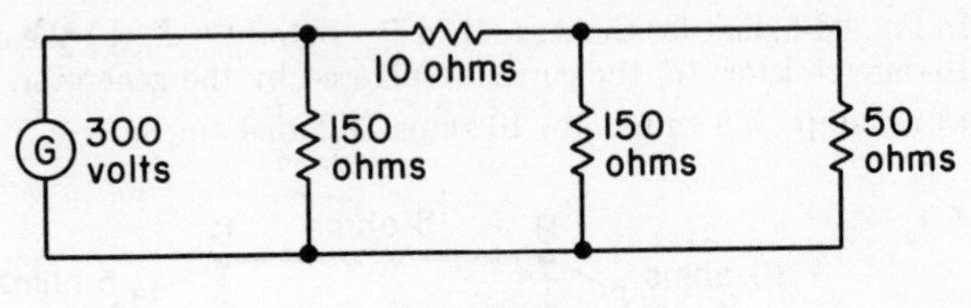

Fig. P4-8.

P4-9. In Fig. P4-9, by Thévenin's theorem, find the current and power in the 60-ohm resistance. What is the current in the 25-ohm and 45-ohm resistances?

Ans. 2.2 amps, 290 watts, 6.2 amps, 9 amps.

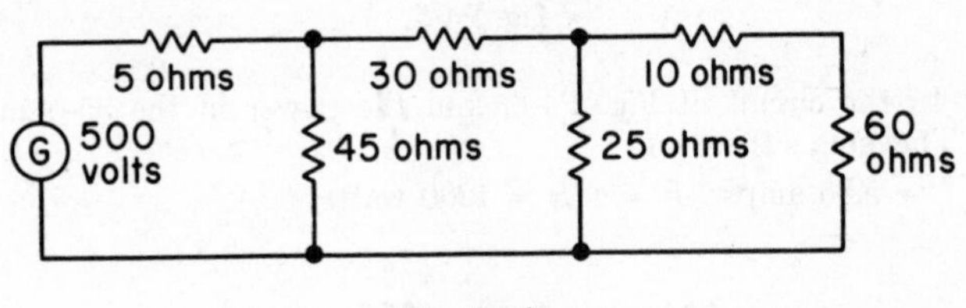

Fig. P4-9.

P4-10. In Fig. P4-10, find the current in the 5-ohm load by Norton's theorem. What current is supplied by each battery?

Ans. 2 amps, 2 amps, and 0 amp.

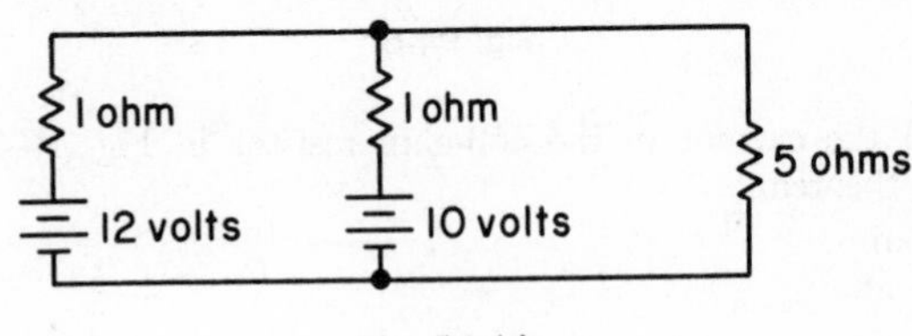

Fig. P4-10.

P4-11. In Fig. P4-11, find the current in the 0.1-ohm load, using Norton's theorem. What current is supplied by each generator?

Ans. 731 amps, 192 amps, 154 amps, 257 amps, 128 amps.

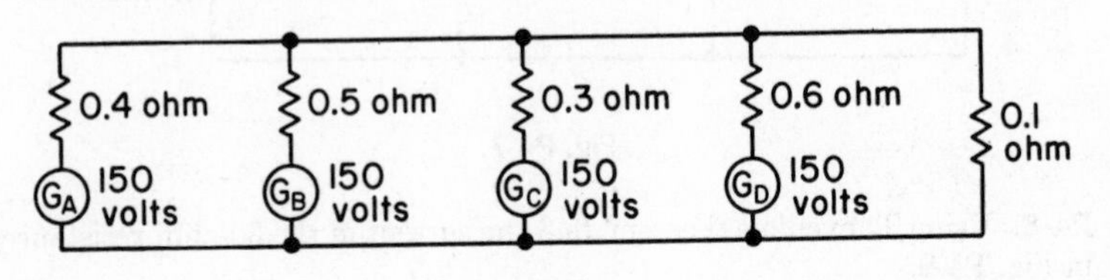

Fig. P4-11.

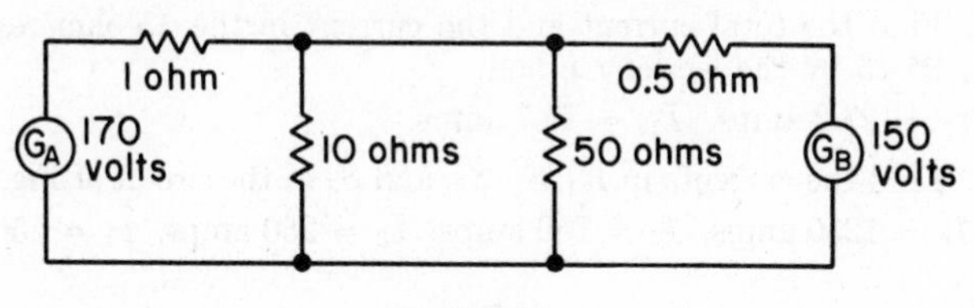

Fig. P4-12.

P4-12. Find the currents in the two load resistances and in the generators in Fig. P4-12. Use Norton's theorem.

Ans. I_{10} = 15.07 amps, I_{50} = 3.01 amps, I_A = 19.36 amps, I_B = − 1.28 amps. (G_B acts as a load.)

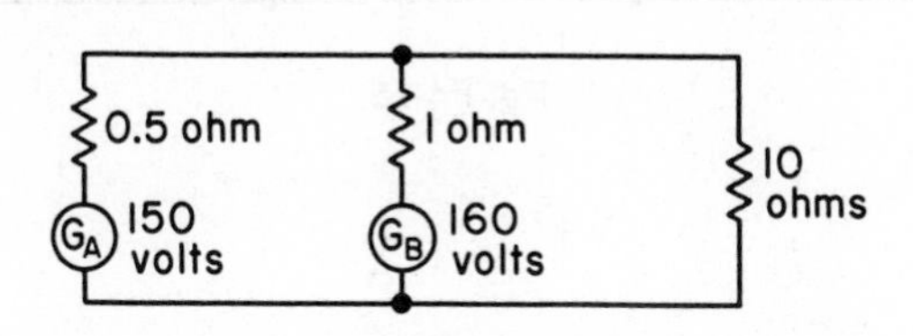

Fig. P4-13.

P4-13. Find the currents in the load and in the two generators of Fig. P4-13. Use the superposition theorem.

Ans. 14.8 amps, 11.6 amps, 3.2 amps.

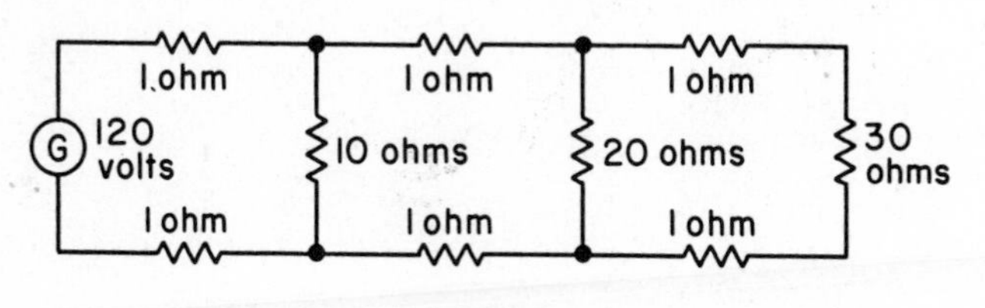

Fig. P4-14.

P4-14. In Fig. P4-14, by use of the ladder method, find the total current and the currents in the 10-ohm, 20-ohm, and 30-ohm resistances.

Ans. I_T = 15.2 amps. I_{10} = 8.96 amps. I_{20} = 3.86 amps. I_{30} = 2.41 amps.

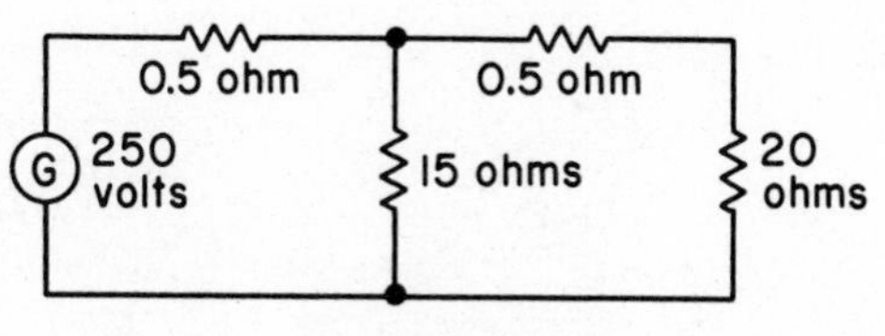

Fig. P4-15.

P4-15. Find the total current and the current in the 15-ohm resistance in Fig. P4-15 by the ladder method.
Ans. $I_T = 27.2$ amps. $I_{15} = 15.7$ amps.

P4-16. Find the currents in R_4, S_1, S_2, and S_3 in the circuit of Fig. P4-16.
Ans. $I_4 = 1250$ amps. $I_3 = 750$ amps. $I_2 = 250$ amps. $I_1 = 250$ amps.

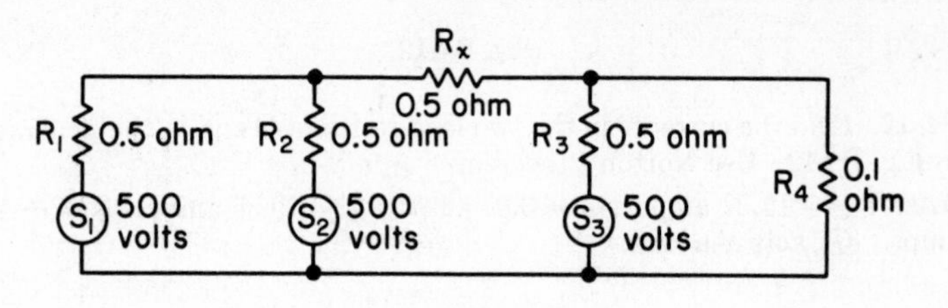

Fig. P4-16.

5 RESISTANCE AND TEMPERATURE

5-1. Wire Sizes. As indicated in Table 5-1, standard annealed copper wire used in nearly all electrical work is made in sizes based on the circular mil area of the wire. The standard for sizing or gaging electrical conductors in the United States is the American Wire Gage (AWG) or Brown and Sharpe Wire Gage (B & S).*

In the AWG (or B & S), wires are given numbers from 1 to 46, the wire size getting larger as the numbers get smaller. Conductors larger than No. 1 are designated "0" (or "aught"), "00" (or "2-aught"), "000" (or "3-aught"), and "0000" ("4-aught"). These four sizes are given shorthand designations as 1/0 (for 0), 2/0 (for 00), 3/0 (for 000), and 4/0 (for 0000). Sizes larger than 4/0 are designated by their circular mil area, as 250,000 CM, 300,000 CM, etc. These larger sizes are also designated 300 MCM where MCM is the abbreviation for "thousand circular mils."

The wire gage is arranged so that for every third size, the area is approximately doubled or cut in half, depending on which way the numbers go in the scale. If this arrangement of the gage is kept in mind and the area measurement of No. 10 wire is memorized to serve as a basis of calculation, it is possible to estimate areas of wire sizes if a table giving the exact figures is not at hand. For example, No. 10 wire has an area of 10,380 CM. No. 13 is three sizes smaller than No. 10 and should have an area of 5190 CM. Table 5-1 shows that it has 5178 CM. No. 7 wire is three sizes larger than No. 10, so it should have an area about two times 10,380, or 20,760 CM. Table 5-1 shows that No. 7 actually has an area of 20,820 CM.

---

* The Brown & Sharpe Company originated the B & S Gage, which was later adopted as the standard for the United States and called the American Wire Gage (AWG). Literature referring to this gage may use either designation, and some authors use both to indicate that it is actually one gage that can be called by either designation.

Table 5-1. Table of Standard Annealed Bare Copper Wire Using American Wire Gage (B & S)

Gage (AWG or B & S)	Diameter	Area	Weight	Length	Resistance at 68° F	
	Inches (Nom.)	Circular Mils	Pounds per M'	Feet per lb	Ohms per M'	Feet per Ohm
0000	.4600	211,600	640.5	1.561	.04901	20,400
000	.4096	167,800	570.9	1.968	.06180	16,180
00	.3648	133,100	402.8	2.482	.07793	12,830
0	.3249	105,500	319.5	3.130	.09827	10,180
1	.2893	83,690	253.3	3.947	.1239	8,070
2	.2550	66,370	200.9	4.977	.1563	6,400
3	.2294	52,640	159.3	6.276	.1970	5,075
4	.2043	41,740	126.4	7.914	.2485	4,025
5	.1819	33,100	100.2	9.980	.3133	3,129
6	.1620	26,250	79.46	12.58	.3951	2,531
7	.1443	20,820	63.02	15.87	.4982	2,007
8	.1285	16,510	49.98	20.01	.6282	1,592
9	.1144	13,090	39.63	25.23	.7921	1,262
10	.1019	10,380	31.43	31.82	.9989	1,001
11	.09074	8,234	24.92	40.12	1.260	794
12	.08081	6,530	19.77	50.59	1.588	629.6
13	.07196	5,178	15.68	63.80	2.003	499.3
14	.06408	4,107	12.43	80.44	2.525	396.0
15	.05707	3,257	9.858	101.4	3.184	314.0
16	.05082	2,583	7.818	127.9	4.016	249.0
17	.04526	2,048	6.200	161.3	5.064	197.5
18	.04030	1,624	4.917	203.4	6.385	156.5
19	.03589	1,288	3.899	256.5	8.051	124.2
20	.03196	1,022	3.092	323.4	10.15	98.5
21	.02846	810.1	2.452	407.8	12.80	78.11
22	.02535	642.4	1.945	514.2	16.14	61.95
23	.02257	509.5	1.542	648.4	20.36	49.13
24	.02010	404.0	1.223	817.7	25.67	38.96
25	.01790	320.4	.9699	1,031	32.37	30.90
26	.01594	254.1	.7692	1,300	40.81	24.50
27	.01420	201.5	.6100	1,639	51.47	19.43
28	.01264	159.8	.4837	2,067	64.90	15.41
29	.01126	126.7	.3836	2,607	81.83	12.22
30	.01003	100.5	.3042	3,287	103.2	9.691
31	.008928	79.7	.2413	4,145	130.1	7.685
32	.007950	63.21	.1913	5,227	164.1	6.095
33	.007080	50.13	.1517	6,591	206.9	4.833
34	.006305	39.75	.1203	8,310	260.9	3.833
35	.005615	31.52	.09542	10,480	329.0	3.040
36	.005000	25.00	.07568	13,210	414.8	2.411
37	.004453	19.83	.06001	16,660	523.1	1.912
38	.003965	15.72	.04759	21,010	659.6	1.516
39	.003531	12.47	.03774	26,500	831.8	1.202
40	.003145	9.888	.02993	33,410	1,049	0.9534
41	.00280	7.8400	.02373	42,140	1,323	.7559
42	.00249	6.2001	.01877	52,270	1,673	.5977
43	.00222	4.9284	.01492	67,020	2,104	.4753
44	.00197	3.8809	.01175	85,100	2,672	.3743
45	.00176	3.0976	.00938	106,600	3,348	.2987
46	.00157	2.4649	.00746	134,040	4,207	.2377

Adjacent sizes differ by a factor of $\sqrt[3]{2}$, or approximately 1.26. Therefore, No. 11, being smaller than No. 10, should have an area of about 10,380/1.26, or 8238 CM. Table 5-1 gives it a value of 8234 CM.

No. 1/0, which is ten sizes removed from No. 10, should have an area approximately ten times that of No. 10, or 103,800 CM. The actual value, in Table 5-1, is 105,500 CM.

Such calculations do not give exact values for the conductors, but they give a reasonable approximation of the area.

Example 5-1. What is the CM area of No. 3† wire by the approximate method?

Solution. Starting with 10,380 CM for No. 10 wire, we can take every three gage numbers as having double the area:

Gage No.	*Area (CM)*
10	10,380
7	20,760
4	41,520

No. 3 is larger than No. 4 by the factor 1.26. Therefore, No. 3 has an area of (1.26) (41,520) = 52,315 CM. Table 5-1 shows that the area of No. 3 wire is 52,640 CM.

A second method for estimating the area of No. 3 wire is to find the approximate area of No. 1/0, which is about ten times that of No. 10.

$$(10)\ (10{,}380) = 103{,}800 \text{ CM}$$

No. 3 wire has an area one-half that of No. 1/0, since it is three gage sizes smaller than No. 1/0.

$$\frac{103{,}800}{2} = 51{,}900 \text{ CM}$$

Obviously, the first method, although longer, is more accurate.

5-2. Wire Resistances.

Table 5-1 shows that the resistance of No. 10 wire at 68° Fahrenheit is 0.9989 ohm per 1000 feet. This figure is very close to 1 ohm per thousand feet, a figure that is easier to remember. The resistance of a wire is inversely pro-

---

† Although No. 3 wire is listed in the National Electrical Code and in Table 5-2, and is used in Example 5-1, it cannot be considered as being "commercially available" in the United States because it is not usually manufactured except on special order. If No. 3 wire is needed according to circuit or feeder calculations described in this chapter, No. 2 wire should be used unless the cable manufacturer can supply No. 3 in sufficient quantity at a reasonable price.

portional to the area. In Chapter 1, the resistance of copper was given as 10.4 ohms per CM foot. If a copper wire has an area of 2 CM, its resistance would be 5.2 ohms per foot. The resistance of No. 7 wire, therefore, would be half that of No. 10 since it has twice the area. Assuming 1 ohm per 1000 feet for No. 10 wire, we estimate 0.5 ohm for No. 7. Table 5-1 gives the actual resistance as 0.4982 ohm.

Example 5-2. Find the resistance of No. 2 wire without using Table 5-1.
Solution. Starting with 1 ohm per 1000 feet for No. 10 wire, we can make a table of values of resistance for every third gage.

Gage No.	*Resistance*
10	1 ohm
7	0.5 ohm
4	0.25 ohm
1	0.125 ohm

Since No. 2 is one size smaller than No. 1, its resistance will be larger by the factor of 1.26.

$$R = (1.26)\,(0.125) = 0.1575 \text{ ohm}$$

The resistance of No. 2 wire as given in the table is 0.1563 ohm.

5-3. Wire Capacities. In the United States, the only recognized authority for determining the current-carrying capacities of copper wire and cables is the National Electrical Code of the National Fire Protection Association (NFPA). The main purpose of assigning current capacities for conductors is to prevent fire, and the ability of the insulation around the wire to resist heat is the important consideration. For example, No. 14 TW (Thermoplastic Weatherproof insulation) in free air will carry 20 amperes safely, but the same wire in an enclosure or raceway is limited to 15 amperes. If an asbestos insulated wire of No. 14 gage is enclosed in a raceway it can carry 30 amperes, and the same wire in free air may carry up to 40 or 50 amperes.

The current capacity of a wire or cable cannot be calculated, as there is no relationship between the area or the resistance and the capacity. For example, No. 10 TW wire in a raceway will carry 30 amperes. Although No. 1/0 wire is ten times as large as No. 10, it can carry only about four times the current, or 125 amperes, because it cannot dissipate ten times the heat. A conductor that will carry ten times as much current as No. 10 would have to be more than forty-three times as large in area.

Table 5-2 lists the current-carrying capacities of some of the conductors used, such as R (rubber), RW (rubber, weatherproof), T (thermoplastic), TW (thermoplastic, weatherproof), RHW (rubber, heat-resistant, weatherproof), THW (thermoplastic, heat-resistant, weatherproof), and AVA (asbestos, varnished cambric).

Table 5-2. Current-Carrying Capacities of Standard Size Conductors for Power Circuits and Feeders

(Based on the National Electrical Code.)

Size AWG	Type* R, RW, T, TW	Type* RHW THW	Type* AVA	Size MCM†	Type* R, RW, T, TW	Type* RHW THW	Type* AVA
14	15	15	30	250	215	255	315
12	20	20	35	300	240	285	345
10	30	30	45	350	260	310	390
8	40	45	60	400	280	335	420
6	55	65	80	500	320	380	470
4	70	85	105	600	355	420	525
3	80	100	120	700	385	460	560
2	95	115	135	750	400	475	580
1	110	130	160	800	410	490	600
0	125	150	190	900	435	520	—
00	145	175	215	1000	455	545	680
000	165	200	245	1250	495	590	—
0000	195	230	275	1500	520	625	785
				1750	545	650	—
				2000	560	665	840

*R (rubber); RW (rubber, weatherproof); T (thermoplastic); TW (thermoplastic, weatherproof); RHW (rubber, heat-resistant, weatherproof); THW (thermoplastic, heat-resistant, weatherproof); AVA (asbestos, varnished cambric).

†MCM is 1000 circular mils. The figures in this column are multiplied by 1000, as 250 MCM = 250,000 CM.

Example 5-3. What is the smallest size of TW conductor that can be used to carry 135 amperes?

Solution. Table 5-2 shows that No. 1/0 will carry 125 amperes and No. 2/0 will carry 145 amperes. No. 2/0 is required.

If the 135-ampere load is to be sustained for any appreciable length of time, however, this fact must be taken into consideration and the capacity of conductors must be reduced to 80 per cent of that given in the table. For this condition, the allowable capacity of No. 2/0 is only 116 amperes. The capacity of No. 3/0 is only 132 amperes for this sustained load, and No. 4/0 must therefore be used. The capacity of No. 4/0 cable for a long continued or sustained load is

$$(195)\ (0.8) = 156 \text{ amps}$$

5-4. Choosing the Right Size of Wire. For all practical purposes, the current capacities of conductors listed in the National Electrical Code and in Table 5-2 are of little value except as a limit. This fact has become increasingly recognized during recent years and is being written into local electrical codes, especially those of large cities. Although Table 5-2 shows that No. 14 wire is approved for loads up to 15 amperes, some codes will not permit its use for lighting or power circuits. The size of wire is now required to be chosen on the basis of the voltage drop from a circuit-feeding device, such as a lighting panel, to the load on the branch circuit.

The illumination output of an incandescent light drops approximately 3 per cent for every 1 per cent drop in voltage below the manufacturer's rating of the lamp. The amount of light for voltages 23 per cent to 108 per cent of rated lamp voltage is shown in Table 5-3. For all practical purposes, the incandescent lamp is blacked out (no output) if the voltage drops to 70 per cent of the lamp voltage rating, but serious loss of light and increased cost of electricity will take place at even 95 per cent of rated voltage. Fluorescent lights will black out if the voltage drops to approximately 80 per cent of the rated voltage of the lamp and ballast.

The voltage drop in a direct-current or a single-phase alternating-current line is calculated on the basis of the ampere load and the circular mil area of the wire or cable. Some electrical codes (laws governing electrical wiring) specify a formula to be used for the calculation of voltage drops. Although copper wire has a resistivity of 10.4 ohms per CM foot at 20° C, a higher value is considered indicative of actual conditions in the circuit under operating conditions when calculating the voltage drop. Because of the possi-

Table 5-3. Light Intensity Versus Lamp Voltage for 120-Volt Incandescent Lamp

Per Cent Normal Voltage*	Voltage at Lamp	Per Cent Normal Foot Candles of Light*
108	129.6	126
100	120.0	100
92	110.4	74
83	99.6	54
75	90.0	37
70	84.0	28
67	80.4	23
58	69.6	13
50	60.0	7.0
42	50.4	2.7
33	39.6	0.8
25	30.0	0.2
23	27.6	0.1

**Based on information furnished by Automatic Switch Co., Florham Park, New Jersey, through its Los Angeles, California, office.*

bility of high atmospheric temperatures and the temperature rise of the copper when current is flowing, the value of 10.8 ohms per CM foot gives better results in voltage drop calculations.

The voltage drop in any direct current circuit is, from Ohm's law,

$$V_d = IR \tag{5-1}$$

where V_d is the voltage drop in the line, I is the current in amperes, and R is the total resistance of the line from the current source—such as a lighting panel—to the load and back (twice the length l of the circuit). The resistance is, therefore,

$$R = \frac{(2\,l)\,(10.8)}{\text{CM}} \tag{5-2}$$

where 10.8 is the resistivity of the copper, l is the one-way length of the circuit, and CM is the circular mil area of the conductor.

Substituting equation (5-2) in equation (5-1) gives the voltage drop equation.

$$V_d = \frac{21.6\, Il}{\text{CM}} \qquad (5\text{-}3)$$

The per cent voltage drop is then found from the equation

$$\%V_d = \frac{V_d}{V} \times 100 \qquad (5\text{-}4)$$

where V is the rated voltage of the system, as 120, 240, etc.

Equations (5-3) and (5-4) should be used for the calculation of voltage drops for actual electrical construction which is regulated by law, or when no temperature is specified. Voltage drops for specific temperatures are calculated from Ohm's law and the equations and data given in Section 5-5 of this chapter.

Example 5-4. A load of six 200-watt lamps is fed from a 120-volt lighting panel. If the length of the circuit is 150 feet, what is the smallest standard size of wire that can be used if a 2 per cent voltage drop is allowed for the circuit?

Solution. The total wattage of the load is

$$P = (6)\,(200) = 1200 \text{ watts}$$

If we assume that the actual load is 1200 watts and that this load is not reduced by voltage drop in the line, the current is

$$I = \frac{P}{E} = \frac{1200}{120} = 10 \text{ amps}$$

According to Table 5-2, No. 14 gage wire will carry up to 15 amperes. The CM area required for the circuit is found by solving equation (5-3) for the area.

$$\text{CM} = \frac{21.6\, Il}{V_d} = \frac{(21.6)\,(10)\,(150)}{(0.02)\,(120)} = \frac{32{,}400}{2.4} = 13{,}500 \text{ CM}$$

From Table 5-1 we learn that No. 8 gage wire with an area of 16,510 CM must be used, even though its allowable current-carrying capacity, from Table 5-2, is 40 amperes.

Example 5-5. What would be the actual voltage drop for the load in Example 5-4 for No. 14 wire? For No. 12 wire? For No. 10 wire?

Solution. For No. 14 wire, the drop is found from equation (5-3).

$$V_d = \frac{(21.6)\,(10)\,(150)}{4107} = 7.89 \text{ volts}$$

The per cent voltage drop, from equation (5-4), is

$$\%V_d = \frac{V_d}{V} \times 100 = \frac{7.89}{120} \times 100 = 6.6\% \text{ (nearly)}$$

For No. 12 wire, the voltage drop and per cent voltage drop are

$$V_d = \frac{(21.6)(10)(150)}{6530} = 4.96 \text{ volts}$$

$$\%V_d = \frac{4.96}{120} \times 100 = 4.1\%$$

For No. 10 wire, the voltage drop and per cent voltage drop are

$$V_d = \frac{(21.6)(10)(150)}{10{,}380} = 3.12 \text{ volts}$$

$$\%V_d = \frac{3.12}{120} \times 100 = 2.6\%$$

For most circuits, the size of wire required for the voltage drop limitation will be much larger than that permitted by the current-carrying capacities given in Table 5-2.

5-5. Temperature Coefficient of Resistance. Most metals increase in resistance as the temperature increases. Table 5-1 gives the resistance of standard annealed copper wire at 68° F (20° C), but the operating temperatures of the wires are usually much higher. Based on its resistance at 20° C, a copper conductor will increase its resistance by approximately 0.393 of 1 per cent per degree Celsius or 0.218 of 1 per cent per degree Fahrenheit. This percentage rise—with respect to the standard temperature of 20° C (68° F)—is approximately constant over the range of temperatures from about 0° to 200° C (32° to about 390° F).

The rise in resistance can be expressed as

$$R_2 = R_1 + \alpha R_1 (t_2 - t_1) \tag{5-5}$$

where R_2 is the resistance at temperature t_2, R_1 is the resistance at temperature t_1, and α is the per cent rise (or fall) of the resistance with respect to the standard temperature.

Equation (5-5) may be rewritten in the form

$$R_2 = R_1 [1 + \alpha (t_2 - t_1)] \tag{5-6}$$

Accurate results can be obtained by using equation (5-6) only if R_1 is the resistance at the standard temperature and t_1 is the standard temperature. The change in resistance per degree is essentially constant over the operating range of temperatures, but the per cent change is not constant. For example, the per cent change at 90° C is quite different from the per cent change at 20° C, even though the actual change in ohms is the same. The change in resistance in ohms per CM foot is 0.0408 in the Celsius scale and 0.0223 in the Fahrenheit scale.

Since the increase (or decrease) in resistance is constant over the operating range of temperatures, the resistance of a conductor can be represented as a straight line above 0° C, as shown in Fig. 5-1. Below the freezing point of water (0° C or 32° F) the change in resistance per degree is slightly less than at higher temperatures, and the graph in Fig. 5-1 curves until it crosses the zero resistance line at Z, which is very close to absolute zero (− 273.15° C or − 459.67° F). If the change was constant for all temperatures, the conductor would have zero resistance at the value M.

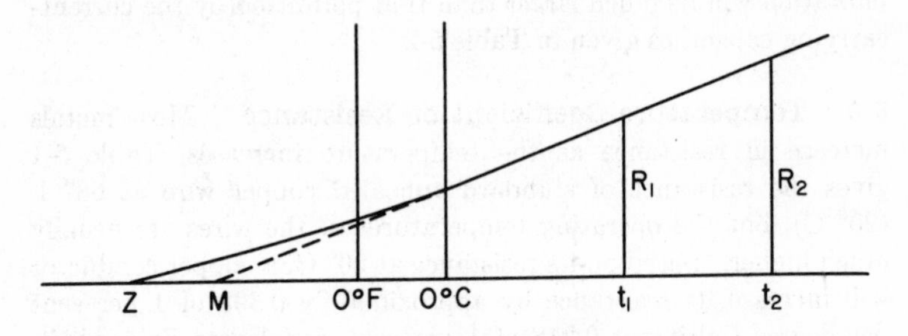

Fig. 5-1. Relationship between resistance and temperature of some electrical conductors.

If R_1 and R_2 are the resistances at temperatures t_1 and t_2, respectively—where t_1 and t_2 are any temperature between 20° and 200° C—from the similar triangles in the figure we may write

$$\frac{R_2}{R_1} = \frac{T + t_2}{T + t_1} \tag{5-7}$$

where T is in degrees Celsius or degrees Fahrenheit below zero. For copper conductors, the value of T in the Celsius scale is 234.5° and in the Fahrenheit scale it is 390.1°. Table 5-4 gives temperature constants for several materials.‡

Another method of calculating the changes in resistance of copper conductors resulting from changes in temperatures is indicated in Table 5-5. If the resistance of the wire at 20° C is known, its

‡ Most of the values in Table 5-4 are from "Calculating Temperature from Resistance Changes" by Eugene George Key and Michael J. Coppola, *Power Plant Engineering*, Vol. 43 (September, 1939), p. 603.

Table 5-4. Temperature Constants for Conducting Materials

Conductor	Temperature Constant M	
	Fahrenheit	Celsius
Silver, pure annealed	405.6	243.1
Copper, pure annealed	385.6	232.0
Copper, annealed	416.7	249.3
Copper, hard drawn	417.4	249.7
Copper, standard annealed	390.1	234.5
Aluminum (99.5% pure)	391.5	235.3
Aluminum (commercial 97.5% pure)	379.1	228.4
Iron (approximately pure)	255.8	159.9
"E.B.B." iron wire	352.8	213.8
"B.B." iron wire	355.7	215.4
Nickel	256.2	160.1
Tin (pure)	373.2	225.1
Steel Wire	355.5	215.3
Tungsten	348.9	176.0

resistance at a higher temperature can be found by the formula

$$R_2 = K_2 R_{20} \tag{5-8}$$

where R_2 is the resistance at the higher temperature, R_{20} is the resistance at 20° C, and K_2 is the constant from column 2 of Table 5-5 corresponding to the temperature of R_2. If the resistance R_1 is known for a temperature t_1, then, from equation (5-8),

$$R_1 = K_1 R_{20}$$

Dividing this equation into equation (5-8) gives

$$\frac{R_2}{R_1} = \frac{K_2}{K_1} \tag{5-8a}$$

or

$$R_2 = R_1 \left(\frac{K_2}{K_1}\right) \tag{5-9}$$

Equation (5-9) allows Table 5-5 to be used for converting resistance between any two temperatures listed in the table.

Table 5-5. Multiplying Constants for Copper Wire at Various Temperatures

Temperature (degrees C)	Multiplying Factor for Temperatures above 20° C	Temperature (degrees F)
20	1.000	68
25	1.019	77
30	1.039	86
35	1.059	95
40	1.079	104
45	1.098	113
50	1.118	122
55	1.137	131
60	1.157	140
65	1.176	149
70	1.196	158
75	1.216	167
80	1.236	176
85	1.255	185
90	1.275	194
95	1.294	203
100	1.314	212

Example 5-6. A No. 8 copper conductor 300 feet long is operating at a temperature of 50° C. What is its resistance at that temperature?

Solution. From Table 5-1 we find that No. 8 wire has a resistance of 0.6282 ohm per thousand feet at 68° F or 20° C. The resistance of 300 feet of this conductor is

$$R_1 = \frac{300}{1000}(0.6282) = 0.1885 \text{ ohm}$$

(a) From equation (5-6), the resistance at 50° C is found to be

$$R_2 = R_1 [1 + \alpha (t_2 - t_1)] = 0.1885 [1 + (0.00393) (30)]$$
$$= (0.1885) (1 + 0.118) = (0.1885) (1.118) = 0.2107 \text{ ohm}$$

(b) Equation (5-7) may also be used.

$$R_2 = R_1 \left(\frac{T + t_2}{T + t_1}\right) = 0.1885 \left(\frac{234.5 + 50}{234.5 + 20}\right)$$
$$= (0.1885) \left(\frac{284.5}{254.5}\right) = (0.1885) (1.118) = 0.2107 \text{ ohm}$$

(c) Equation (5-8) can also be used with values from Table 5-5.

$$R_2 = K_2 R_{20} = (1.118) (0.1885) = 0.2107 \text{ ohm}$$

5-6. Converting Celsius and Fahrenheit Temperatures. Since both Celsius and Fahrenheit temperatures are used in electrical engineering, conversions from one scale to another are often necessary. Graphs and tables are available which can be used to convert from one scale to another. However, when tables and graphs are not available, the conversion must be calculated.

The formulas given in most text and reference books are

$$C = \frac{5}{9} (F - 32) \quad (5\text{-}10)$$

$$F = \frac{9}{5} C + 32 \quad (5\text{-}11)$$

Equations (5-10) and (5-11) are not easy to remember because they are different in form. In 1939, Stanley F. Davis§ proposed two formulas based on the fact that the Celsius and Fahrenheit scales are identical at 40° below zero. These formulas are of the same form, are easy to remember, and are simple to use. The Davis formulas are

$$C = \frac{5}{9} (F + 40) - 40 \quad (5\text{-}12)$$

$$F = \frac{9}{5} (C + 40) - 40 \quad (5\text{-}13)$$

§ See "Converting Centigrade and Fahrenheit" by Stanley F. Davis, *Power Plant Engineering*, Vol. 43 (September, 1939), p. 603. See also *Elementary Engineering Mechanics* by Eugene George Key (New York: John Wiley & Sons, Inc., 1960), p. 408.

Equations (5-12) and (5-13) give the identical results as do equations (5-10) and (5-11) and have much to recommend them.

When only a change in temperature is to be converted from one scale to the other, the following formulas will give the desired results:

$$C_2 - C_1 = \frac{5}{9}(F_2 - F_1) \tag{5-14}$$

$$F_2 - F_1 = \frac{9}{5}(C_2 - C_1) \tag{5-15}$$

where C_2, C_1, F_2, and F_1 are the high and low temperatures on the Celsius and Fahrenheit scales, respectively. If $C_2 - C_1$ is replaced by T_C and $F_2 - F_1$ is replaced by T_F, the change may be represented as

$$T_C = \frac{5}{9} T_F \tag{5-16}$$

$$T_F = \frac{9}{5} T_C \tag{5-17}$$

Example 5-7. A temperature of 150° C is to be converted to the Fahrenheit scale. Find the temperature in degrees F.

Solution. Equation (5-11) gives

$$F = \frac{9}{5}\mathrm{C} + 32 = \frac{9}{5}(150) + 32 = 270 + 32 = 302^\circ\ \mathrm{F}$$

The result obtained by using equation (5-13) is the same:

$$F = \frac{9}{5}(\mathrm{C} + 40) - 40 = 342 - 40 = 302^\circ\ \mathrm{F}$$

Example 5-8. Motors are rated to allow a 40° C rise above ambient‖ temperature during operation. What is this rise on the Fahrenheit scale?

Solution. From equation (5-17) we obtain

$$T_F = \frac{9}{5} T_C = \frac{9}{5}(40) = 72^\circ\ \mathrm{F}$$

5-7. Resistance Thermometry. Since the average operating temperatures of motors, generators, conductors, and other electrical wire-wound devices cannot be determined by direct

‖ Ambient temperature is defined as the temperature of the air, oil, water, or other medium surrounding an object.

measurement, equation (5-7) can be used to obtain them. Even equation (5-9) will yield fair results if the temperatures are within the range of Table 5-5 and are interpolated for temperatures and resistances between tabular values.

When temperatures are extremely high (beyond 200° C), formulas based on a constant change in resistance per degree are very inaccurate, the inaccuracy increasing as the temperatures increase. The actual change in resistance is then defined by the formula

$$R_2 = R_0 (1 + \alpha_0 t - \beta_0 t^2) \tag{5-18}$$

Since copper cannot be used for high temperature resistance measurements, other metals, such as platinum, are used in resistance thermometers. Platinum has the values, for equation (5-18), of $\alpha_0 = 0.00392$ and $\beta_0 = 5.83 \times 10^{-7}$. Resistance thermometers can be used to determine temperatures of definite points —or hot spots—in electrical or other equipment in which high temperatures exist.

Some metals, called semi-conductors, have high temperature coefficients—about ten times that of ordinary metals—and their coefficients are negative. In other words, the resistance decreases as the temperature rises and, conversely, increases as the temperature drops. These resistors, called thermistors, are used to a great extent in the testing and operating of electronic equipment, particularly radar. Thermistors are usually made of various combinations of copper, nickel, cobalt, manganese, uranium, etc. Thermistors are confined to applications in which a small current flows, with consequent low variation in temperatures.

Example 5-9. A motor is stored in a room where the temperature is 25° C. The resistance of its windings is measured and found to be 80 ohms. The motor is then connected to a load and operated for one hour, after which the resistance is again measured and found to be 91 ohms. What is the temperature rise as determined from the resistance measurements?

Solution. Equation (5-7) can be used. If t_2 is the final temperature, then

$$t_2 = \frac{R_2 (T + t_1)}{R_1} - T = \frac{91 (234.5 + 25)}{80} - 234.5$$

$$= 295 - 234.5 = 60.5° \text{ C}$$

This represents a rise of $60.5 - 25 = 35.5°$ C. Since motors are allowed a 40° C rise above ambient in one hour, this motor satisfies that requirement.

5-8. Resistance of Rectangular Conductors.[#] Resistance in the engineering system of calculations is based on the circular mil foot, but not all conductors are circular. The most common non-circular conductor used in power work is the bus bar, which is rectangular in shape. The dimensions of bus bars range from ⅛ to ½ inch in thickness, and from 1 to 8 inches in width.

In Chapter 1, the resistance of circular conductors was given as

$$R_C = \frac{\rho l}{A_C} \qquad \text{[see equation (1-12)]}$$

where ρ is the resistivity in ohms per CM foot, l is the length in feet, and A_C is the area in circular mils, equal to the square of the diameter when the diameter is expressed in mils or in numbers of thousandths of an inch. A mil is equal to 0.001 inch. The area in square mils, then, is smaller by the factor $\pi/4$, or 0.7854, since a square mil is larger than a circular mil. The difference is expressed by the equation

$$A_R = \frac{\pi}{4} A_C \quad \text{or} \quad A_C = \frac{4}{\pi} A_R$$

where A_R is the área of the rectangular conductor in square mils. The resistance of rectangular conductors is, therefore,

$$R_R = \frac{\rho\, l}{\frac{4}{\pi} A_R} = \frac{\pi \rho l}{4 A_R} \tag{5-19}$$

Taking 10.4 ohms per CM foot as the resistivity of copper wire, we find that the resistivity for bus bars is (10.4) ($\pi/4$), or 8.17 ohms per square mil foot. When this value of resistivity is used, equation (5-19) can be used in the form

$$R_R = \frac{\rho_R\, l}{A_R} \tag{5-20}$$

where ρ_R is the resistivity in ohms per square mil per foot, or 8.17, and the other symbols have the significance already given them. The change in this constant resulting from changes in temperature can be found by any of the methods that apply to the resistivity of circular wires.

[#] See "Resistance of Rectangular Conductors" by Eugene George Key, *Power Plant Engineering*, Vol. 43 (July, 1939), p. 467.

Example 5-10. What is the resistance of a $\frac{3}{8} \times 4$ bus bar at 20° C if the bus is 100 feet long? At 60° C?

Solution. From equation (5-20) we obtain the value at 20° C.

$$R_R = \frac{\rho_R\, l}{A_R} = \frac{(8.17)\,(100)}{\frac{3}{8}\,(4)\,(1000)^2} = 0.000545 \text{ ohm}$$

Using equation (5-9) and Table 5-5, we obtain the resistance at 60° C.

$$R = (1.157)\,(0.000545) = 0.000631 \text{ ohm}$$

The carrying capacities of rectangular conductors depend on the size of the bars, the number of bars, and the spacing between the bars when more than one bar is used.

5-9. Stranded Wire.

Since most wires and cables are pulled through wireways such as conduits (specially constructed pipes), large conductors are made of two or more smaller conductors wound around each other for greater flexibility. This type of conductor is called "stranded" to differentiate it from the solid or rod-type often used in the smaller gages.**

For accurate results in resistance and voltage drop calculations, the additional length of the copper resulting from the spiral arrangement of the strands must be taken into consideration. Wire tables issued by cable manufacturers usually list the resistance of both solid and stranded wires for those sizes for which both types are available. When only the resistance of solid wires is given in the table, a factor of 2 per cent can be added to the value of the resistance of the solid wire in finding the resistance of the stranded wire. Some stranded conductors require that a factor of other than 2 per cent be used.

Practical engineering design, however, does not require this extreme accuracy. If the voltage drop for the No. 14 wire of

** The National Electrical Code requires that all conductors of No. 6 and larger be stranded if they are used in raceways such as conduits. Many engineering firms, such as the Fluor Corporation in Los Angeles, require that all wires used in instrument circuits and sizes No. 8 and larger in all other circuits—including power and lighting—must be stranded. According to William J. E. Jones, Assistant to the Chief Electrical Engineer at the Fluor Corporation, the trend in electrical construction is toward using stranded wire for all sizes down to No. 12 gage for nearly all purposes, especially when nine or more wires are to be pulled through the same conduit. Pulling that many rod-type conductors through a conduit is a task bordering on the extremely difficult, if not the impossible.

Example 5-5 were calculated for stranded wire, the actual drop might be 8.05 volts instead of 7.89, or a difference of 0.16 volt. This difference is generally considered to be unimportant.

5-10. Current Calculations. When a circuit or feeder is designed, the power in watts is usually determined first and the current is obtained by dividing the power by the voltage. Since voltages are standardized, this division can be changed into multiplication by finding a constant for the voltage used in a particular system.

If the voltage used is 110, for example, the multiplying factor is found by dividing the voltage into 1000.

$$C_P = \frac{1000}{110} = 9.1$$

Constants can be found for other voltages for direct-current systems by the same method of calculation. Constants for all standard voltages from 110 to 600 volts are given in Table 5-6. The constant C_P for any voltage is used in the formula

$$I = kw \times C_P \qquad (5\text{-}21)$$

where I is the current in amperes, kw is the power in kilowatts, and C_P is the constant from Table 5-6.

Table 5-6. Constants for Calculating Current from Power at Standard Voltages

Volts	C_P
110	9.1
120	8.33
220	4.54
240	4.17
440	2.27
480	2.08
500	2.00
600	1.67

Example 5-11. A circuit has a load to 5000 watts at 440 volts. What is the current in amperes?

Solution. Equation (5-21) gives the result by direct substitution, using the constant from Table 5-6.

$$I = kw \times C_P = (5)\ (2.27) = 11.35 \text{ amps}$$

5-11. Resistance of Incandescent Lamps. The incandescent lamp is probably the most outstanding example of the effect of heat on the resistance of conductors. The cold resistance of the

Table 5-7. Inrush and Normal Currents in Incandescent Lamps*

Lamp (watts)	Inrush current (amperes)	Time to reach maximum (seconds)	Normal operating current (amperes)	Time to reach normal (seconds)
75	9.38	0.0004	0.625	0.07
100	13.0	0.0007	0.835	0.10
200	26.2	0.0008	1.67	0.10
300	40.0	0.0011	2.5	0.13
500	67.9	0.0014	4.17	0.15
750	101.4	0.0021	6.25	0.17
1000	142.4	0.0031	8.33	0.23

*Currents are based on 120 volts across the lamp.
Data were furnished by the Los Angeles office of Automatic Switch Co. (ASCO), Florham Park, New Jersey.

tungsten filament is so low that the initial inrush current—at the instant the switch is closed—amounts, theoretically, to as much as fifteen to seventeen times the normal running current for the lamp.

As indicated in Table 5-7, the current inrush to a 75-watt lamp may reach 9.38 amperes during the first 0.0004 second, a value more than fifteen times the normal 0.625 ampere when the lamp reaches operating temperature at the end of 0.07 second. Since one cycle in a 60-cycle alternating current is equal to 0.0167 second, 0.07 second represents 4.2 cycles. The time for the other lamps listed in Table 5-7 to return to normal represents 5.98 cycles for the 100 and 200-watt lamps, 7.78 cycles for the 300, 9 cycles for the 500, 10.15 cycles for the 750, and 13.8 cycles for the 1000-watt lamp.

Since the filament starts heating as soon as current starts to flow, the actual inrush currents are reduced to slightly less than the theoretical values listed in Table 5-7, but, for safety and adequate operating characteristics, switching equipment is designed to handle more than the maximum theoretical current. The punishment that a 20-ampere switch and breaker—as well as the line conductors—must take at the instant a circuit is closed with a load of twelve 75-watt lamps can be appreciated when it is realized that although the normal current for such a circuit is only 7.5 amperes, the inrush current may be 112.56 amperes but the breaker must not trip open during that load.

Example 5-12. Using the currents given in Table 5-7, find the temperature of the filament for the 75-watt lamp when normal current is flowing.

Solution. The resistance at the instant the switch is closed is

$$R_1 = \frac{V}{I} = \frac{120}{9.38} = 12.8 \text{ ohms}$$

The resistance at the end of 0.07 second when normal current flows is

$$R_2 = \frac{V}{I} = \frac{120}{0.625} = 192 \text{ ohms}$$

Assuming that R_1 is at 20° C, we may use equation (5-7) and the constants given in Table 5-4.

$$t_2 = \frac{192\,(176 + 20)}{12.8} - 176 = 2940 - 176 = 2764° \text{ C}$$

This temperature may be converted to Fahrenheit by using equation (5-13).

$$F = \frac{9}{5}(C + 40) - 40 = \frac{9}{5}(2804) - 40 = 5007° \text{ F}$$

Note that these temperatures are beyond the straight line part of the resistance curve and therefore cannot be considered accurate. However, they do give a good indication of the heat lost in an incandescent lamp.

Problems Based on Chapter 5

P5-1. Using the method explained in Section 5-1, find the CM area of No. 4/0 cable.

Ans. 209,260 CM.

P5-2. What is the resistance of No. 4/0 cable by the method explained in Section 5-2?

Ans. 0.0495 ohm per 1000 ft.

P5-3. What is the smallest commercially available TW copper wire that can be used to supply a long continued load of 60 amps?

Ans. No. 2 will carry 72 amps. (No. 3 is not commercially available.)

P5-4. The maximum voltage drop on a feeder from a voltage source to a lighting panel is 1%. A 240-volt feeder which is 500 ft long supplies 108 amps to a lighting panel. What conductor is required?

Ans. With 2.4 volts drop allowed, 500 MCM (500,000 CM) is required.

P5-5. Five 500-watt lamps are supplied by a 120-volt lighting circuit. If the length of the circuit is 200 ft from the lighting panel to the center of the load and a voltage drop of 2% is allowed, what conductor is needed?

Ans. With 2.4 volts drop allowed, No. 4 is required.

P5-6. A lighting branch circuit 175 ft long supplies eight 75-watt lamps and three 200-watt lamps at 120 volts. If the conductor were chosen from Table 5-2 on the basis of carrying capacity alone, what would be the voltage drop?

Ans. 10 amps would require No. 14 wire, which would give a 9.2 volt drop, or 7.7%.

P5-7. A 500-volt feeder from a generator bus to a distribution panel carries a load of 1000 kw. If the feeder is 1000 ft long and a voltage drop of 1% is permitted, what size feeder is required?

Ans. The current is 2000 amps. With a 5-volt drop, 4,320,000 CM is required. The largest conductor listed in Table 5-2 is 2,000,000 CM. The job can be done best by using six 750,000-CM cables in parallel (a total of 12 cables for two-way transmission of current).

P5-8. A test bench 100 ft long requires a 12.5-volt feeder which will never carry more than 0.05 amp. If the voltage at the far end is to be not less than 12.49 volts, and the 0.05 amp load is assumed for the entire length of the feeder, what size conductor is required?

Ans. 10,800 CM is required, so that No. 8 is the smallest commercially available conductor that can be used.

P5-9. Ten 75-watt lamps will give the desired level of illumination in an area if the voltage is 120 volts. If the voltage drops to 92% of normal, how many lamps will be required to give the correct amount of illumination?

Ans. 14.

P5-10. Copper has a resistivity of 10.4 ohms per CM foot at 20° C, but equation (5-3) uses the value of 10.8. What temperature does this value represent?

Ans. 30° C or 86° F.

P5-11. The San Fernando Valley in Southern California records temperatures of 116° F during the summer period. If a circuit is assumed to have an operating temperature of 20° C above the ambient temperature, what is the resistivity of the copper wire?

Ans. Temperature is 152° F or 66.7° C. Resistivity is 12.3 ohms per CM foot.

P5-12. A coil is kept in a room where the temperature is 30° C. A Wheatstone Bridge shows the coil resistance to be 512 ohms. After the coil has operated for a period of time in a room whose temperature is 35° C, its resistance is found to have increased to 590 ohms. If standard annealed copper wire is used for the coil, how many degrees has the coil risen above the ambient temperature of the room in which it is operating?

Ans. 70.3° C − 35° C = 35.3° C.

P5-13. A line which was heavily loaded opens because of a ground fault. A Varley Loop test is made while the line is still hot and indicates that, based on the cold resistance of the cable, the fault is 5 miles from the point where the test is made. The next day, after the line has had a chance to cool, the same test indicates that the fault is only 4.2 miles from the test point. If the ambient temperature is 20° C, what was the operating temperature of the line at the time the fault occurred?

Ans. $R_2 = 5R_1/4.2 = 1.19R_1$. Operating temperature was 48.3° above ambient temperature.

P5-14. A No. 4/0 cable is to be replaced by a bus bar. If the cable is 250 ft long and the bus is to be 275 ft long but with the same resistance for the run as the cable, what is the area of the bus bar in square inches?

Ans. 182,716 square mils or 0.183 square in. The bar could be 1/8 in. × 1½ in.

P5-15. If the cool resistance of a 1000-watt lamp is at 20° C, what is the operating temperature of the lamp?

Ans. 3180° C or 5740° F.

6 CONDUCTION OF ELECTRICITY IN SOLIDS AND LIQUIDS

6-1. Types of Conduction. Electric currents can flow in solids (as in wire), in gases, or in liquids. An electric current consists of the net motion of electric charges. The motion of a negative charge in one direction is equal to the motion of a positive charge in the opposite direction and is recorded as the same value of current. If a positive charge moves in one direction and a negative charge moves in the opposite direction, the current is doubled.

The flow of electricity in solids is confined to the movement of electrons. Metals consist of atoms with free electrons. (Free electrons are electrons that are not attached to any atom.) The more free electrons present in the metal, the better it is as a conductor.

A positive ion is an atom or group of atoms that has lost one or more electrons. A single atom may lose an electron and have a positive charge equal to $+ 1.6 \times 10^{-19}$ coulomb. If two atoms are joined and each has lost an electron, the two atoms form an ion with a positive charge equal to 2 times 1.6×10^{-19} coulomb or $+ 3.2 \times 10^{-19}$ coulombs. A single atom may lose one, two, three, four, or sometimes even more electrons. If a single atom loses two electrons, it, too, has a positive charge of 2 times 1.6×10^{-19} coulomb.

A negative ion is an electron or an atom or group of atoms that has gained one or more electrons.

Positive or negative ions may exist in a liquid or solution even when there is no difference in electrical potential present. Even in the solid crystal which is common table salt (sodium chloride, NaCl), the molecules exist as sodium ions (Na^+) and chlorine ions (Cl^-). When the salt is placed in water, the ions are set free as the crystals dissolve. If two conductors—called plates or electrodes—to which a direct current source of voltage is connected are now placed in the solution, the Na^+ ions will travel toward the negative electrode and the Cl^- ions will travel toward the positive electrode. The movement of the ions constitutes an electric current, as is indicated if an ammeter is connected in the circuit (see Fig. 6-1, which shows three such cells connected in series). In addition, some of the water molecules become ionized* and cause a slight increase in current. The chemical reaction is given by the equation

$$H_2O = H^+ + (OH)^-$$

The $(OH)^-$ is a negative hydroxl ion. This ionization takes place even in pure water in the presence of an electric voltage, but the ionization is so slight that pure water offers a resistance of 500,000 ohms (0.5 megohm) at 18° C.

6-2. Primary Cells. When bars or plates of two different metals are immersed in an aqueous solution of acids, bases, or salts, an electric voltage can be measured, even though no outside source of voltage is present. The solution is called an *electrolyte*. The combination of electrodes and electrolyte is called a *primary cell* because it produces a voltage without requiring that it be given an electric charge before being put in operation. In fact, a primary cell cannot be charged in order to restore it to its original condition after it has been used.

One primary cell that is commonly used has a copper plate and a zinc plate and sulphuric acid as the electrolyte. The copper plate is positive and the zinc plate is negative. The sulphuric acid—H_2SO_4—in water will produce positive and negative ions according to the equation

$$H_2SO_4 \rightarrow 2H^+ + SO_4^{--}$$

When the two plates are connected through an external load, an electric current starts to flow. The hydrogen ions travel toward the zinc plate and there pick up some of the excess electrons.

---

* Ionization of water takes place to a very slight extent whether or not a potential exists between electrodes. Ionization is so slight in pure (distilled) water, even with a direct current potential applied, that only an extremely small current can flow. In fact, the current flow is so minute that pure water is generally considered to be an insulator. However, the addition of even a slight amount of impurities will cause a considerable rise in current flow through the resulting solution.

The reaction is as follows:

$$2H^+ + 2e \rightarrow H_2 \uparrow$$

Although some of the hydrogen is given off at the zinc electrode, most of it remains, forming a gas shield around the zinc. When the gas covers enough of the zinc plate to stop the action of the cell, the cell is said to be "polarized." The gas shield must be removed or disturbed to restore the cell to its conducting condition.

In the dry cell, carbon is used in place of copper and chemical inhibitors are used to prevent or retard polarization. The action of the dry cell is similar to that of the copper-zinc cell.

A variation of the copper-zinc cell is the *gravity* or *crowfoot* cell. A zinc electrode that looks much like the foot of a crow is fastened at the top of the container and a copper electrode is placed at the bottom. Two electrolytes are used, the copper being covered by a copper sulphate solution and the zinc being immersed in a zinc sulphate solution. The zinc sulphate, having a lower specific gravity than the copper sulphate, will remain on top and the solutions will not mix unless stirred or violently shaken. In this cell, the zinc is the negative electrode and the copper is the positive electrode.[†]

6-3. Electrolysis — Faraday's Principles. If the two electrodes that are immersed in an electrolyte are of identical materials, the galvanic—or battery—action described in Section 6-2 will not take place. However, if a voltage is applied to the electrode terminals, the cell will conduct current by *electrolysis*.

Assume that three cells are to be checked to determine what effect an electric current produces with three different electrolytes. This circuit is shown in Fig. 6-1. Platinum is used for all six electrodes. The electrolyte in Cell number 1 is silver nitrate,

---

† To an electrical engineer, the positive plate is the anode and the negative plate is the cathode. To the chemist, however, the anode is the electrode at which oxidation occurs. Oxidation is defined as any process which increases the proportion of oxygen or acid-forming element or radical in a compound. This process occurs at the zinc or negative plate in the cell described here. The reaction is

$$Zn \rightarrow Zn^{++} + 2e$$

Consequently, to the chemist, the negative plate of this cell is the anode and the positive plate is the cathode.

$AgNO_3$. The electrolyte in Cell number 2 is copper sulphate, $CuSO_4$. The electrolyte in Cell number 3 is antimony chloride, $SbCL_3$.

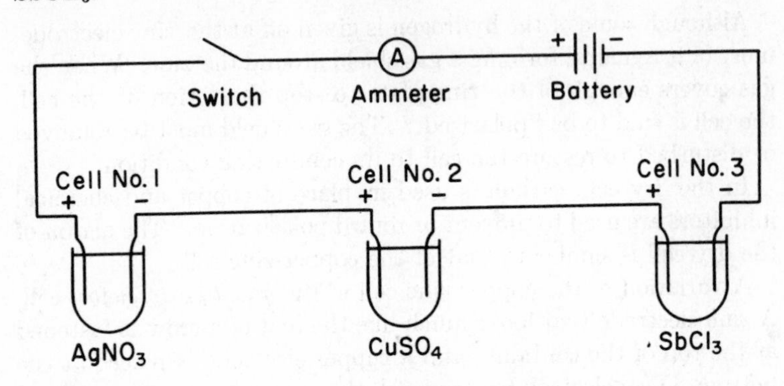

Fig. 6-1. Electrolysis.

When the circuit is closed, current flows. The silver, copper, and antimony from the electrolytes are deposited on the negative electrodes of their respective cells. After a certain period of time, the circuit is opened (current flow is stopped) and the negative electrodes of the three cells are weighed. The results show that the three electrodes have increased in weight as follows:

Cell No. 1 (with $AgNO_3$)
Ag (silver): 107.87 grams = 107.87/1 grams

Cell No. 2 (with $CuSO_4$)
Cu (copper): 31.77 grams = 63.54/2 grams

Cell No. 3 (with $SbCl_3$)
Sb (Antimony): 40.58 grams = 121.74/3 grams

These fractions indicate that the amount of metal deposited on the negative electrode is equal to the atomic weight of the metal, expressed in grams, divided by the valence of the metallic element. When this result is obtained, we can determine that the quantity of electricity that has been transferred through each cell is equal to 96,522 coulombs.

The principles relating to the transfer of material by electrolysis were first discovered by Michael Faraday (1791-1867). These principles may be stated as follows:

Faraday's principles of electrolysis. The quantity of an element undergoing chemical reaction at an electrode is proportional to the quantity of electric charge passing through a cell and to the atomic mass of the element, and is inversely proportional to the valence of the element.

These principles may be summarized in the formula

$$M = \frac{wQ}{96{,}500n} \tag{6-1}$$

where M is the mass of the element deposited (expressed in grams), w is the atomic weight of the material, n is the valence of the material, and Q is the charge passed through the electrolyte. The quantity given previously as 96,522 coulombs is expressed as 96,500 in the formula to allow computation on the slide rule and gives sufficient accuracy for engineering purposes. This quantity is called a *faraday*. The charge Q is in coulombs in equation (6-1).

The quantity w, expressed in grams, is equal to one mole of the material (atomic weight expressed in grams), and w/n is the amount of material deposited per faraday. The quantity $w/96{,}500n$ is called the *electrochemical equivalent* of the material.

In 1811, Amadeo Avogadro theorized that every substance contains the same number of molecules per mole of the material. His theory was proved by later chemists who found that one mole of any substance contains 6.02×10^{23} molecules (called Avogadro's number). Assuming that a material exists that has a unit molecular weight,‡ we can obtain the constant

$$\frac{1 \text{ gram per mole}}{6.02 \times 10^{23} \text{ molecules per mole}} = 1.67 \times 10^{-24} \text{ grams per molecule}$$

This constant is the mass of a molecule (or of an atom) of unit molecular (or atomic) weight. Since the current (and, consequently, the charge) is carried through the electrolyte by means of ions, the charge on a single ion is found to be

$$q = (1.67 \times 10^{-24})(96{,}500n) = 1.6 \times 10^{-19} n \text{ coulomb} \tag{6-2}$$

The constant, 1.6×10^{-19} coulomb, is the charge on an electron or on any positive or negative ion with a unit charge. Since the valence n is always a whole number, the charge on an ion is always a whole number multiplied by the charge on an electron.

‡ Although no such material exists, the hydrogen ion H^+ has unit molecular weight and, consequently, is directly applicable to this discussion.

Table 6-1. Chemical Elements and Their Atomic Weights (1961)
Based on Carbon-12.

Elements	Symbol	Atomic Weight	Elements	Symbol	Atomic Weight
Aluminum	Al	26.9815	Manganese	Mn	54.9381
Antimony	Sb	121.75	Neon	Ne	20.183
Argon	Ar	39.948	Nickel	Ni	58.71
Arsenic	As	74.9216	Niobium	Nb	92.906
Barium	Ba	137.34	Nitrogen	N	14.0067
Beryllium	Be	9.0122	Osmium	Os	190.2
Bismuth	Bi	208.98	Oxygen	O	15.9994
Boron	B	10.811	Palladium	Pd	106.4
Bromine	Br	79.909	Phosphorus	P	30.9738
Cadmium	Cd	112.40	Platinum	Pt	195.09
Calcium	Ca	40.08	Potassium	K	39.102
Carbon	C	12.01115	Praseodymium	Pr	140.907
Cerium	Ce	140.12	Rhenium	Re	186.2
Cesium	Cs	132.905	Rhodium	Rh	102.905
Chlorine	Cl	35.453	Rubidium	Rb	85.47
Chromium	Cr	51.996	Ruthenium	Ru	101.07
Cobalt	Co	58.9332	Samarium	Sm	150.35
Copper	Cu	63.54	Scandium	Sc	44.956
Dysprosium	Dy	162.50	Selenium	Se	78.96
Erbium	Er	167.26	Silicon	Si	28.086
Europium	Eu	151.96	Silver	Ag	107.870
Fluorine	F	18.9984	Sodium	Na	22.9898
Gadolinium	Gd	157.25	Strontium	Sr	87.62
Gallium	Ga	69.72	Sulfur	S	32.064
Germanium	Ge	72.59	Tantalum	Ta	180.948
Gold	Au	196.967	Tellurium	Te	127.60
Hafnium	Hf	178.49	Terbium	Tb	158.924
Helium	He	4.0026	Thallium	Tl	204.37
Holmium	Ho	164.930	Thorium	Th	232.038
Hydrogen	H	1.00797	Thulium	Tm	168.934
Indium	In	114.82	Tin	Sn	118.69
Iodine	I	126.9044	Titanium	Ti	47.90
Iridium	Ir	192.2	Tungsten	W	183.85
Iron	Fe	55.847	Uranium	U	238.03
Krypton	Kr	83.80	Vanadium	V	50.942
Lanthanum	La	138.91	Xenon	Xe	131.30
Lead	Pb	207.19	Ytterbium	Yb	173.04
Lithium	Li	6.939	Yttrium	Y	88.905
Lutetium	Lu	174.97	Zinc	Zn	65.37
Magnesium	Mg	24.312	Zirconium	Zr	91.22

Example 6-1. How many coulombs are required to purify 5 lbs of electrolytic copper? If an average current of 200 amperes flows during the process, how long will it take?

Solution. A pound is equal to 454 grams.§ By solving equation (6-1)

§ The actual value is 453.5924 grams per pound, but using 454 introduces an error of only about 4 parts in more than 4,500, or less than 9/100 of 1 per cent.

for Q, we obtain the relationship (copper has a valence of 2)

$$Q = \frac{96{,}500nM}{w} = \frac{(96{,}500)\,(2)\,(5)\,(454)}{63.54} = 6{,}888{,}527 \text{ coulombs}$$

Since an ampere is equal to one coulomb per second, the time t is equal to

$$t = \frac{6{,}888{,}527}{200} = 34{,}443 \text{ seconds}$$

This problem can also be solved in one step, since

$$t = \frac{Q}{I} \tag{6-3}$$

where t is in seconds, Q is in coulombs, and I is in amperes. Substituting equation (6-3) in equation (6-1) gives

$$t = \frac{96{,}500nM}{wI} \tag{6-4}$$

6-4. Storage Batteries. As explained in Section 6-2, if any two dissimilar metals are placed in a weak acid solution, an electrical potential will be present at the two metals (electrodes). Because the generation of this potential is accompanied by destruction of one of the electrodes, this type of cell—called a primary cell—cannot be renewed except by replacing the electrodes and, sometimes, the electrolyte. The primary cell is usually capable of delivering only small amounts of current because of its high internal resistance, and, consequently, cannot be used in an automobile or in any other type of power-operated equipment.

If one electrode is made of metallic lead and another of lead dioxide (PbO_2) and these electrodes are immersed in a sulphuric acid solution, a potential difference is also measured between the electrodes. This cell, however, is different from the primary cell in several ways. It can be returned to its original condition—or nearly so—by causing the current to flow in the reverse direction through the cell. The voltage between the electrodes is generally higher than that of the usual primary cell (2.1 volts per cell as compared to 1.1 volt for the copper-zinc cell). It has a higher capacity than the primary cell, being able to deliver more than 100 amperes for short periods to drive motors such as the starter in an automobile.

The metallic lead plate is the negative electrode of the secondary cell or storage battery of the lead-acid type used in automobiles. Since the area of the plates is important in this type of cell—the greater the area the greater being the ampere-hour capacity of the cell—the lead is in a spongy condition. The positive plate is lead dioxide (PbO_2).

Some authorities give the following equations for the anode, the cathode, and the complete cell reaction:

Negative Plate

$$Pb + HSO_4^- \rightleftarrows PbSO_4 + 2e^- + H^+$$

Positive Plate

$$PbO_2 + HSO_4^- + 3H^+ + 2e^- \rightleftarrows PbSO_4 + 2H_2O$$

Complete Reaction

$$Pb + 2HSO_4^- + 2H^+ + PbO_2 \rightleftarrows 2PbSO_4 + 2H_2O$$

Other authorities give the following equations:

Negative Plate

$$Pb + SO_4^{--} \rightleftarrows PbSO_4 + 2e^-$$

Positive Plate

$$PbO_2 + SO_4^{--} + 4H^+ + 2e^- \rightleftarrows PbSO_4 + 2H_2O$$

Complete Reaction

$$Pb + PbO_2 + 2H_2SO_4 \rightleftarrows 2PbSO_4 + 2H_2O$$

Whichever equations are used, the end results are the same. The double arrows indicate that the reaction can proceed in either direction. When the battery is discharging, the reaction is to the right. When the battery is being charged, the reaction is to the left.

The lead sulphate is a solid and remains on the plates, while the water replaces the sulphuric acid of the electrolyte. A cell which is discharged sufficiently for appreciable quantities of lead sulphate and water to be present has a high internal resistance and consequently a decreased output. Since a sulphuric acid solution has a higher specific gravity than water, the specific gravity of the electrolyte can be used as an indication of the condition of the cell when no load is applied.

A new cell has a specific gravity of 1.300 and an output of 2.1 volts. A cell which has a specific gravity of 1.100 and an output of about 1.8 volts is considered fully discharged for all practical purposes. When the cell is recharged, the electrolyte will not return to its original reading of 1.300 but will probably reach no higher than about 1.275. A cell should always be recharged if its specific gravity drops to 1.150, because at lower readings the lead sulphate tends to harden and break off, settling to the bottom of the cell. When this happens, the cell is usually beyond recovery. The cell is said to be "sulphated."

As used in practice, the lead cell is generally connected in series with other similar cells. For the automobile, either three or six cells are connected in series in a single container with voltage outputs of 6.3 or 12.6 volts. For other uses, single cells of large physical size, and consequent high current outputs, are used in series with other single cells. As many as 50 or more cells may be used, with voltage outputs of more than 100 volts.

A second commonly used cell is the nickel-iron or alkaline battery, known as the Edison cell after its inventor, Thomas A. Edison. This cell is much stronger structurally and can withstand much more abuse than the lead cell, but has a current output rating too low for use in many installations. Cost of the cell also limits its use.

The chemical reaction of the Edison cell is not entirely understood. At one time, the reaction was assumed to be

$$2Fe + 2Ni_2O_3 \cdot 6H_2O \rightleftarrows 4Ni(OH)_2 + 2Fe(OH)_2$$

More recent tests indicate that the reaction is probably given by the equation

$$NiO_2 \cdot 2H_2O + Fe \rightleftarrows Fe(OH)_2 + Ni(OH)_2$$

The compound NiO_2 is called nickel dioxide. The electromotive force of the Edison cell during discharge is about 1.2 volts.

The positive plate of the Edison cell is a nickel trioxide (Ni_2O_3), and the negative plate is finely divided iron. The electrolyte is a 21 per cent solution of potassium hydroxide with some lithium hydroxide.

Secondary cells or storage batteries are rated in ampere-hours, indicating the number of hours a cell can deliver a given current, or

$$\text{ampere-hours} = \text{amperes} \times \text{hours} \tag{6-5}$$

Theoretically, at least, after a cell has discharged at a certain rate for a time, it can still be expected to have remaining the original capacity minus the ampere-hour discharge. Within some limits, this is true, but if the rate of discharge is too high, the battery gets hot and the plates tend to buckle. If this happens, the battery may not be able to deliver its full rated capacity.

In Europe, a storage battery using nickel and cadmium electrodes is used for automobiles. Other types of storage batteries are in the experimental or developmental stage but are not yet ready for commercial use.

Example 6-2. A storage battery is rated at 100 ampere-hours. If it is discharged at the rate of 2.8 amperes for 25 hours, what capacity may still be available?

Solution. From equation (6-5) the discharge is found to be

$$(2.8)\ (25) = 70 \text{ ampere-hours}$$

The remaining capacity is, therefore,

$$100 - 70 = 30 \text{ ampere-hours}$$

Problems Based on Chapter 6

P6-1. Charles M. Hall, while a student at Oberlin College, devised the first practical method for preparing pure aluminum from bauxite ($Al_2O_3 \cdot 2H_2O$). The aluminum oxide (Al_2O_3) is prepared and then electrolyzed, using carbon anodes. How many ampere-hours are required to prepare one pound of aluminum from the oxide?

Ans. 1352 ampere-hours.

P6-2. Three cells having platinum electrodes contain, respectively, electrolytic solutions of zinc chloride ($ZnCl_2$), stannous chloride ($SnCl_2$), and ferric chloride ($FeCl_3$). When 5 grams of zinc are deposited in the first cell, how much tin and tungsten are deposited in cells 2 and 3 if the same current flows in all three cells?

Ans. $Q = 14{,}800$ coul. 9.15 gm of tin and 2.85 gm of iron.

P6-3. A current of 10 amps is used to plate silver in a silver nitrate solution ($AgNO_3$). If a surface 30×20 cm is to be plated to a thickness of 0.004 cm, how long will the process be in operation if silver weighs 10.5 gm per cubic cm?

Ans. $Q = 21{,}500$ coul. $t = 2150$ sec or about 36 min.

P6-4. How long will it take to decompose 36 gm of water (H_2O) by electrolysis with a current of 3 amps?

Ans. Using either the oxygen or the hydrogen, 36 hrs ($Q = 386{,}000$ coul).

P6-5. How many gm of silver will be deposited by 1 amp of current flowing for 1 sec?

Ans. 0.00112 gm.

P6-6. A copper sheet measuring 30×50 cm is to be plated on both sides with nickel 0.002 cm thick. Nickel weighs 8.9 gm per cubic cm and has a valence of 2. How long will the plating process require if a current of 20 amps is used?

Ans. 7450 sec or 124 min, 10 sec.

P6-7. A zinc plate in a primary cell measures 2 × 4 × 8 cm. How many coulombs will the cell deliver before the zinc plate is completely dissolved? Assume constant current. Zinc weighs 7.14 gm per cubic cm.

Ans. 1,350,000 coul.

7 INDUCTANCE AND CAPACITANCE IN DIRECT-CURRENT CIRCUITS

7-1. Inductance. The circuits studied so far have contained only resistance as the load on the voltage source. Only a few circuits, however, can accomplish their purpose unless something else besides resistance is present. Bells must be rung, relay contacts must be operated, and motors must be driven. These loads all require that coils of wire be used as the driving force—the force that causes electrical energy to be converted into mechanical energy and mechanical energy into some form of work.

The circuit components by means of which this conversion is accomplished are called *inductance* and *capacitance*. Inductance can be defined as that property of an electric circuit that opposes any change in the current through that circuit. Capacitance is that property of an electric circuit that opposes any change in the voltage across that circuit.

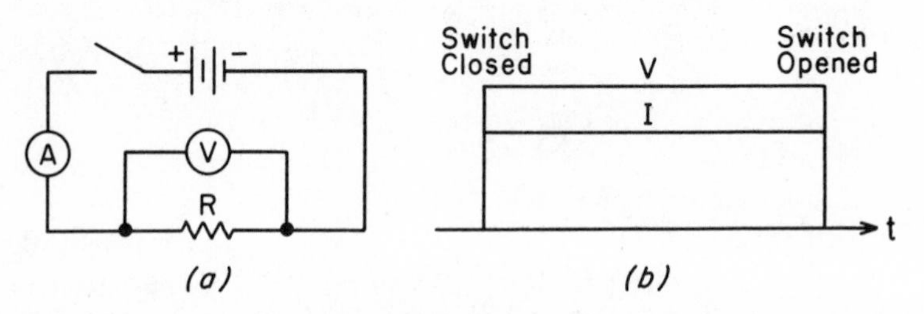

Fig. 7-1. Circuit containing resistance.

When a switch is closed in a circuit containing only resistance, as in Fig. 7-1*a*, the ammeter A and the voltmeter V both rise instantly to a value and remain steady at that value. If the resistance R and the voltage V are known, the current I, in amperes, can be calculated by Ohm's law,

$$V = IR \tag{7-1}$$

where V is in volts and R is in ohms. When the circuit is opened, the current and voltage drop instantly to zero. The voltage and current conditions are indicated graphically in Fig. 7-1*b*.

When a coil of wire—such as is present in many electrical appliances—is used in place of a pure resistance, we have the circuit shown in Fig. 7-2*a*. In this circuit, L represents the characteristic of the coil—called the *inductance*—and R represents the resistance of the coil. The inductance and resistance cannot be separated but they are shown this way in Fig. 7-2*a* to simplify the discussion.*

When the switch is closed, voltmeter V_1 rises instantly to the voltage output of the battery or other direct-current source but the current rises very slowly, as indicated in Fig. 7-2*b*. At point 1 in Fig. 7-2*b*, the current reaches the maximum value as determined from Ohm's law (equation (7-1)) and the current acts as if the inductance L were not present. The voltage across L is zero when the current reaches its Ohm's law value.

The voltage across the resistance R is zero at the instant the switch is closed, but rises slowly to the maximum value at point 1, as shown in Fig. 7-2*c*. The circuit is now assumed to be operating under stable conditions from point 1 to point 2, since no physical or other change is imposed on it. At point 2, however, the switch is opened. The voltage across the coil goes to a value at least equal to the applied voltage E,† but in the opposite direction, as shown in Fig. 7-2*b*. The current flows in the same direction as it did before the switch was opened. Both current and voltage decay gradually to zero, as shown in Fig. 7-2*b*. The voltage across the resistance is equal and opposite to the voltage across the inductance, as shown in Fig. 7-2*c*.

A non-inductive discharge resistance R_N is shown connected across the battery in Fig. 7-2*a* to form a path for the current to flow during the period after the switch is opened. If this resistance were not in the circuit, a large arc might appear between the contacting surfaces of the switch and eventually destroy the switch and the voltage source. The voltage across the resistance (see

* The conditions illustrated in Fig. 7-2*a* can be very closely approximated in an actual circuit. Coils with a very high inductance and negligible resistance are common and can be used in series with a pure resistance. The conditions found in this type of circuit are very nearly those described in connection with Fig. 7-2*a*.

† In some circuits, the voltage across the coil can reach several times the value of the voltage E.

Fig. 7-2*c*)—and, consequently, the voltage across the inductance—is not as high as it might otherwise be without R_N or some other resistance.

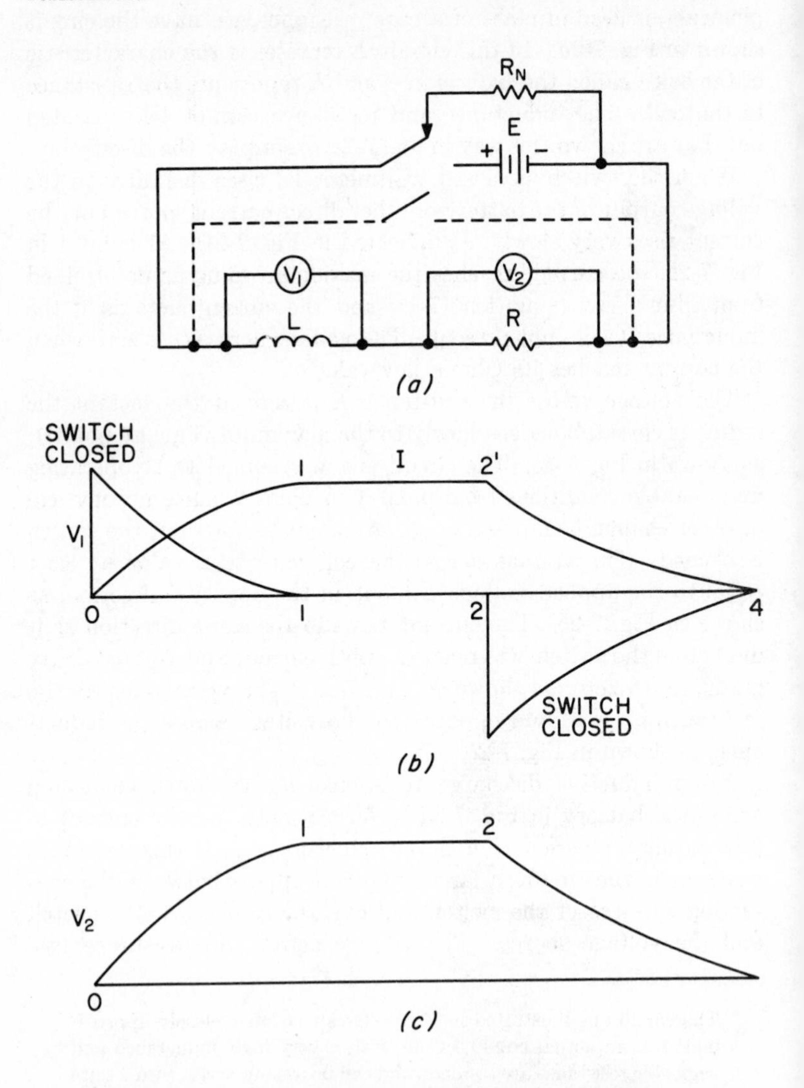

Fig. 7-2. Circuit containing resistance and inductance.

From an examination of the voltage and current relations shown in Fig. 7-2*b* and *c*, we see that when an inductance is present in the circuit, the voltage across the inductance reaches its maximum value instantaneously but the current does not reach its maximum value until some time later. The current, therefore, lags behind the voltage. This lagging current is an important characteristic of inductance in either alternating- or direct-current circuits.

If L is the inductance in henrys, e is the voltage induced across the coil at a given instant, and di is the change in current in a small time dt, then,

$$e = -L \frac{di}{dt} \tag{7-2}$$

The negative sign in equation (7-2) indicates that the action of an inductance is always in such a direction that it opposes any change in the flow of current. The actual voltage of the circuit effective in causing current flow is

$$\text{emf} = E - L \frac{di}{dt} \tag{7-3}$$

where emf is the electromotive force that is effective in causing current flow and E is the terminal voltage of the direct current source. (The internal resistance of the voltage source will have some effect on the characteristics of the circuit, but this resistance is so low that it can usually be neglected.)

Coils are rated in henrys of inductance. The henry is named after Joseph Henry, the American physicist (1797-1878) who did considerable work with coils and capacitors. A circuit (or coil) has an inductance of one henry if a current changing at the rate of one ampere per second produces an emf of one volt. This emf is sometimes called *back emf* or *counter emf*. Its value is determined from equation (7-2).

In the circuit of Fig. 7-2*a*, if i is the current flowing through L and R, the voltage E is expressed by the equation

$$E = Ri + L \frac{di}{dt} \tag{7-4}$$

Equation (7-4) follows from equation (7-3) if the emf of equation (7-3) is considered to be Ri in equation (7-4).

Equation (7-3) can be solved only by use of differential equations. The solution for the current i is

$$i = \frac{E}{R}\left(1 - \epsilon^{-\frac{Rt}{L}}\right) \tag{7-5}$$

All the symbols in equation (7-5) have previously been explained except the Greek letter ϵ (epsilon) which is the natural or Naperian logarithmic base, 2.71828183 . . . . The value of ϵ may be taken as 2.718 or even 2.72 in most calculations, as these figures will yield results that are sufficiently accurate for practical purposes.

Equation (7-5) is true only for the special case where the current is zero at the instant that the switch is closed to energize the circuit. It does not apply to conditions where current is flowing at the time the voltage, resistance, or inductance is changed. The steady-state current, from Ohm's law, is $I = E/R$, where I is the maximum value of the current. Making this substitution in equation (7-5) we obtain the relationship

$$i = I\left(1 - \epsilon^{-\frac{Rt}{L}}\right) \tag{7-6}$$

The current relationships found from equations (7-5) and (7-6) are indicated by the current curve from 0 to 1 in Fig. 7-2*b*.

When the switch is opened, the voltage source is removed. The differential equation for the conditions then present in the circuit illustrated in Fig. 7-2*a* is

$$i\,(R + R_N) + L\,\frac{di}{dt} = 0 \tag{7-7}$$

If the circuit is so arranged that opening the main switch closes the circuit indicated by the dotted lines but disconnects R_N from the circuit, we have only R and L present during decay of the current. Under these circumstances, equation (7-7) will not include R_N and may be written

$$Ri + L\,\frac{di}{dt} = 0 \tag{7-8}$$

Equation (7-8) is the one usually found in textbooks. The solution of this equation is

$$i = \frac{E}{R}\,\epsilon^{-\frac{Rt}{L}} \tag{7-9}$$

The steady current I may be substituted in equation (7-9) for its Ohm's law equivalent, E/R.

$$i = I\,\epsilon^{-\frac{Rt}{L}} \tag{7-10}$$

Even though R_N is in series with R during discharge of the inductance, the current I will not change when the switch is opened from the direct-current source and closed to R_N. The inductance acts to prevent any change in the current. Therefore, the current decays in accordance with the relationship

$$i = I \epsilon^{-\frac{t(R + R_N)}{L}} \tag{7-11}$$

Equation (7-11) indicates that the current decreases along a logarithmic curve as shown in Fig. 7-2*b* between points 2 and 4. Since $R_N + R$ is greater than R, the current will decay more rapidly with equation (7-11) than with equation (7-10). Equations (7-9), (7-10), and (7-11) are valid only if the final current is zero, as at point 4 in Fig. 7-2*b*.

If the main switch is opened, as shown in Fig. 7-3, with no discharge resistance, the resistance in equation (7-10) reduces to zero very rapidly, since R_N equals infinity. From equation (7-2), the current change di from I to zero is in zero time dt, and e therefore is infinite. In actual practice, this voltage e will rise to such a high value that the circuit insulation may be punctured, and any electrical equipment in the circuit would therefore be destroyed or severely damaged.

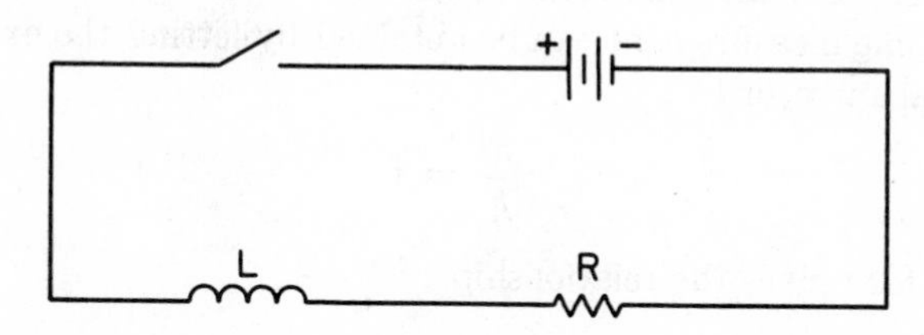

Fig. 7-3. Open circuit without a discharge resistance.

Example 7-1. In the circuit of Fig. 7-2, R = 5 ohms, L = 20 henrys, and E = 25 volts. What is the current one second after the switch is closed? What is the final value of the current?

Solution. Equation (7-5) will give the current one second after the switch is closed.

$$i = \frac{E}{R}\left(1 - \epsilon^{-\frac{Rt}{L}}\right) = \frac{25}{5}\left(1 - 2.72^{-\frac{(5)\,(1)}{20}}\right) = 5\left(1 - \frac{1}{2.72^{0.25}}\right)$$

$$= 5\left(1 - \frac{1}{1.283}\right) = 5\,(1 - 0.78) = 5 - 3.90 = 1.10 \text{ amps}$$

The final or steady state current is found from Ohm's law.

$$i = \frac{E}{R} = \frac{25}{5} = 5 \text{ amps}$$

Example 7-2. If the circuit of Fig. 7-2*a* is opened from the battery and closed to the dotted circuit so that the current decays through L and R, what will the current be in 2 seconds?

Solution. From equation (7-10),

$$i = I\epsilon^{-\frac{Rt}{L}} = \frac{5}{\epsilon^{\frac{(5)(2)}{20}}} = \frac{5}{\epsilon^{0.5}} = \frac{5}{\sqrt{\epsilon}} = 3.03 \text{ amps}$$

7-2. Time Constant in an Inductive Circuit. When studying the rise and fall of the current in an inductive circuit, the student naturally wants to know how much time is required to reach the steady-state value of current or voltage. An examination of equations (7-5), (7-6), (7-9), and (7-11) shows that any value of t can be inserted and a corresponding value of the current i or the voltage e can be found. Theoretically, therefore, the current never reaches the steady-state value of E/R on rise, nor zero on decay. From a practical standpoint, however, we know that the ammeter does indicate steady current values a finite number of seconds after the circuit is closed or opened.

When the current reaches its steady value, Rt/L theoretically equals zero and the time must therefore be infinite. A convenient unit of time measurement can be obtained by letting the exponent of ϵ equal unity, or 1.

$$\frac{Rt}{L} = 1$$

Solving for t gives the relationship

$$t = T = \frac{L}{R} \tag{7-12}$$

The ratio L/R is known as the time constant T of the inductive circuit. If equation (7-5) is solved for one time constant ($Rt/L = 1$), we obtain

$$i = \frac{E}{R}(1 - \epsilon^{-1}) = \frac{E}{R}(1 - 0.368) = (0.632)\frac{E}{R} \tag{7-13}$$

One time constant, therefore, is the time in seconds required for the current in an inductive circuit to rise to 63.2 per cent of its Ohm's law value. After a period of time in seconds equal to two time constants ($Rt/L = 2$), we obtain

$$i = \frac{E}{R}(1 - \epsilon^{-2}) = \frac{E}{R}(1 - 0.135) = 0.865\frac{E}{R} \tag{7-14}$$

The rise during the second time constant is, therefore,

$$i_{\text{rise}} = \frac{E}{R}(0.865 - 0.632) = 0.233\frac{E}{R} \qquad (7\text{-}15)$$

Equation (7-15) can be used to determine how much the current rose during the second time constant compared to the difference between its Ohm's law value and its value at the end of one time constant. Since the current at the end of the period of time corresponding to one time constant is, from equation (7-13), 0.632 of its Ohm's law value, the rise yet to take place is

$$\frac{E}{R}(1 - 0.632) = 0.368\frac{E}{R} \qquad (7\text{-}16)$$

Dividing equation (7-15) by equation (7-16) gives the ratio

$$\frac{0.233}{0.368} = 0.632$$

Therefore, during the second time constant, the current rises 63.2 per cent of the difference between its Ohm's law value and its value at the end of the first time constant. Further checks show that this rate of rise per time constant (or, more precisely, per period of time corresponding to a time constant) is consistent, because during every time period the rise is 63.2 per cent of the remaining difference between the Ohm's law value and its instantaneous value for the instant under consideration.

Table 7-1. Value of $\epsilon^{-\frac{Rt}{L}}$ and $1 - \epsilon^{-\frac{Rt}{L}}$ for Time Constants from 0 to 6

Time Constant	0	1	2	3	4	5	6
$\epsilon^{-\frac{Rt}{L}}$	1.000	0.368	0.135	0.0498	0.0183	0.00674	0.00248
$1 - \epsilon^{-\frac{Rt}{L}}$	0.000	0.632	0.864	0.9502	0.9817	0.9933	0.9975

Table 7-1 shows the value of the quantities $\epsilon^{-Rt/L}$ and $1 - \epsilon^{-Rt/L}$ for time constants ranging from 0 to 6. This table shows that the current reaches more than 99 per cent of its Ohm's law value in five time constants. Since the rise during the sixth time constant is less than 0.005, the current is considered to have reached its steady or Ohm's law value at the end of five time constants, from a

Table 7-2. Values of $\epsilon^{-\frac{Rt}{L}}$ (or $\epsilon^{-\frac{t}{RC}}$)

$\frac{Rt}{L}$	0.00	0.01	0.02	0.03	0.04	0.05	0.06	0.07	0.08	0.09
0.0	1.0000	0.9900	0.9802	0.9704	0.9608	0.9512	0.9418	0.9324	0.9231	0.9139
0.1	0.9048	0.8958	0.8869	0.8781	0.8694	0.8607	0.8521	0.8437	0.8353	0.8270
0.2	0.8187	0.8106	0.8025	0.7945	0.7866	0.7788	0.7711	0.7634	0.7558	0.7483
0.3	0.7408	0.7334	0.7261	0.7189	0.7118	0.7047	0.6977	0.6907	0.6839	0.6771
0.4	0.6703	0.6637	0.6570	0.6505	0.6440	0.6376	0.6313	0.6250	0.6188	0.6126
0.5	0.6065	0.6005	0.5945	0.5886	0.5827	0.5769	0.5712	0.5655	0.5599	0.5543
0.6	0.5488	0.5434	0.5379	0.5326	0.5273	0.5220	0.5169	0.5117	0.5066	0.5017
0.7	0.4966	0.4916	0.4868	0.4819	0.4771	0.4724	0.4677	0.4630	0.4584	0.4538
0.8	0.4493	0.4449	0.4404	0.4360	0.4317	0.4274	0.4232	0.4190	0.4148	0.4107
0.9	0.4066	0.4025	0.3985	0.3946	0.3906	0.3867	0.3829	0.3791	0.3753	0.3716
1.0	0.3679	0.3642	0.3606	0.3570	0.3535	0.3499	0.3465	0.3430	0.3396	0.3362
1.1	0.3329	0.3296	0.3263	0.3230	0.3198	0.3166	0.3135	0.3104	0.3073	0.3042
1.2	0.3012	0.2982	0.2952	0.2923	0.2894	0.2865	0.2837	0.2808	0.2780	0.2753
1.3	0.2725	0.2698	0.2671	0.2645	0.2618	0.2592	0.2567	0.2541	0.2516	0.2491
1.4	0.2466	0.2441	0.2417	0.2393	0.2369	0.2346	0.2322	0.2299	0.2276	0.2254
1.5	0.2231	0.2209	0.2187	0.2165	0.2144	0.2122	0.2101	0.2080	0.2060	0.2039
1.6	0.2019	0.1999	0.1979	0.1959	0.1940	0.1920	0.1901	0.1882	0.1864	0.1845
1.7	0.1827	0.1809	0.1791	0.1773	0.1755	0.1738	0.1720	0.1703	0.1686	0.1670
1.8	0.1653	0.1637	0.1620	0.1604	0.1588	0.1572	0.1557	0.1541	0.1526	0.1511
1.9	0.1496	0.1481	0.1466	0.1451	0.1437	0.1423	0.1409	0.1395	0.1381	0.1367
2.0	0.1353	0.1340	0.1327	0.1313	0.1300	0.1287	0.1275	0.1262	0.1249	0.1237
2.1	0.1225	0.1212	0.1200	0.1188	0.1177	0.1165	0.1153	0.1142	0.1130	0.1119
2.2	0.1108	0.1097	0.1086	0.1075	0.1065	0.1054	0.1044	0.1033	0.1023	0.1013
2.3	0.1003	0.0993	0.0983	0.0973	0.0963	0.0954	0.0944	0.0935	0.0926	0.0916
2.4	0.0907	0.0898	0.0889	0.0880	0.0872	0.0863	0.0854	0.0846	0.0837	0.0829
2.5	0.0821	0.0813	0.0805	0.0797	0.0789	0.0781	0.0773	0.0765	0.0758	0.0750
2.6	0.0743	0.0735	0.0728	0.0721	0.0714	0.0707	0.0699	0.0693	0.0686	0.0679
2.7	0.0672	0.0665	0.0659	0.0652	0.0646	0.0639	0.0633	0.0627	0.0620	0.0614
2.8	0.0608	0.0602	0.0596	0.0590	0.0584	0.0578	0.0573	0.0567	0.0561	0.0556
2.9	0.0550	0.0545	0.0539	0.0534	0.0529	0.0523	0.0518	0.0513	0.0508	0.0503
3.0	0.0498	0.0493	0.0488	0.0483	0.0478	0.0474	0.0469	0.0464	0.0460	0.0455
3.1	0.0450	0.0446	0.0442	0.0437	0.0433	0.0429	0.0424	0.0420	0.0416	0.0412
3.2	0.0408	0.0404	0.0400	0.0396	0.0392	0.0388	0.0384	0.0380	0.0376	0.0373
3.3	0.0369	0.0365	0.0362	0.0358	0.0354	0.0351	0.0347	0.0344	0.0340	0.0337
3.4	0.0334	0.0330	0.0327	0.0324	0.0321	0.0317	0.0314	0.0311	0.0308	0.0305
3.5	0.0302	0.0299	0.0296	0.0293	0.0290	0.0287	0.0284	0.0282	0.0279	0.0276
3.6	0.0273	0.0271	0.0268	0.0265	0.0263	0.0260	0.0257	0.0255	0.0252	0.0250
3.7	0.0247	0.0245	0.0242	0.0240	0.0238	0.0235	0.0233	0.0231	0.0228	0.0226
3.8	0.0224	0.0221	0.0219	0.0217	0.0215	0.0213	0.0211	0.0209	0.0207	0.0204
3.9	0.0202	0.0200	0.0198	0.0196	0.0195	0.0193	0.0191	0.0189	0.0187	0.0185
4.0	0.0183	0.0181	0.0180	0.0178	0.0176	0.0174	0.0172	0.0171	0.0169	0.0167
4.1	0.0166	0.0164	0.0162	0.0161	0.0159	0.0158	0.0156	0.0155	0.0153	0.0151
4.2	0.0150	0.0148	0.0147	0.0146	0.0144	0.0143	0.0141	0.0140	0.0138	0.0137
4.3	0.0136	0.0134	0.0133	0.0132	0.0130	0.0129	0.0128	0.0127	0.0125	0.0124
4.4	0.0123	0.0122	0.0120	0.0119	0.0118	0.0117	0.0116	0.0114	0.0113	0.0112
4.5	0.0111	0.0110	0.0109	0.0108	0.0107	0.0106	0.0105	0.0104	0.0103	0.0102
4.6	0.0101	0.0100	0.0099	0.0098	0.0097	0.0096	0.0095	0.0094	0.0093	0.0092
4.7	0.0091	0.0090	0.0089	0.0088	0.0087	0.0087	0.0086	0.0085	0.0084	0.0083
4.8	0.0082	0.0081	0.0081	0.0080	0.0079	0.0078	0.0078	0.0077	0.0076	0.0075
4.9	0.0074	0.0074	0.0073	0.0072	0.0072	0.0071	0.0070	0.0069	0.0069	0.0068
5.0	0.0067	0.0067	0.0066	0.0065	0.0065	0.0064	0.0063	0.0063	0.0062	0.0062
5.1	0.0061	0.0060	0.0060	0.0059	0.0059	0.0058	0.0057	0.0057	0.0056	0.0056
5.2	0.0055	0.0055	0.0054	0.0054	0.0053	0.0052	0.0052	0.0051	0.0051	0.0050
5.3	0.0050	0.0049	0.0049	0.0048	0.0048	0.0047	0.0047	0.0047	0.0046	0.0046
5.4	0.0045	0.0045	0.0044	0.0044	0.0043	0.0043	0.0043	0.0042	0.0042	0.0041
5.5	0.0041	0.0040	0.0040	0.0040	0.0039	0.0039	0.0038	0.0038	0.0038	0.0037
5.6	0.0037	0.0037	0.0036	0.0036	0.0036	0.0035	0.0035	0.0034	0.0034	0.0034
5.7	0.0033	0.0033	0.0033	0.0032	0.0032	0.0032	0.0032	0.0031	0.0031	0.0031
5.8	0.0030	0.0030	0.0030	0.0029	0.0029	0.0029	0.0029	0.0028	0.0028	0.0028
5.9	0.0027	0.0027	0.0027	0.0027	0.0026	0.0026	0.0026	0.0026	0.0025	0.0025

practical standpoint. Although Table 7-1 was calculated by the use of five-place logarithms, slide rule accuracy is generally acceptable in circuit calculations.

Values for $\epsilon^{-Rt/L}$ when Rt/L equals 0 to 5.9 are given in Table 7-2. Table 7-2 will help solve or check computations in inductive circuits. Its use for circuits containing capacitance will be explained later.

Example 7-3. A circuit has a total resistance of 5 ohms and an inductance of 25 henrys. In how many seconds will the current reach its maximum value?

Solution. The value of a time constant is found from equation (7-12).

$$t = \frac{L}{R} = \frac{25}{5} = 5 \text{ seconds}$$

The total time to reach the maximum value of current is equal to five time constants.

$$\text{Total time} = (5)\,(5) = 25 \text{ seconds}$$

7-3. Capacitance. When a circuit containing resistance and capacitance (see Fig. 7-4*a*) is closed, ammeter A and voltmeter V_1 rise instantly to a maximum value, but V_2 does not move. If the circuit remains closed through switch 1, the ammeter A and voltmeter V_1 gradually fall to zero while voltmeter V_2 rises gradually to a steady value. The conditions are shown graphically in Fig. 7-4*b* between points 0 and 1.

When switch 1 is closed (with switch 2 open) the initial value of the current reading is equal to the Ohm's law value and the voltage reading of V_1 is equal to the full voltage output E of the battery or other direct-current voltage source. As the current decreases and V_2 starts to rise, the readings of V_1 and V_2 are equal to E. At point 1 in Fig. 7-4*b*, $V_1 = 0$ and $V_2 = E$ and the current is zero, indicating that under steady-state conditions, a capacitor is an open circuit for direct current. The graph between 1 and 2 represents this steady-state condition.

At point 2, switch 1 is opened and switch 2 is closed at the same instant. Current now flows out of the capacitor in the direction opposite to that during which the capacitor was being charged. The current rises instantly to its Ohm's law value and V_1 is numerically equal to V_2 but opposite in direction, as shown in Fig. 7-4*b*. The current and the two voltages fall gradually to zero at point 3 in the graph.

Capacitance is defined as the charge (in coulombs) per volt,

$$q = VC \tag{7-17}$$

where q is the charge in coulombs, V is the emf in volts, and C is

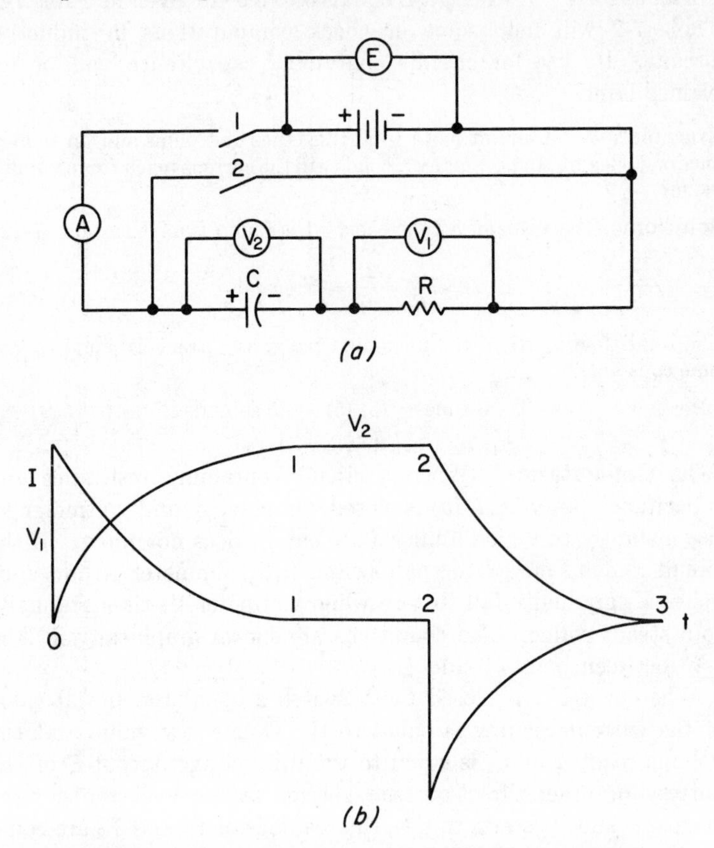

Fig. 7-4. Circuit containing capacitance and resistance.

the capacitance in farads. The current in amperes is equal to coulombs per second, or

$$I = \frac{q}{t} \tag{7-18}$$

Since the current is constantly changing during the charge or discharge of a capacitor, the instantaneous value of the current i is

$$i = \frac{dq}{dt} = \frac{d}{dt} VC = C \frac{dV}{dt} \tag{7-19}$$

If v_c is the voltage across the capacitor and Ri is the voltage across the resistance (in Fig. 7-4, $V_1 = Ri$ and $V_2 = v_c$), then, during the current rise,

$$Ri + v_c = E \tag{7-20}$$

Equations (7-19) and (7-20) can be solved simultaneously (since $V = v_c$) by differential equations. The final solution for the current is

$$i = \frac{E}{R}\,\epsilon^{-\frac{t}{RC}} \tag{7-21}$$

The voltage across the capacitor during this period is

$$v_c = E\left(1 - \epsilon^{-\frac{t}{RC}}\right) \tag{7-22}$$

The voltage v_r across the resistor is found by subtracting equation (7-22) from the applied voltage E.

$$v_r = E - v_c = E - E\left(1 - \epsilon^{-\frac{t}{RC}}\right)$$

or

$$v_r = E\,\epsilon^{-\frac{t}{RC}} \tag{7-23}$$

Equations (7-21), (7-22), and (7-23) can be used only if the voltage across the capacitor is zero when the voltage E is impressed on the circuit. If the capacitor has a voltage v across it when E is impressed on the circuit, the current in the circuit is

$$i = \left(\frac{E - V}{R}\right)\epsilon^{-\frac{t}{RC}} \tag{7-24}$$

Under this condition, the voltage across the capacitor is

$$v_c = E\left(1 - \epsilon^{-\frac{t}{RC}}\right) + V\,\epsilon^{-\frac{t}{RC}} \tag{7-25a}$$

or

$$v_c = E + (V - E)\,\epsilon^{-\frac{t}{RC}} \tag{7-25b}$$

When $V = 0$, equations (7-24), (7-25a), and (7-25b) reduce to equations (7-21) and (7-22).

Equations (7-25a) or (7-25b) can be used for all values of E or V. If an emf V is already present across a capacitor, a new emf E which may be either larger or smaller than V may be impressed. By using the correct values for V and E, we can find the actual change of voltage across the capacitor for any time t.

When the circuit is opened and the capacitor is allowed to discharge through resistor R, the value of the current is found by the equation

$$i = \frac{V}{R} \epsilon^{-\frac{t}{RC}} \tag{7-26}$$

where i is the current in amperes at time t, V is the voltage across the capacitor at the instant it starts to discharge, and R is the series resistance in ohms. The voltage across the capacitor during discharge is found as follows:

$$v_c = V \epsilon^{-\frac{t}{RC}} \tag{7-27}$$

Since only the capacitor and the resistance are present in the circuit during discharge of the capacitor, we may state that

$$v_c + v_r = 0 \tag{7-28}$$

so that

$$v_r = -v_c \tag{7-29}$$

Example 7-4. A 1000-microfarad capacitor and a 2000-ohm resistance are connected in series across a 120-volt direct-current source. What is the current one second after the circuit is closed? What are the potentials across the capacitor and across the resistance at that instant of time? What is the initial current at the instant the circuit is closed?

Solution. The current is found by use of equation (7-21). Since the capacitance of 1000 microfarads (or 1000 μ f) may be expressed as 1000 $\times$ 10^{-6} farads,

$$i = \frac{E}{R} \epsilon^{-\frac{t}{RC}} = \frac{120}{2000} \epsilon^{-\frac{1}{(2000)\,(1000 \times 10^{-6})}}$$

$$= 0.06\, \epsilon^{-0.5} = (0.06)\,(0.6065) = 0.03639 \text{ amp, or } 0.036 \text{ amp}$$

Table 7-2 can be used in evaluating the above equation.

The voltage or potential across the capacitor is found from equation (7-22).

$$v_c = E\left(1 - \epsilon^{-\frac{t}{RC}}\right) = 120\,(1 - 0.6065) = (120)\,(0.3935) = 47.22 \text{ volts}$$

The voltage across the resistance is found from equation (7-23).

$$v_r = E\, \epsilon^{-\frac{t}{RC}} = (120)\,(0.6065) = 72.78 \text{ volts}$$

As a check, we should get E by adding v_c to v_r.

$$v_c + v_r = E = 47.22 + 72.78 = 120 \text{ volts}$$

The initial current at the instant the circuit is closed is found from Ohm's law, or by letting $t = 0$ in equation (7-21).

$$i = \frac{E}{R} = \frac{120}{2000} = 0.06 \text{ amp}$$

7-4. Time Constant in a Capacitive Circuit. The time constant for a capacitive circuit is calculated from the exponent of ϵ in equation (7-21). Solving that equation for t, we obtain

$$t = T = RC \tag{7-30}$$

The product RC is known as the time constant T of the capacitive circuit. The time constant of a capacitive circuit is usually extremely short because the capacitance of the circuit may be only a few microfarads or even micro-microfarads. If a circuit had a capacitance of 100 microfarads and a time constant of one second was desired, the resistance would have to be 10,000 ohms.

Voltage and current values in capacitive circuits are assumed to reach their steady-state values after five time constants, just as in inductive circuits. Tables 7-1 and 7-2 apply to capacitive circuits if $\epsilon^{-Rt/L}$ is replaced by $\epsilon^{-t/RC}$.

Example 7-5. A circuit consists of a 1,000,000-ohm resistance in series with a 10-microfarad capacitor. How long will the current flow in the circuit?

Solution. We can use equation (7-30) to determine the length of the time constant.

$$T = RC = (1 \times 10^6)(10 \times 10^{-6}) = 10 \text{ seconds}$$

Since the current is assumed to be zero after five time constants, the total time is 50 seconds.

7-5. Inductances in Series and Parallel. When several inductances are connected in series as in Fig. 7-5, the voltage E is equal to the sum of the voltages across the inductances, so that

$$E = V_1 + V_2 + \cdots + V_{n-1} + V_n \tag{7-31}$$

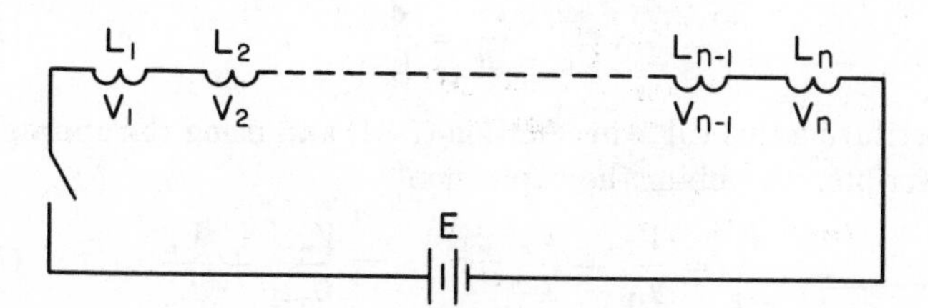

Fig. 7-5. Inductances in series.

Substituting equation (7-2) in equation (7-31) and using appropriate subscripts to identify the resulting values, we obtain the equation

$$L_T\frac{di}{dt} = L_1\frac{di}{dt} + L_2\frac{di}{dt} + \cdots + L_{n-1}\frac{di}{dt} + L_n\frac{di}{dt} \tag{7-32}$$

The negative sign of equation (7-2) is omitted from equation (7-32) because the value of the total inductance L_T is being sought, and the direction of the induced voltage need not be considered in this type of problem.

Dividing equation (7-32) by di/dt gives the total inductance of the circuit.

$$L_T = L_1 + L_2 + \cdots + L_{n-1} + L_n \tag{7-33}$$

Therefore, the total inductance of a series circuit is the sum of the inductances connected in series. Series inductances thus are comparable to series resistances.

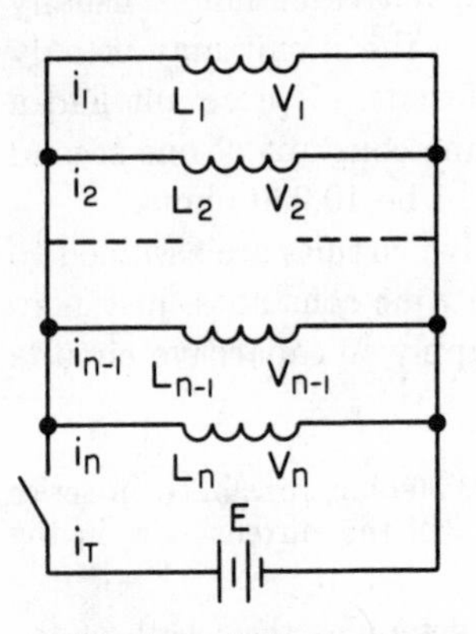

Fig. 7-6. Inductances in parallel.

When several inductances are connected in parallel as indicated in Fig. 7-6, the voltages across all the inductances are equal (identical). The total current i_T is the sum of the individual branch currents from i_1 to i_n. Since both current and the time are equal at a given instant, we may write

$$\frac{di_T}{dt} = \frac{di_1}{dt} + \frac{di_2}{dt} + \cdots + \frac{di_{n-1}}{dt} + \frac{di_n}{dt} \tag{7-34}$$

If we solve equation (7-2) for di/dt, we obtain

$$\frac{di}{dt} = \frac{e}{L} \tag{7-35}$$

Substituting this value in equation (7-34) and using the appropriate subscripts, we obtain the expression

$$\frac{E}{L_T} = \frac{V_1}{L_1} + \frac{V_2}{L_2} + \cdots + \frac{V_{n-1}}{L_{n-1}} + \frac{V_n}{L_n} \tag{7-36}$$

Since all the voltages are equal, we may divide both sides of equation (7-36) by the respective voltages to obtain the relationship

$$\frac{1}{L_T} = \frac{1}{L_1} + \frac{1}{L_2} + \cdots + \frac{1}{L_{n-1}} + \frac{1}{L_n} \tag{7-37}$$

Equation (7-37) gives the total inductance L_T of a circuit containing two or more inductances in parallel.

Example 7-6. The circuit in Fig. 7-7 contains six inductances and a resistance connected as shown. If $L_1 = 5$ henrys, $L_2 = 3$ henrys, $L_3 = 10$

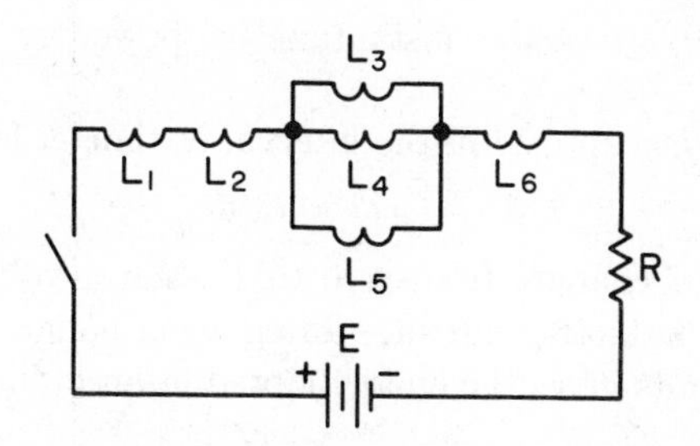

Fig. 7-7. Inductances in series and in parallel in the same circuit.

henrys, $L_4 = 6$ henrys, $L_5 = 15$ henrys, $L_6 = 12$ henrys, and $R = 15$ ohms, find the total inductance and the time constant of the circuit. What is $\epsilon^{-Rt/L}$ for $t = 2$ seconds?

Solution. The inductance of the parallel branch is found from equation (7-37).

$$\frac{1}{L_{3-4-5}} = \frac{1}{L_3} + \frac{1}{L_4} + \frac{1}{L_5} = \frac{1}{10} + \frac{1}{6} + \frac{1}{15} = 0.1 + 0.167 + 0.067 = 0.334$$

$$L_{3-4-5} = \frac{1}{0.334} = 3 \text{ henrys}$$

The total inductance can now be found by use of equation (7-33).

$$L_T = L_1 + L_2 + L_{3-4-5} + L_6 = 5 + 3 + 3 + 12 = 23 \text{ henrys}$$

The time constant is found by use of equation (7-12) when $L = L_T$.

$$T = \frac{L_T}{R} = \frac{23}{15} = 1.53 \text{ seconds}$$

When $t = 2$ seconds, the exponent Rt/L is found as follows:

$$\frac{Rt}{L} = \frac{(15)\,(2)}{23} = 1.30$$

From Table 7-2, $\epsilon^{-1.30} = 0.2725$.

7-6. Energy Stored in an Inductance. Power in a direct-current circuit at any instant is found from the equation

$$p = ei \tag{7-38}$$

where p, e, and i are the instantaneous values of power, voltage, and current. When the value of e from equation (7-2) is substituted in equation (7-38), we obtain the relationship

$$p = Li\,\frac{di}{dt} \tag{7-39}$$

Equation (7-39) gives the instantaneous power or energy in an inductance.

The energy dw supplied in the interval of time dt is

$$dw = p\,dt = Li\,di \tag{7-40}$$

The current i changes from zero to I when a voltage E is impressed on an inductive circuit. Integrating equation (7-40) between these limits gives the energy stored in an induction coil.

$$W = \int dw = L\int_0^I i\,di$$

$$W = \tfrac{1}{2}LI^2 \tag{7-41}$$

This is the energy which is returned to the circuit when a switch—such as that shown in Fig. 7-2*a*—is opened, and is the energy responsible for the voltages and currents indicated by equations (7-8) through (7-11).

Example 7-7. In Example 7-1, how much energy is stored in the inductance when the current reaches its full value and at the end of one second?

Solution. In the example, L is 20 henrys and I is 5 amperes. Inserting these values in equation (7-41) gives the energy.

$$W = \tfrac{1}{2}LI^2 = \tfrac{1}{2}(20)(5)^2 = (10)(25) = 250 \text{ joules}$$

From Example 7-1, the current at the end of one second is 1.10 amperes. The energy is found from equation (7-41).

$$W = \tfrac{1}{2}(20)(1.10)^2 = (10)(1.21) = 12.1 \text{ joules}$$

A joule is a watt-second.

7-7. Capacitances in Series and Parallel. When several capacitances are connected in series, as in Fig. 7-8, the voltage E is equal to the sum of the voltages across the capacitances so that E is equal to $V_1 + V_2$, etc. The equation is the same as equation (7-31). From equation (7-17), we see that the voltage across a capacitor is equal to q/C. Therefore, we may write

$$E = \frac{q_T}{C_T} = \frac{q_1}{C_1} + \frac{q_2}{C_2} + \cdots + \frac{q_{n-1}}{C_{n-1}} + \frac{q_n}{C_n} \tag{7-42}$$

The current and charge are proportional, as indicated by equation (7-19). Since the current through C_1 is equal to the current at any other part of the circuit, the charges on the capacitors are equal. Therefore,

$$q_T = q_1 = q_2 = \cdots = q_{n-1} = q_n \tag{7-43}$$

Dividing equation (7-42) by q_T or its equivalent, we obtain

$$\frac{1}{C_T} = \frac{1}{C_1} + \frac{1}{C_2} + \cdots + \frac{1}{C_{n-1}} + \frac{1}{C_n} \tag{7-44}$$

Equation (7-44) is the equation used to determine the total capacitance of a circuit containing two or more capacitors in series.

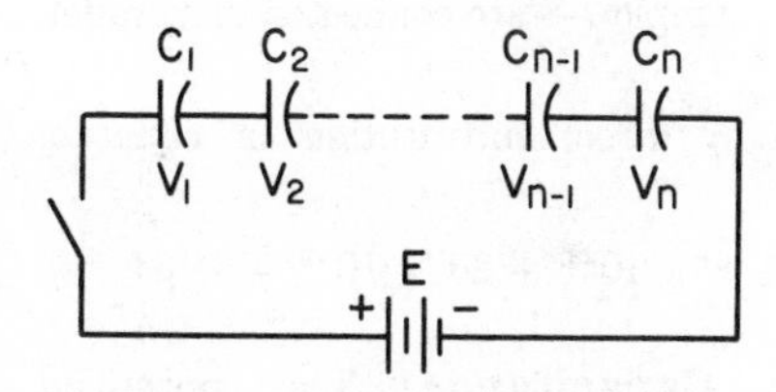

Fig. 7-8. Capacitances in series.

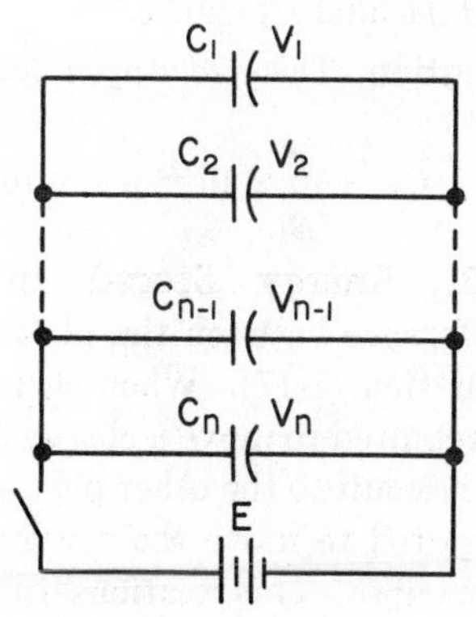

Fig. 7-9. Capacitances in parallel.

When several capacitors are connected in parallel, as in Fig. 7-9, the voltage is the same across every capacitor, so that

$$E = V_1 = V_2 = \cdots = V_{n-1} = V_n \tag{7-45}$$

Since the total current is equal to the sum of the currents in all the branches, we may write

$$q_T = q_1 + q_2 + \cdots + q_{n-1} + q_n \tag{7-46}$$

From equation (7-17) we may write

$$EC_T = V_1C_1 + V_2C_2 + \cdots + V_{n-1}C_{n-1} + V_nC_n \tag{7-47}$$

Substituting equation (7-45) in equation (7-47), we obtain the relationship

$$C_T = C_1 + C_2 + \cdots + C_{n-1} + C_n \tag{7-48}$$

Equation (7-48) gives the total capacitance of a number of capacitances connected in parallel.

Example 7-8. If capacitors rated at 10 μf, 6 μf, 8 μf, and 20 μf are connected in series, what is their total capacitance?

Solution. This problem is solved by direct substitution in equation (7-44).

$$\frac{1}{C_T} = \frac{1}{10 \times 10^{-6}} + \frac{1}{6 \times 10^{-6}} + \frac{1}{8 \times 10^{-6}} + \frac{1}{20 \times 10^{-6}}$$

$$= 0.1 \times 10^6 + 0.167 \times 10^6 + 0.125 \times 10^6 + 0.05 \times 10^6$$

$$= 0.442 \times 10^6$$

$$C_T = \frac{1}{0.442 \times 10^6} = 2.26\ \mu\text{f}$$

Example 7-9. If the capacitors of Example 7-8 are connected in parallel, find the total capacitance.

Solution. This problem is solved by direct substitution in equation (7-48).

$$C_T = 10 \times 10^{-6} + 6 \times 10^{-6} + 8 \times 10^{-6} + 20 \times 10^{-6} = 44\ \mu\text{f}$$

7-8. Energy Stored in a Capacitance. The potential difference between the plates of a capacitor is always found from equation (7-17). When current flows in a capacitive circuit, work is required to move a charge from one plate of the capacitor around the circuit to the other plate of the capacitor. The amount of work required to move the charge depends on the potential across the capacitor. This relationship is expressed by the equation

$$dw = V\,dq \tag{7-49}$$

where dw is a small amount of work required to move a small charge dq. Since $V = q/C$, we may write

$$dw = \frac{1}{C}\,q\,dq \tag{7-50}$$

The total work W required during the charging process is the integral of equation (7-50).

$$W = \int dw = \frac{1}{C}\int_{q=0}^{q=Q} q\,dq \tag{7-51}$$

When equation (7-51) is completed, we obtain the relationship

$$W = \frac{1}{2}\frac{Q^2}{C} \tag{7-52}$$

where W is the work in joules required to charge the capacitor to Q coulombs. The work, therefore, is equal to the energy in joules stored in the capacitor when a charge of Q coulombs exists in the plates. From equation (7-17) we may derive two other expressions for this energy. These are

$$W = \frac{1}{2}CV^2 \tag{7-53}$$

$$W = \frac{1}{2}QV \tag{7-54}$$

Example 7-10. If 120 volts are impressed across the capacitors in Example 7-8, what is the energy stored?

Solution. We may obtain the charge Q from equation (7-17), letting $q = Q$.

$$Q = (120)(2.26 \times 10^{-6}) = 272 \times 10^{-6} \text{ coulombs}$$

The energy can be found from equation (7-52), (7-53), or (7-54).

$$W = \frac{1}{2}\frac{Q^2}{C} = \frac{(1)(272 \times 10^{-6})^2}{(2.26 \times 10^{-6})(2)} = \frac{73{,}500 \times 10^{-6}}{4.52}$$

$$= 16{,}300 \times 10^{-6} = 0.0163 \text{ joule}$$

$$W = \frac{1}{2}CV^2 = \frac{1}{2}(2.26 \times 10^{-6})(120)^2 = 0.0163 \text{ joule}$$

$$W = \frac{1}{2}QV = \frac{1}{2}(272 \times 10^{-6})(120) = 0.0163 \text{ joule}$$

7-9. Reconnecting Charged Capacitors. Sometimes capacitors which are previously charged are reconnected into another circuit. When this is done, the voltages across the capacitors are equalized by the circuit after the reconnection.

Fig. 7-10*a* shows capacitors C_1 and C_2, which are charged separately to voltages V_1 and V_2, respectively. The charges are, therefore, Q_1 and Q_2. The total charge on the two capacitors, Q_T, is equal to the sum of the charges Q_1 and Q_2. Algebraically, the relationship is expressed as

$$Q_T = Q_1 + Q_2 \tag{7-55}$$

Since $Q = CV$ for charged capacitors, equation (7-55) may be written

$$Q_T = C_1V_1 + C_2V_2 \tag{7-56}$$

These capacitors are now reconnected as shown in Fig. 7-10*b* so that their positive terminals are joined. As soon as this connection is made, the charge will flow from one capacitor to the other until the voltages are equal. Since no charge is added or taken away,

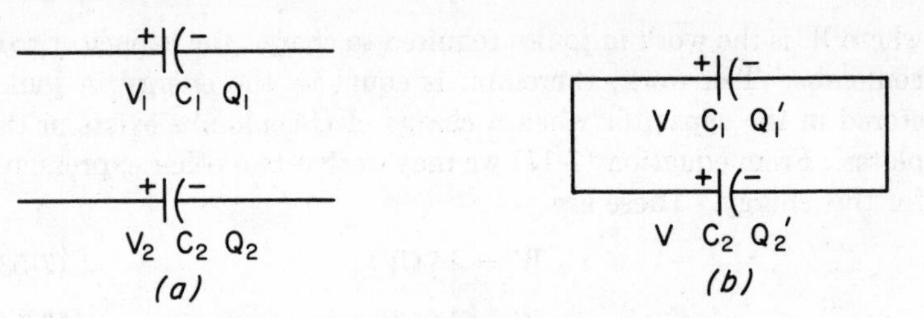

Fig. 7-10. Reconnecting charged capacitors.

Q_T is still the total charge after the reconnection. If V is the new voltage across the capacitors C_1 and C_2, and Q_1' and Q_2' are the respective charges at this time, we may write the relationship as

$$Q_T = Q_1' + Q_2' = C_1V + C_2V = V(C_1 + C_2) \qquad (7\text{-}57)$$

Equating Q_T for equations (7-56) and (7-57), we obtain the expression

$$V\,(C_1 + C_2) = C_1V_1 + C_2V_2 \qquad (7\text{-}58)$$

Solving equation (7-58) for the new voltage V, we obtain the relationship

$$V = \frac{C_1V_1 + C_2V_2}{C_1 + C_2} \qquad (7\text{-}59)$$

Example 7-11. In Fig. 7-11*a*, $C_1 = 10\ \mu f$, $C_2 = 5\ \mu f$, $C_3 = 15\ \mu f$, and $E = 500$ volts. After the three capacitors are charged, they are reconnected as shown in Fig. 7-11*b*. What is the final voltage across the capacitors?

Solution. The capacitance of the parallel combination is found by using equation (7-48).

$$C_P = C_2 + C_3 = 5 + 15 = 20\ \mu f$$

The total capacitance of the entire combination can now be found by use of equation (7-44).

$$\frac{1}{C_T} = \frac{1}{C_1} + \frac{1}{C_P} = \frac{1}{10} + \frac{1}{20} = (0.1 + 0.05) \times 10^6 = 0.15 \times 10^6$$

$$C_T = \frac{10^{-6}}{0.15} = 6.67\ \mu f$$

The total charge can be found from equation (7-17).

$$Q_1 = VC_T = (500)(6.67 \times 10^{-6}) = 3335 \times 10^{-6}\text{ coulombs}$$

This is the charge on capacitor C_1. The voltage across this capacitor is found by the equation

$$V_1 = \frac{Q_1}{C_1} = \frac{3335 \times 10^{-6}}{10 \times 10^{-6}} = 333.5 \text{ volts}$$

Q_1 is also the charge on the combination of C_1 and C_2. The voltage across this combination is

$$V_P = \frac{Q_1}{C_P} = \frac{3335 \times 10^{-6}}{20 \times 10^{-6}} = 166.5 \text{ volts}$$

V_P is the voltage across both C_2 and C_3.

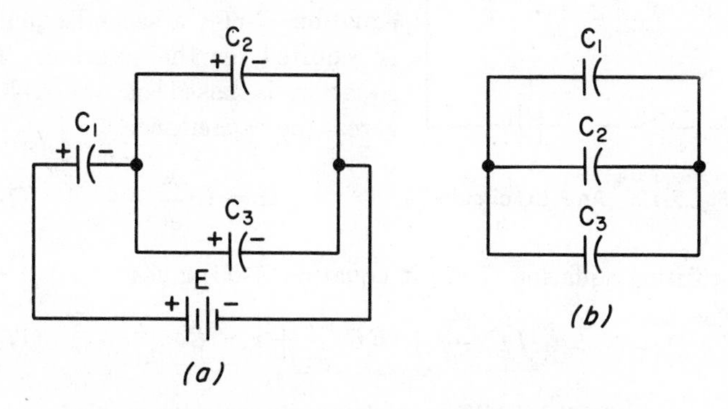

Fig. 7-11. Charging and reconnecting capacitors.

The voltage across the three capacitors, when reconnected as shown in Fig. 7-11*b*, is obtained by use of equation (7-59). When three capacitors are used, the equation is

$$V = \frac{C_1V_1 + C_2V_2 + C_3V_3}{C_1 + C_2 + C_3}$$

$$= \frac{[(10)(333.5) + (5)(166.5) + (15)(166.5)] \times 10^{-6}}{(10 + 5 + 15) \times 10^{-6}}$$

$$= \frac{3335 + 833 + 2500}{30} = \frac{6668}{30} = 222.3 \text{ volts}$$

7-10. The *RLC* Circuit. When resistance, inductance, and capacitance are connected in series—as in Fig. 7-12—the current and voltage relations at any instant depend on the relative values of the parameters in the circuit. At the instant the switch is closed, the voltage across the coil L is equal to the source voltage E and the current is zero. Sometime later, the voltage across the capacitor is equal to E and the current is again zero. Between these extremes, the exact current and voltage relations can be determined by plotting curves for the values found.

Kirchhoff's laws for the circuit shown in Fig. 7-12 give the voltage equation

$$L\frac{di}{dt} + Ri + v = E \tag{7-60}$$

where the symbols on the left side of the equation are the voltages across the inductance, the resistance, and the capacitor.

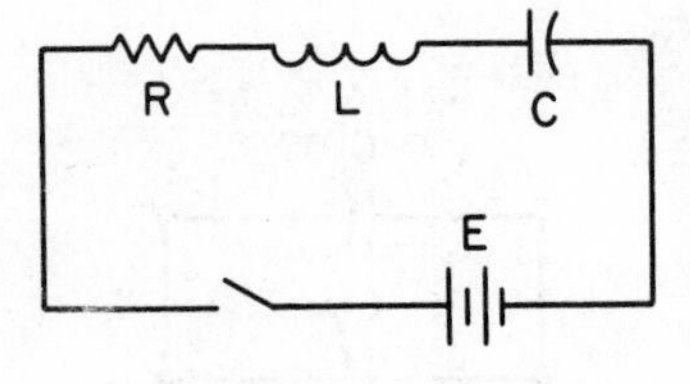

Fig. 7-12. An *RLC* circuit.

Since i and v are unknown in equation (7-60), a second equation is required for the solution. This equation is based on the voltage across the capacitance.

$$i = C\frac{dv}{dt} \tag{7-61}$$

Substituting equation (7-61) in equation (7-60) gives

$$LC\frac{d^2v}{dt^2} + RC\frac{dv}{dt} + v = E \tag{7-62}$$

Equation (7-62) is a differential equation in only one unknown—v. This voltage v is the voltage across the capacitor at any given instant of time. When this equation is solved, we obtain

$$v = V_1 \epsilon^{-\frac{t}{T_1}} + V_2 \epsilon^{-\frac{t}{T_2}} + V_c \tag{7-63}$$

where v is the instantaneous voltage across the capacitor at time t, and V_c is the final voltage across the capacitor after the current has stopped flowing in the circuit. V_c, then, is usually equal to the applied voltage E. V_1, V_2, T_1, and T_2 have values as follows:

$$V_1 = \frac{1}{1 - \frac{T_2}{T_1}}\left(V_o - V_c + \frac{T_2 I_o}{C}\right) \tag{7-64}$$

$$V_2 = V_o - V_c - V_1 \tag{7-65}$$

$$T_1 = \frac{RC}{2} + \sqrt{(RC/2)^2 - LC} \tag{7-66}$$

$$T_2 = \frac{RC}{2} - \sqrt{(RC/2)^2 - LC} \tag{7-67}$$

In these four equations, V_o is the voltage across the capacitor before any change in the circuit is made. If the capacitor is uncharged at that instant, V_o is zero. I_o is the current that is flowing at the time a change is made in the circuit. If the circuit is open at that time, no current is flowing and I_o is equal to zero. T_1 and T_2 are time constants.

The current in the circuit is obtained by differentiating equation (7-63) and multiplying by the capacitance C, as indicated by equation (7-61).

$$i = C\left(\frac{V_1}{-T_1}\epsilon^{-\frac{t}{T_1}} + \frac{V_2}{-T_2}\epsilon^{-\frac{t}{T_2}}\right) \qquad (7\text{-}68)$$

The method recommended for solving RLC circuits is as follows:

1. Determine the values of R, L, and C in the circuit.

2. Determine I_o. If the circuit is open when $t = 0$, then $I_o = 0$.

3. Determine V_o. If the capacitor is in an uncharged condition when $t = 0$, then $V_o = 0$.

4. Solve for V_c. Under the conditions stated in (2) and (3), $V_c = E$. Under other conditions, V_c may or may not be equal to E. The circuit conditions may have to be analyzed to determine the actual value of V_c.

5. Solve for T_1 and T_2.

6. Solve for V_1 and V_2.

7. Insert T_1, T_2, V_1, and V_2 in equation (7-63) to obtain the voltage across the capacitor, and in equation (7-68) to obtain the current.

8. If the voltages across the inductance and resistance are desired, these values can be calculated from the following relationships:

$$V_R = Ri \qquad (7\text{-}69)$$

$$V_L = v - V_R \qquad (7\text{-}70)$$

In this type of circuit, the current can never equal the Ohm's law value of E/R, since there is always a voltage present across L or C or across both L and C.

A useful solution can be found with these equations only when $(RC/2)^2 \geqq LC$. When $(RC/2)^2 = LC$, $R = 2\sqrt{L/C}$. When R is less than this value, the circuit cannot be solved by the equations given previously.

When $R < 2\sqrt{L/C}$, the equations that are used are:

$$v = V_1 \epsilon^{-\frac{t}{T}} \cos(\omega t + \phi) + V_c \quad (7\text{-}71)$$

The time constant T is found by the equation

$$T = \frac{2L}{R} \quad (7\text{-}72)$$

The other constants are calculated as follows:

$$\omega = \sqrt{\frac{1}{LC} - \frac{1}{T^2}} \quad (7\text{-}73)$$

$$\phi = \tan^{-1}\left(\frac{-I_o}{\omega C\,(V_o - V_c)} - \frac{1}{\omega T}\right) \quad (7\text{-}74)$$

$$V_1 = \frac{V_o - V_c}{\cos\phi} \quad (7\text{-}75)$$

Example 7-12. In the circuit in Fig. 7-12, R = 8000 ohms, L = 18 henrys, C = 2 microfarads, and E = 150 volts. The switch is closed at $t = 0$ and C is not previously charged. Find the voltage across the capacitor and the current in the circuit for any time t.

Solution. Since $t = 0$ and the capacitor is not charged, $I_o = 0$ and $V_o = 0$. V_c = 150 volts. The problem should be checked for the value of $2\sqrt{L/C}$:

$$2\sqrt{\frac{L}{C}} = 2\sqrt{\frac{18}{2 \times 10^{-6}}} = 2\sqrt{9 \times 10^6} = 6000$$

Since R is 8000 ohms, equation (7-63) is used for the solution.

The constants T_1, T_2, V_1, and V_2 are now found by use of equations (7-64), (7-65), (7-66), and (7-67).

$$T_1 = \frac{(8 \times 10^3)(2 \times 10^{-6})}{2} + \sqrt{\left[\frac{(8 \times 10^3)(2 \times 10^{-6})}{2}\right]^2 - (18)(2 \times 10^{-6})}$$

$$= 8 \times 10^{-3} + \sqrt{64 \times 10^{-6} - 36 \times 10^{-6}}$$

$$= 8 \times 10^{-3} + \sqrt{28 \times 10^{-6}} = 8 \times 10^{-3} + 5.29 \times 10^{-3}$$

$$= 13.29 \times 10^{-3} = 0.01329 \text{ second}$$

$$T_2 = 8 \times 10^{-3} - 5.29 \times 10^{-3} = 2.71 \times 10^{-3} = 0.00271 \text{ second}$$

$$V_1 = \frac{1}{1 - \frac{0.00271}{0.01329}}(-150) = \frac{-150}{1 - 0.204} = \frac{-150}{0.796} = -188 \text{ volts}$$

$V_2 = -150 + 188 = 38$ volts

These values are now inserted in equation (7-63).

$$v = -188\,\epsilon^{-\frac{t}{0.01329}} + 38\,\epsilon^{-\frac{t}{0.00271}} + 150 \text{ volts}$$

This is the voltage across the capacitor. The current in the circuit is determined by use of equation (7-68).

$$i = (2 \times 10^{-6})\left(\frac{-188}{-0.01329}\,\epsilon^{-\frac{t}{0.01329}} + \frac{38}{-0.00271}\,\epsilon^{-\frac{t}{0.00271}}\right)$$

$$= \left(2830\,\epsilon^{-\frac{t}{0.01329}} + 2800\,\epsilon^{-\frac{t}{0.00271}}\right) \text{ micro-amps}$$

Problems Based on Chapter 7

P7-1. A current of 5 amps flows in a circuit containing an inductance of 10 henrys. If the circuit is suddenly opened and the current stops flowing in 0.1 second, what is the resulting induced voltage?

Ans. 500 volts.

P7-2. A series circuit contains an inductance of 15 henrys and a resistance of 20 ohms connected across a voltage source of 80 volts. What is the current one second after the circuit is closed? What are the voltages across the inductance and across the resistance at this time?

Ans. $i = 2.94$ amps. $e_R = 58.8$ volts. $e_L = 21.2$ volts.

P7-3. A series circuit has the following values: $E = 75$ volts, $R = 5$ ohms, and $L = 15$ henrys. What is the time constant? How long after the circuit is energized will the current reach a constant value?

Ans. $T = 3$ sec. $t = 15$ sec.

P7-4. The circuit of problem P7-3 is opened by a switch similar to that shown in Fig. 7-2*a* by dotted lines, so that L and R are in the circuit by themselves. What will be the value of the current 8 seconds later?

Ans. 1.04 amps.

P7-5. A circuit contains an inductance of 8 henrys and a resistance of 2 ohms. How long after the circuit is energized will the current reach one-half of its Ohm's law value?

Ans. 2.78 sec.

P7-6. A circuit contains three inductances in series with a resistance across a 120-volt source. If $L_1 = 8$ henrys, $L_2 = 10$ henrys, $L_3 = 6$ henrys, and $R = 15$ ohms, what is the time constant? What is the value of the current one second after the circuit is closed? After 2 seconds?

Ans. $T = 1.6$ sec. $i_1 = 3.72$ amps. $i_2 = 5.71$ amps.

P7-7. A circuit contains three inductances in parallel and a series resistance across a 125-volt source. If $L_1 = 10$ henrys, $L_2 = 8$ henrys, $L_3 = 6$ henrys, and $R = 15$ ohms, what is the time constant? What is the current 0.2 second after the circuit is closed?

Ans. $T = 0.17$ sec. $i = 5.77$ amps.

P7-8. In Fig. P7-8, $L_1 = 5$ henrys, $L_2 = 1$ henry, $L_3 = 3$ henrys, $L_4 = 8$ henrys, $L_5 = 10$ henrys, and $L_6 = 2$ henrys. Find the total inductance. Assume that a current of 10 amps is flowing when a 10-ohm resistance is connected as shown in Fig. P7-8 (switching arrangement not shown in the figure). What is the current 2 seconds later?

Ans. 5.21 henrys. $i = 0.215$ amp.

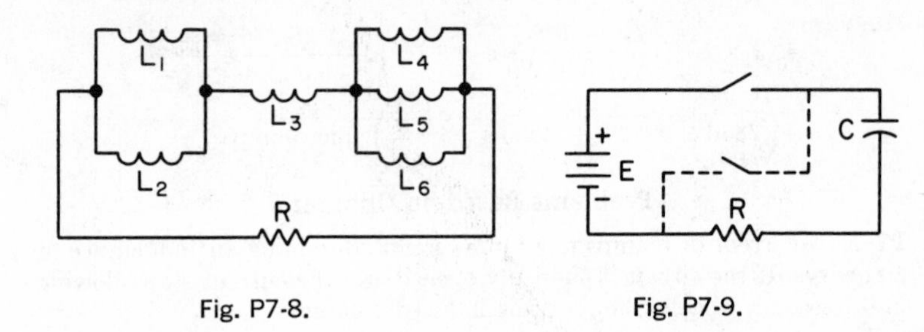

Fig. P7-8. Fig. P7-9.

P7-9. In Fig. P7-9, $R = 1000$ ohms, $C = 10$ microfarads, and $E = 300$ volts. What is the time constant? What is the current 0.015 second after the circuit is closed? What are the voltages across the capacitor and the resistance?

Ans. $T = 0.01$ sec. $i = 0.0669$ amp. $v_c = 233$ volts. $v_R = 67$ volts.

P7-10. After stable conditions are reached, the circuit in problem P7-9 is opened from the voltage source and closed to form the circuit indicated by the dotted lines in Fig. P7-9. Find the current 0.03 second after this connection is made. What are the voltages across the capacitor and across the resistance at this instant?

Ans. $i = 0.0149$ amp. $v_c = 14.9$ volts. $v_R = Ri = 14.9$ volts.

P7-11. Three capacitances are connected in series. If $C_1 = 1000$ microfarads, $C_2 = 50$ microfarads, and $C_3 = 100$ microfarads, what is the total capacitance?

Ans. $C_T = 32.3$ microfarads.

P7-12. If the capacitances of problem P7-11 are connected in parallel, what is the total capacitance?

Ans. $C_T = 1150$ microfarads.

P7-13. In Fig. P7-13, capacitors $C_1 = C_2 = C_3 = C_4 = C_5 = C_6 = C_7 = C_8 = C_9 = 3$ microfarads, and $C_{10} = C_{11} = C_{12} = 2$ microfarads. Find the capacitance between g and h, e and f, c and d, and a and b.

Ans. $C_{gh} = C_{ef} = C_{cd} = C_{ab} = 1$ microfarad.

P7-14. If the voltage across terminals a and b of Fig. P7-13 is 1500 volts, find the charge on every one of the capacitors and on the entire network. Use the values given in problem P7-13.

Ans. $q_{ab} = 1500 \times 10^{-6}$ coul. $q_1 = q_9 = 1500 \times 10^{-6}$ coul. $q_{10} = 1000 \times 10^{-6}$ coul. $q_2 = q_8 = 500 \times 10^{-6}$ coul. $q_{11} = 333 \times 10^{-6}$ coul. $q_3 = q_7 =$

167×10^{-6} coul. $q_{12} = 111 \times 10^{-6}$ coul. $q_4 = q_5 = q_6 = 56 \times 10^{-6}$ coul. Check: $q_{10} + q_{11} + q_{12} + q_5 = q_{ab} = 1500 \times 10^{-6}$ coul.

P7-15. In Fig. P7-9, $R = 1000$ ohms and $C = 1000$ microfarads. An emf of 200 volts is impressed on the circuit for 3 seconds. (a) What are the current in the circuit and the voltage across the capacitor? (b) An emf of 500 volts is impressed on the circuit when $t = 3$ sec. What are the current in the circuit and the voltage across the capacitor 3 seconds later?

Ans. (a) $v_c = 190$ volts. $i = 0.01$ amp. (b) $v_c = 485$ volts. $i = 0.015$ amp.

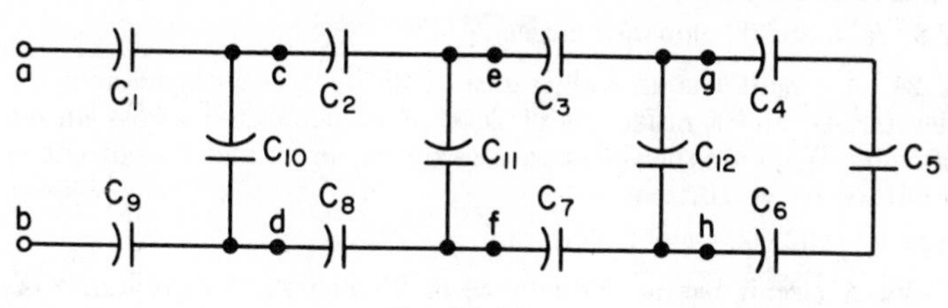

Fig. P7-13.

P7-16. In problem P7-7, what is the energy stored in the inductance when $t = 0.17$ sec?

Ans. 35.5 joules.

P7-17. In problem P7-9, what is the energy stored in the capacitor when $t = 0.015$ sec? When $i = 0$?

Ans. 0.27 joule. 0.45 joule.

P7-18. A 10-microfarad capacitor charged to 3000 volts is connected across a 20-microfarad capacitor which has been charged to 1500 volts. If the positive terminals of the capacitors are connected together, what is the final voltage across each capacitor?

Ans. $V = 2000$ volts.

P7-19. If the capacitors of problem P7-18 had been connected so that the positive terminal of one were connected to the negative terminal of the other, what would be the final voltage?

Ans. Zero volts.

P7-20. A 10-microfarad capacitor charged to 3000 volts is connected across a 20-microfarad capacitor which has been charged to 2000 volts. If the positive terminal of one is connected to the negative terminal of the other, what is the final voltage?

Ans. 333 volts.

P7-21. What is the total energy stored in the capacitors of problem P7-18 before and after the reconnection?

Ans. 67.5 joules before reconnection and 60 joules after reconnection. (Although the total charge remains the same, some energy is lost through radiation and as heat in the connecting wires as the charges move through them.)

P7-22. A 1000-microfarad capacitor is charged to a potential of 500 volts. The capacitor is now connected in series with a 1000-ohm resistor across a 300-volt source. Find the voltage across the capacitor and the current 1.5 seconds later.

Ans. 345 volts and 0.045 amp.

P7-23. A circuit has an inductance L, a capacitance C, and a resistance R, in series. If $L = 10$ henrys and $C = 1000$ microfarads, what value of R is required if equations (7-62) and (7-68) are to be used to determine the voltage and the current?

Ans. $R = 20{,}000$ ohms (or larger).

P7-24. A circuit has an inductance of 25 henrys, a capacitance of 100 microfarads, and a resistance of 2000 ohms connected across an emf of 200 volts. What are the voltage across the capacitor and the current in the circuit when $t = 0.07$ sec?

Ans. $v_c = 52$ volts. $i = 0.055$ amp.

P7-25. A circuit has an inductance of 25 henrys, a capacitance of 100 microfarads, and a resistance of 500 ohms connected across an emf of 200 volts. Find the value of T, ω, ϕ, and V_1.

Ans. $T = 0.1$ sec. $\omega = 17.32$. $\phi = \tan^{-1}\left(-\frac{\sqrt{3}}{3}\right) = 330°$.

$V_1 = -231$ volts.

8 ALTERNATING-CURRENT CIRCUITS

8-1. The *j*-Operator. Since nearly all quantities encountered in the study of alternating currents are vectorial, some sort of vector notation is necessary. For most purposes, the complex notation —sometimes called "imaginary numbers"—is found to be convenient. The complex notation requires the use of the letter *j*—called the *j*-operator—and the Cartesian coordinate axes as shown in Fig. 8-1.

In Fig. 8-1, the axis starting at the origin 0 and going to the right is the positive or "real" axis. Any division along this axis is equal to $+1$ multiplied by the absolute value of the division. Thus, any division whose absolute value along this axis may be represented by the letter a has the relative value of $+a$ as indicated in the figure. If we multiply this vector by minus 1 (-1), we obtain the value $-a$ which is measured to the left of 0 as indicated in the figure. Multiplying $+a$ by -1 has thus rotated the vector a counterclockwise through an angle of 180°.

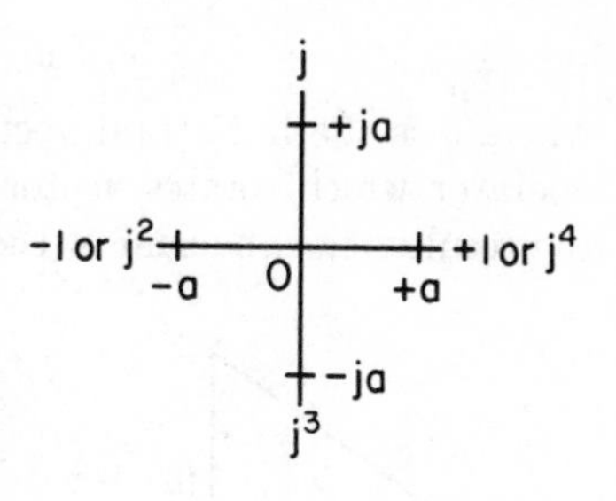

Fig. 8-1. The *j*-operator on the coordinate axes.

The value -1 *may therefore be defined as an operator which will rotate any vector counterclockwise through an angle of 180°.* As will be seen later, -1 causes this rotation no matter where the vector is located. For example, if $-a$ is multiplied by -1, it is again equal to the original vector, a.

Since we are interested in distances along the axis perpendicular to the 1 to -1 axis, we need an operator which will rotate the given vector half way, or 90°, counterclockwise. This operator, to be of any use in vector algebra, must be one which, multiplied by itself, will equal the operator -1. If we represent this operator by the letter j, then

$$j^2 = -1 \tag{8-1}$$

If we solve equation (8-1) for j, we obtain

$$j = \sqrt{-1} \tag{8-2}$$

From this explanation and from equation (8-2) we may write the definition for the operator j.

j is an operator which will rotate any vector counterclockwise through an angle of 90°. The operator j is equal to the square root of minus one.

With this operator j we may rotate the original vector $+a$ to the position represented by $+ja$ in Fig. 8-1. When multiplied by j, $+ja$ becomes j^2a. Equation 8-1 shows that $j^2 = -1$, so that $j^2a = -a$, which we obtained by use of the operator -1. Multiplying $-a$ (or j^2a) by j gives $-ja$ (or j^3a, since $j^3 = j^2$ times j). This value is plotted in Fig. 8-1. When $-ja$ is multiplied by j, it becomes $-j^2a$, or $+a$, the original vector. This vector may also be represented by j^4a, since $j^4 = j^2$ times j^2, or $+1$.

The complex form for vector notation is

$$c = a + jb \tag{8-3}$$

where a is the horizontal vector, b is the vertical vector, j is the operator which rotates vector b to the vertical position, and c is the resultant of the sum of the vectors a and jb. This relationship is shown in Fig. 8-2 for positive values of a and b. The vector c is always considered positive, regardless of its position or direction.

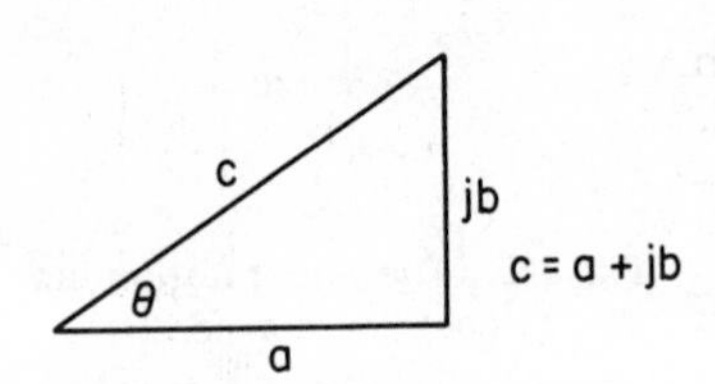

Fig. 8-2. Complex form for vector notation.

Vectors of the form $a + jb$ can be added, subtracted, multiplied, or divided. The methods of manipulating these vectors are illustrated in the following examples.

Example 8-1. Find the sum and the difference of two vectors designated as $5 + j6$ and $8 + j4$.

Solution. The sum is determined as follows:

$$5 + j6 + 8 + j4 = (5 + 8) + j(6 + 4) = 13 + j10$$

The difference is determined as follows:

$$5 + j6 - (8 + j4) = (5 - 8) + j(6 - 4) = -3 + j2$$

Example 8-2. Find the product of vectors $3 + j5$ and $8 - j6$.

Solution. The process is straight algebraic multiplication.

$$(3 + j5)(8 - j6) = 24 - j18 + j40 - j^2 30$$

Since $j^2 = -1$, we may rewrite this product as follows:

$$24 + 30 - 18 + j40 = 54 + j22$$

Example 8-3. Find the quotient of $6 + j2$ divided by $3 - j4$.

Solution. We may express this relationship by a fraction.

$$\frac{6 + j2}{3 - j4}$$

Since j is irrational, we must clear the denominator by multiplying both numerator and denominator by the conjugate of the denominator.

$$\frac{(6 + j2)(3 + j4)}{(3 - j4)(3 + j4)} = \frac{18 + j24 + j6 + j^2 8}{9 + 16}$$

$$= \frac{18 - 8 + j30}{25} = \frac{10}{25} + j\frac{30}{25} = 0.4 + j1.2$$

8-2. The Polar Form of Vector Notation. Although vectors in the complex form may be added, subtracted, multiplied, and divided, the multiplication and division processes are somewhat complicated at times. For this reason, the polar form of vector notation may sometimes be preferable.

From Fig. 8-2, we may write

$$\bar{c} = c\,\underline{/\theta} \qquad (8\text{-}4)$$

where $\bar{c}$ refers to side c as a vector, c is the numerical value of this vector, and θ is the angle between c and the positive horizontal axis.

Vectors of the form indicated in equation (8-4) may be multiplied or divided but cannot be added or subtracted. If two vectors, $c\,\underline{/\theta}$ and $d\,\underline{/\alpha}$, are to be multiplied, the process is

$$(c\,\underline{/\theta})(d\,\underline{/\alpha}) = cd\,\underline{/\theta + \alpha} \qquad (8\text{-}5)$$

If these two vectors are to be divided, the process is

$$\frac{c\,\underline{/\theta}}{d\,\underline{/\alpha}} = \frac{c\,\underline{/\theta - \alpha}}{d} \qquad (8\text{-}6)$$

Example 8-4. Multiply the vectors $10\,\underline{/20^\circ}$ and $5\,\underline{/30^\circ}$.

Solution. Equation (8-5) indicates that the solution is as follows:

$$(10\,\underline{/20^\circ})(5\,\underline{/30^\circ}) = (10)(5)\,\underline{/20^\circ + 30^\circ} = 50\,\underline{/50^\circ}$$

Example 8-5. Divide $10 \underline{/20^\circ}$ by $5 \underline{/30^\circ}$.

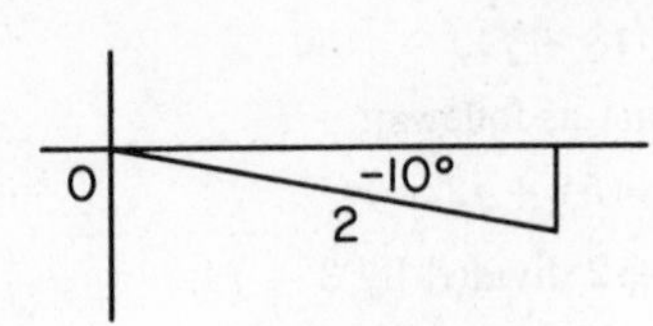

Fig. 8-3. Representation of a negative angle.

Solution. Equation (8-6) shows that

$$\frac{10 \underline{/20^\circ}}{5 \underline{/30^\circ}} = 2 \underline{/20^\circ - 30^\circ} = 2 \underline{/-10^\circ}$$

The negative angle indicates that the new vector is 10° in a clockwise direction with respect to the positive horizontal axis. This position is indicated in Fig. 8-3.

8-3. Converting Between Polar and Complex Forms.

The analysis of an alternating-current system may require that vectors be converted from one form of notation to another. This conversion is accomplished by the use of fundamental trigonometric relations as follows:

$$a = c \cos \theta \tag{8-7}$$

$$jb = jc \sin \theta \tag{8-8}$$

If equations (8-7) and (8-8) are added, we obtain the relationship

$$a + jb = c\,(\cos \theta + j \sin \theta) \tag{8-9}$$

By use of equation (8-9) we may convert from the polar form to the complex form of vector notation.

The conversion from the complex to the polar form is accomplished by finding the tangent of the angle θ. Since j is merely an operator and does not affect the absolute value of b, we may write

$$\tan \theta = \frac{b}{a} \tag{8-10}$$

From equation (8-10) we can determine θ, and from either equation (8-7) or equation (8-8) we can find c.

Example 8-6. Convert $5 + j3$ to the polar form.

Solution. The tangent of the angle can be found by use of equation (8-10) and the angle can be found from that value. If a slide rule is used, however, the angle can be determined directly.

$$\tan^{-1} \frac{b}{a} = \tan^{-1} \frac{3}{5} = 31^\circ$$

Equation (8-7) now gives the value of c.

$$c = \frac{a}{\cos \theta} = \frac{5}{\cos 31^\circ} = 5.82$$

The polar form is, therefore,

$$\bar{c} = 5.82 \underline{/31^\circ}$$

Example 8-7. Convert $8 \underline{/26^\circ}$ to the complex form.

Solution. Equation (8-9) can be used, with the aid of either trigonometric tables or the slide rule.

$$a + jb = c(\cos \theta + j \sin \theta) = 8(\cos 26^\circ + j \sin 26^\circ) = 7.2 + j3.5$$

8-4. The Single Phase Sine Wave. Alternating-current generators can be designed to deliver electrical energy in any of a number of wave forms. The voltage of a generator at any instant depends on: (1) the strength of the magnetic field, (2) the velocity of the rotating part of the machine, and (3) the angle between the direction of the magnetic field and the instantaneous direction of travel of the rotating part. Since these three conditions are not constant* while a generator is in operation, the voltage output is variable for every position of the rotating part of the machine.

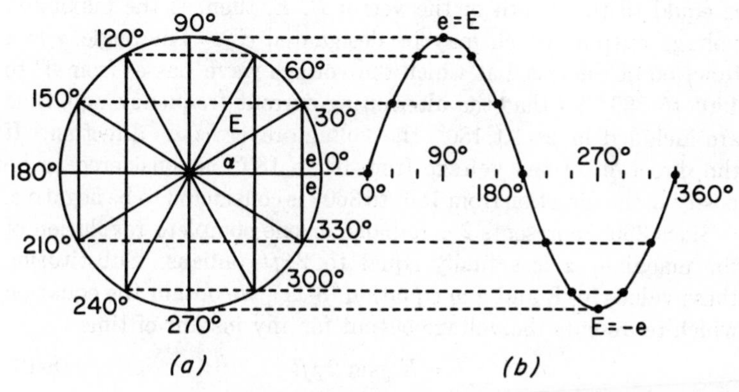

Fig. 8-4. The single phase sine wave.

The rate at which the voltage varies can be controlled by the design of the generator. Experience has shown that electrical systems will operate more efficiently and with less maintenance if the output varies sinusoidally to produce what is known as a sine

* The velocity of the machine is usually considered to be constant, as an increase in velocity of rotation would also increase the frequency output, as will be shown in Chapter 11. However, since an increase in velocity of rotation also increases the voltage output of the generator, this characteristic must be considered as a variable.

wave of voltage. This wave form is illustrated in Fig. 8-4.

Let E be a vector which rotates counterclockwise from the horizontal right position. This position is marked 0° on the coordinate diagram in Fig. 8-4*a*. The vertical distance from the horizontal to the end of the vector E represents the voltage output of the generator, which at that position is zero volts, as indicated on the graph of the output shown in Fig. 8-4*b*.

As the vector rotates, the vertical distance from the horizontal in Fig. 8-4*a* is plotted in Fig. 8-4*b*. If the central angle in Fig. 8-4*a* is called α, and the vertical distance—representing the output—is designated e, then

$$\sin \alpha = \frac{e}{E}$$

and the output is therefore

$$e = E \sin \alpha \qquad (8\text{-}11)$$

As shown in Fig. 8-4*b*, at 90° and at 270°, the voltage output e is equal to the length of the vector E. E, then, is the maximum voltage output, which may be designated E_m. The angle α is a function of the speed at which the voltage wave passes from 0° to 180° to 360°, so that the alternating-current frequency and time are included in α. At 180°, the voltage reverses its direction. If the direction of the voltage from 0° to 180° is considered to be positive, the direction from 180° to 360° is considered to be negative.

Since 360° represents 2π radians, or one complete revolution of the machine, α is actually equal to $2\pi ft$ radians. Substituting these values for E and α in equation (8-11), we obtain the equation which represents the voltage output for any instant of time t.

$$e = E_m \sin 2\pi ft \qquad (8\text{-}12)$$

Since for any given frequency—as 60 cycles per second—the product $2\pi f$ is a constant, we may write

$$e = E_m \sin \omega t \qquad (8\text{-}13)$$

where $\omega = 2\pi f$.

In equations (8-11), (8-12), and (8-13), e and E_m are in volts, f is in cycles per second, and t is in seconds. The product ωt (or $2\pi ft$) is in radians. If the angle α in degrees is desired, we may use the equation

$$e = E_m \sin 57.3\, \omega t \qquad (8\text{-}14)$$

since there are 57.3° in a radian ($180°/\pi = 57.3°$).

Example 8-8. A 60-cycle a-c generator has an output of 100 volts at an instant when $t = 0.023$ second. What is the value of ω? What is the angle in radians with respect to the zero position ($t = 0$) in Fig. 8-4? What is the angle in degrees (called *electrical degrees*)? What is the maximum voltage of the generator?

Solution. Since $f = 60$ cycles per second, $\omega = 2\pi f = (6.28)(60) = 376.99$ radians per second. (The value is generally taken to be 377, since the error amounts to about one part in 38,000.)

The angle in radians is equal to $2\pi ft$:

$$\alpha = (377)(0.023) = 8.67 \text{ radians}$$

The angle in degrees is equal to

$$(8.67)(57.3) = 496.79° \text{ or } 497°$$

The maximum voltage output of the generator is found by solving equation (8-13) or (8-14) for E_m.

$$E_m = \frac{e}{\sin \omega t} = \frac{100}{\sin 8.67} = \frac{100}{\sin 2.39} = 146.7 \text{ volts}$$

$$E_m = \frac{e}{\sin 57.3\, \omega t} = \frac{100}{\sin 497°} = \frac{100}{\sin 137°} = \frac{100}{\sin 43°}$$

$$= 146.7 \text{ volts}$$

8-5. Relation Between Voltage and Current.

When an alternating-current source of voltage is applied to a circuit containing only resistance,† the current in the circuit is expressed by the equation

$$i = \frac{e}{R} \tag{8-15}$$

Substituting the value of the instantaneous voltage e from equation (8-13) in equation (8-15), we obtain the relationship

$$i = \frac{E_m}{R} \sin \omega t \tag{8-16}$$

The fraction E_m/R is equal to the maximum value of the current, which we can call I_m. Therefore,

$$i = I_m \sin \omega t \tag{8-17}$$

---

† Strictly speaking, circuits containing only resistance are impossible to construct. When frequencies of a few hundred or more cycles per second are present in the circuit, the inductance and capacitance of even a straight wire become very noticeable. For power frequencies of 50 or 60 cycles, however, the effect of inductance and capacitance can often be ignored unless actually designed as a part of the circuit.

Equations (8-13) and (8-17) show that the current and voltage are "in phase" when an a-c circuit contains only resistance. When $t = 0$, then $\sin \omega t = 0$ and both the current and voltage are equal to zero. When $\omega t = \pi/2$ radians (equal to 90°), $\sin \omega t = 1$ and the current and voltage are equal to their respective maximum values, I_m and E_m. Other values of current and voltage can be found by assigning values to ωt and solving equations (8-13) and (8-17). These values can be plotted as in Fig. 8-5.

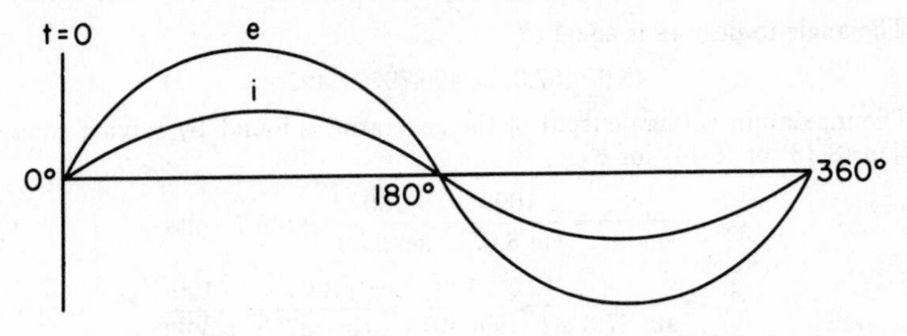

Fig. 8-5. Current and voltage sine waves for a resistive circuit.

If a coil of wire is used either in series with a resistance or in place of the resistance, the voltage across the inductance‡ of the coil is found by the expression

$$e = L \frac{di}{dt} \tag{8-18}$$

Solving equation (8-18) for di, we obtain the relationship

$$di = \frac{e}{L} dt \tag{8-19}$$

Equation (8-19) is a differential equation which can be solved by integration:

$$\int di = \frac{e}{L} \int dt \tag{8-20}$$

Substituting the value of e from equation (8-13) in equation

‡ Since coils are wound with wire, all coils contain resistance as well as inductance. However, since it is possible to obtain coils which have an inductive effect in the circuit equal to 500 or more times the resistance, practical circuits can be designed where the resistance is so nearly zero by comparison with the inductance that the resistance can be ignored.

(8-20), we have

$$\int di = \frac{E_m}{L} \int \sin \omega t \, dt \tag{8-21}$$

By integrating equation (8-21), we obtain the solution

$$i = -\frac{E_m}{L\omega} \cos \omega t \tag{8-22}$$

In trigonometry, we learn that $-\cos \omega t$ is equal to $\sin (\omega t - 90°)$. If we substitute this value in equation (8-22), we have

$$i = \frac{E_m}{\omega L} \sin (\omega t - 90°)^{\S} \tag{8-23}$$

Equation (8-23) shows that the current lags the voltage in an inductance. If equations (8-13) and (8-23) are solved for various values of ωt, the results may be plotted as shown in Fig. 8-6. As shown in Fig. 8-6, when $t = 0$, $e = 0$, and i is at its maximum

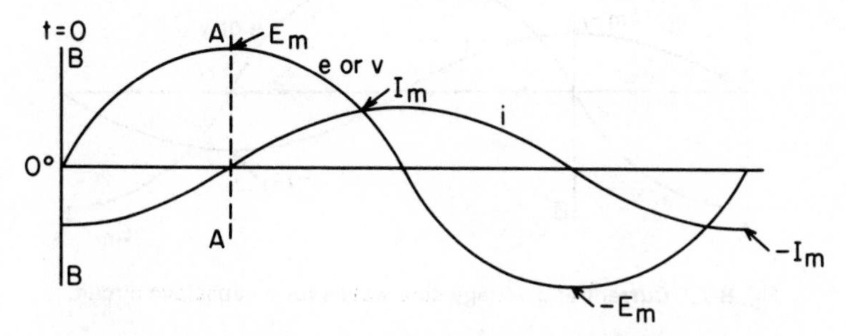

Fig. 8-6. Current and voltage sine waves for an inductive circuit.

negative value, $-I_m$. When $\omega t = 90°$, e is at maximum positive, but i is at zero. The current does not reach its maximum positive value until $\omega t = 180°$, or 90° later than the voltage.

The quantity ωL in equation (8-23) is an important one in alternating current. It is called *inductive reactance,* is given the symbol

---

§ Mathematically speaking, equation (8-23) is incorrect, since ωt is an angle in radians and 90° is an angle in degrees. For convenience, however, engineers will often use this mixed notation since the fundamental angle ωt is more easily calculated in radian form and the phase angle is more accurately designated in degrees. When equations of the form of (8-23) are used, ωt is converted to degrees by multiplying by 57.3, since one radian is equal to 57.3°.

X_L, and is measured in ohms. In equation form, therefore, we may write

$$X_L = \omega L = 2\pi f L \tag{8-24}$$

In equation (8-24), X_L is the inductive reactance in ohms, f is the frequency in cycles per second, and L is the inductance in henrys.

If a capacitor is used in an alternating-current circuit, the instantaneous value of the current is indicated by the equation

$$i = C\,\frac{dv}{dt} \tag{8-25}$$

In equation (8-25), the symbol v is used in place of e for volts. Since v is often used for the voltage across a component of the circuit and e is the voltage across the source, the instantaneous

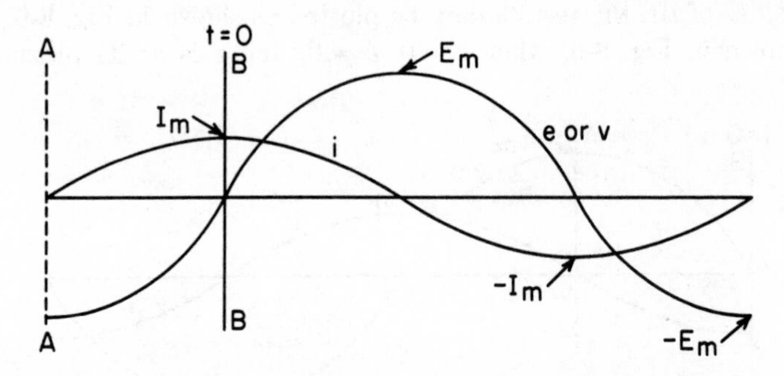

Fig. 8-7. Current and voltage sine waves for a capacitive circuit.

values of both can be found from equation (8-13). If E_m in equation (8-13) is the maximum voltage across the capacitor, we may write

$$v = E_m \sin \omega t \tag{8-26}$$

where v is the voltage across the capacitor. If we substitute equation (8-26) in equation (8-25), we obtain the expression

$$i = C\,\frac{d}{dt}\,(E_m \sin \omega t) \tag{8-27}$$

By performing the indicated differentiation, we obtain the equation for the current:

$$i = \omega C E_m \cos \omega t \tag{8-28}$$

In trigonometry, we learn that $\cos \omega t$ is equal to $\sin(\omega t + 90°)$.

If we substitute this value in equation (8-28), we have

$$i = \omega C E_m \sin(\omega t + 90°) \tag{8-29}$$

Equation (8-29) shows that the current leads the voltage in a capacitance. If equations (8-26) and (8-29) are solved for various values of ωt, the results may be plotted as shown in Fig. 8-7. In Fig. 8-7, when $t = 0$, $v = 0$ but i is at its maximum positive value I_m. The voltage E_m does not reach its maximum value until 90° later. Capacitance, therefore, has an effect exactly the reverse of that of inductance.

The maximum value of the current may be obtained from equation (8-29).

$$I_m = \omega C E_m \tag{8-30}$$

If equation (8-30) is solved for E_m, we obtain

$$E_m = \frac{I_m}{\omega C} \tag{8-31}$$

In equation (8-31), E_m is the maximum value of the emf in volts and I_m is the maximum current in amperes. The quantity $1/\omega C$ is an important one in alternating current. It is called *capacitive reactance*, is given the symbol X_C, and is measured in ohms. In equation form, therefore, we may write

$$X_C = \frac{1}{\omega C} = \frac{1}{2\pi f C} \tag{8-32}$$

In equation (8-32), X_C is the capacitive reactance in ohms, f is the frequency in cycles per second, and C is the capacitance in farads.

If a circuit contains resistance, inductance, and capacitance in series, the voltage across the resistance is in phase with the current, the voltage across the inductance is 90° ahead of the current, and the voltage across the capacitance is 90° behind the current. Since the current is the same in all parts of the series circuit, the current is generally considered as the reference quantity. When the current is the reference, its equation may be written

$$i = I_m \sin \omega t \tag{8-33}$$

Since the voltage across the resistance is in phase with the current, the voltage equation for v_R, the voltage across the resistor, may be written

$$v_R = E_{mR} \sin \omega t \tag{8-34}$$

Since the voltage across the inductance is 90° ahead of the current, the voltage equation for v_L, the voltage across the inductance, may be written

$$v_L = E_{mL} \sin (\omega t + 90°) \tag{8-35}$$

Since the voltage across the capacitance is 90° behind the current, the voltage equation for v_C, the voltage across the capacitance, may be written

$$v_C = E_{mC} \sin (\omega t - 90°) \tag{8-36}$$

Although the voltage and current equations for inductive and capacitive components (see equations (8-13), (8-23), (8-29), (8-34), (8-35), and (8-36)) seem to be contradictory, the only difference is in the time t that is used in reference to a location of $t = 0$. If dotted lines A-A in Figs. 8-6 and 8-7 are used as $t = 0$, then equations (8-35) and (8-36) hold for the voltage. If lines B-B are used as $t = 0$, then equations (8-23) and (8-29) describe the current.

The total voltage of the source e may therefore be written

$$e = v_R + v_L + v_C \tag{8-37a}$$

or

$$e = E_{mR} \sin \omega t + E_{mL} \sin (\omega t + 90°) + E_{mC} \sin (\omega t - 90°) \tag{8-37b}$$

In equation (8-37b), the maximum values of the voltages are as follows:

$$E_{mR} = I_m R \tag{8-38}$$

$$E_{mL} = I_m X_L = I_m (\omega L) \tag{8-39}$$

$$E_{mC} = I_m X_C = \frac{I_m}{\omega C} \tag{8-40}$$

Example 8-9. In Fig. 8-8, $R = 10$ ohms, $X_L = 15$ ohms, $X_C = 8$ ohms, and $I_m = 2$ amperes. Find the voltage e of the alternating-current source. What is the instantaneous value of e when $f = 60$ cycles per second and $t = 1/40$ sec? What is the equation of the current and its value at $t = 1/40$ sec?

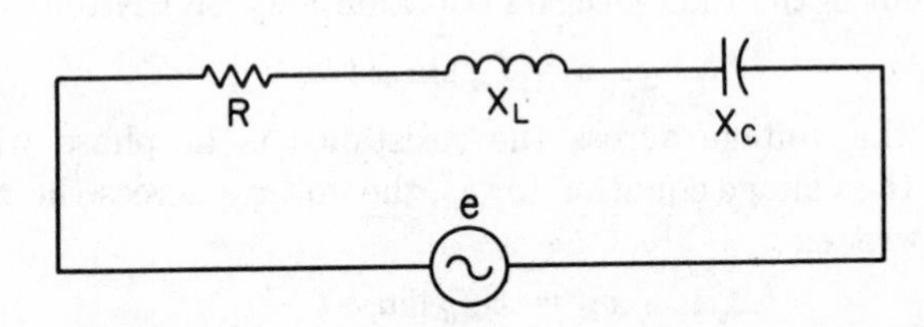

Fig. 8-8. Circuit with resistance, inductance, and capacitance.

Solution. E_{mR}, the maximum voltage across the resistance, can be found from equation (8-38).

$$E_{mR} = I_m R = (2)(10) = 20 \text{ volts}$$

The voltage v_R across the resistance is found by use of equation (8-13) (see also equations (8-37a) and (8-37b)).

$$v_R = E_{mR} \sin \omega t = 20 \sin \omega t$$

E_{mL}, the maximum voltage across the inductance, is found from equation (8-39).

$$E_{mL} = I_m X_L = (2)(15) = 30 \text{ volts}$$

The voltage v_L across the inductance is found by use of equations (8-35) and (8-40).

$$v_L = E_{mL} \sin (\omega t + 90°) = 30 \sin (\omega t + 90°)$$

$$E_{mC} = I_m X_C = (2)\,(8) = 16 \text{ volts}$$

The voltage v_C across the capacitance is found from equation (8-36).

$$v_C = E_{mC} \sin (\omega t - 90°) = 16 \sin (\omega t - 90°)$$

The complete equation for e, the voltage across the source, is found from equations (8-37a) and (8-37b).

$$e = 20 \sin \omega t + 30 \sin (\omega t + 90°) + 16 \sin (\omega t - 90°)$$

When $f = 60$ cycles and $t = 1/40$ sec, the instantaneous value of the voltage at the source is equal to

$$e = 20 \sin \left(\frac{120\,\pi}{40}\right) + 30 \sin \left(\frac{120\,\pi}{40} + 90°\right) + 16 \sin \left(\frac{120\,\pi}{40} - 90°\right)$$

$$= 20 \sin 3\,\pi + 30 \sin (3\,\pi + 90°) + 16 \sin (3\,\pi - 90°)$$

The angle 3π radians is equal to 540°. Therefore,

$$e = 20 \sin 540° + 30 \sin (540° + 90°) + 16 \sin (540° - 90°)$$

$$= 20 \sin 540° + 30 \sin 630° + 16 \sin 450°$$

$$= 20 \sin 180° + 30 \sin 270° + 16 \sin 90°$$

$$= 0 - 30 + 16 = -14 \text{ volts}$$

The equation of the current is given by equation (8-33).

$$i = 2 \sin \omega t$$

At $t = 1/40$ sec, the current is equal to

$$i = 2 \sin 3\,\pi = 2 \sin 180° = 0 \text{ amps}$$

Example 8-10. A 100-cycle a-c source feeds a series circuit which includes an inductance of 5 henrys and a capacitance of 10 microfarads. Find the inductive reactance and the capacitive reactance.

Solution. The inductive reactance is found by using equation (8-24).

$$X_L = 2\,\pi f L = (2\,\pi)(100)(5) = 3140 \text{ ohms}$$

The capacitive reactance is found by using equation (8-32).

$$X_C = \frac{1}{2\pi f C} = \frac{10^6}{(2\pi)(100)(10)} = 159 \text{ ohms}$$

8-6. Effective Values of Current and Voltage. Ammeters and voltmeters are unable to register the instantaneous values of current and voltage because of the mechanical inertia of their moving parts. However, even if these meters could follow the variations, their indications would be of little value in electrical computations because of the rapid changes in values from one instant of time to the next. These meters are constructed and calibrated, therefore, to indicate the effective or heating value of the currents and voltages present in the circuit.

The power in a direct current circuit is given by the equation

$$P_h = I_{dc}^2 R \tag{8-41}$$

where P_h is the power or rate in watts at which heat is produced in a direct current circuit, I_{dc} is the direct current in amperes, and R is the resistance in ohms.

Power in an alternating-current circuit is given by the equation

$$P_h = I_e^2 R \tag{8-42}$$

where P_h has the same significance for alternating current as it has in equation (8-41) for direct current and I_e is the effective—or meter—value of the alternating current.

The instantaneous rate at which heat is produced in an alternating-current circuit depends on the instantaneous value of current i. Therefore,

$$p_h = i^2 R \tag{8-43}$$

where p_h is the heat at any instant, and i is the instantaneous value of the current producing that heat. Since the power (or heat) and current are varying with time t, equation (8-43) is more properly written

$$p_h\, dt = i^2 R\, dt \tag{8-44}$$

Equation (8-43) is a simple differential equation which is integrated between $t = 0$ and $t = 2\pi/\omega$ to determine the heat produced over a period of time equal to one cycle.

$$P_h = \frac{1}{\frac{2\pi}{\omega}} \int_{t=0}^{t=2\pi/\omega} p_h\, dt = \frac{\omega}{2\pi} \int_{t=0}^{t=2\pi/\omega} i^2 R\, dt = \frac{R\omega}{2\pi} \int_{t=0}^{t=2\pi/\omega} i^2\, dt \tag{8-45}$$

When we solve equation (8-42) for I_e^2, we obtain

$$I_e^2 = \frac{P_h}{R} \tag{8-46}$$

If we substitute equation (8-46) in equation (8-45), we obtain the relationship

$$I_e^2 = \frac{\omega}{2\pi} \int_{t=0}^{t=2\pi/\omega} i^2\, dt \tag{8-47}$$

Equation (8-47) may be interpreted to mean

$$I_e = \sqrt{\frac{1}{T} \int_0^T i^2\, dt} \tag{8-48}$$

Equation (8-48) shows that the effective value of a current (or, for that matter, a voltage) is equal to the square root of the average of the squares of the current, or

$$I_e = \sqrt{\text{average } i^2} \tag{8-49}$$

Substituting the value of i from equation (8-33) in equation (8-47), we obtain

$$I_e^2 = \frac{\omega}{2\pi} \int_{t=0}^{t=2\pi/\omega} I_m^2 \sin^2 \omega t\, dt = \frac{I_m^2 \omega}{4\pi} \int_{t=0}^{t=2\pi/\omega} (1 - \cos 2\omega t)\, dt \tag{8-50}$$

The solution of equation (8-50) is

$$I_e^2 = \frac{I_m^2 \omega}{4\pi} \left[\int_{t=0}^{t=2\pi/\omega} dt - \int_{t=0}^{t=2\pi/\omega} \cos 2\omega t\, dt \right]$$

$$= \left(\frac{I_m^2 \omega}{4\pi}\right)\left(\frac{2\pi}{\omega}\right) - 0 = \frac{I_m^2}{2}$$

Extracting the square root of both sides of this equation gives the relationship between the effective and maximum values of the current in an a-c circuit:

$$I_e = \frac{I_m}{\sqrt{2}} = 0.707 I_m \tag{8-51}$$

The effective value is also called the *root-mean-square* or *rms* value, since it is the square root of the average (or mean) of the squares. It is the current that is indicated on the meters in the circuit.

A similar derivation would show that

$$E_e = \frac{E_m}{\sqrt{2}} = 0.707E_m \tag{8-52}$$

Equations (8-51) and (8-52) are based on sine wave forms of current and voltage. From here on, I and E will be used in place of I_e and E_e for the effective or rms values of current and voltage.

Example 8-11. What is the effective value of the currents and voltages if $I_m = 25$ amperes and $E_m = 160$ volts?

Solution. This problem is solved by use of equations (8-51) and (8-52).

$$I = 0.707I_m = (0.707)(25) = 17.7 \text{ amps}$$

$$E = 0.707E_m = (0.707)(160) = 113.1 \text{ volts}$$

8-7. Average Values and Form Factor. The form factor of an alternating wave of voltage or current is an indication of the type of wave. It is defined as the ratio of the effective value of the wave to the average value of the same wave. In equation form, this is expressed as follows:

$$\text{Form factor} = \frac{\text{effective value}}{\text{average value}} \tag{8-53}$$

If I_{av} is the average value of a current wave whose equation is $i = I_m \sin \omega t$, then we may write

$$I_{av} = \frac{1}{T}\int_{t=0}^{t=T} I_m \sin \omega t \, dt \tag{8-54}$$

If this equation is integrated over a period of one-half cycle, then the limits are $t = \pi/\omega$ and $t = 0$.

$$I_{av} = \frac{I_m \omega}{\pi}\int_{t=0}^{t=\pi/\omega} \sin \quad t \, dt = \frac{I_m \omega}{\pi}\left[-\frac{\cos \omega t}{\omega}\right]_{t=0}^{t=\pi/\omega} \tag{8-55}$$

Inserting the indicated limits in the integration gives the result:

$$I_{av} = \frac{2I_m}{\pi} = 0.636\, I_m \tag{8-56}$$

The average voltage is found in the same way and is given by the following equation:

$$E_{av} = \frac{2\,E_m}{\pi} = 0.636\ E_m \tag{8-57}$$

The form factor for a sine wave of current or voltage is, therefore,

$$\text{Form factor} = \frac{0.707}{0.636} = 1.11 \tag{8-58}$$

Example 8-12. An a-c voltage wave is found to have an effective value of 157 volts and a form factor of 1.2. What is its average value?

Solution. From equation (8-53) we find

$$\text{Average value} = \frac{\text{effective value}}{\text{form factor}} = \frac{157}{1.2} = 131 \text{ volts}$$

8-8. The Impedance Triangle. In Section 8-5, we learned that the effects of inductive reactance X_L and capacitive reactance X_C are out of phase with the effect of resistance by 90 electrical degrees, but are out of phase with each other by 180 electrical degrees. These relationships are indicated by equations (8-17), (8-23), (8-29), (8-34), (8-35), (8-36), and (8-37b), and by Example 8-9. These conditions can be indicated graphically on a vector-like diagram.

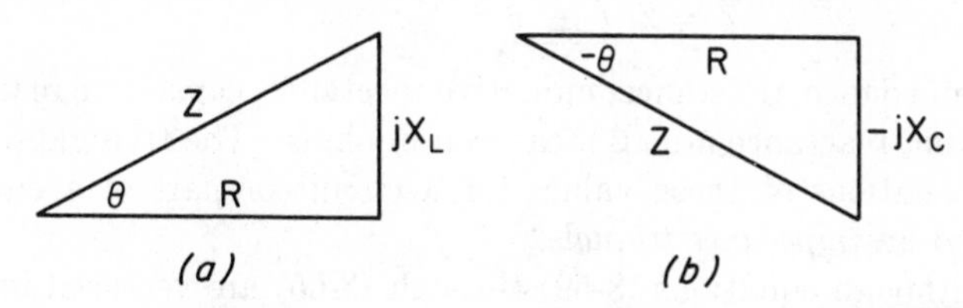

Fig. 8-9. The impedance triangle.

Fig. 8-9*a* is a diagram showing the relations between resistance and inductive reactance. Resistance is drawn as a horizontal line R, and the inductive reactance is drawn from the right end of R, directly (perpendicularly) upward. This inductive reactance is indicated by the symbol X_L. Using the notation introduced in Section 8-1 of this chapter, we identify X_L as jX_L to indicate its direction. The distance from the left end of R to the upper end of jX_L is given the symbol Z and is called the *impedance* of the circuit or of any part of the circuit under consideration.

The value of Z, as shown in Fig. 8-9*a*, is given by vector equations as follows:

$$Z = R + jX_L \quad (8\text{-}59)$$

$$\overline{Z} = Z \underline{/\ \theta} \quad (8\text{-}60)$$

Fig. 8-9*b* is a diagram showing the relations between the resistance R, the capacitive reactance X_C, and the impedance Z. X_C, which is designated as $-jX_C$, is drawn perpendicularly downward because its effect is negative with respect to jX_L. In this triangle, the relationships are

$$Z = R - jX_C \quad (8\text{-}61)$$

$$\overline{Z} = Z \underline{/ -\ \theta} \quad (8\text{-}62)$$

If a circuit or part of a circuit contains both a coil and a capacitor, the capacitive reactance must be subtracted from the inductive reactance to obtain the *net reactance*, X. The value of X can be indicated by the equation

$$X = X_L - X_C \quad (8\text{-}63)$$

The impedance Z may be either positive or negative, depending on the relative sizes of X_L and X_C. The value of the impedance is therefore in the form

$$Z = R + j(X_L - X_C) = R \pm jX \quad (8\text{-}64)$$

$$\overline{Z} = Z \underline{/ \pm\ \theta} \quad (8\text{-}65)$$

Impedance, resistance, inductive reactance, capacitive reactance, and net reactance are all measured in ohms. The triangle showing the relations of these values for a circuit or part of a circuit is called an *impedance triangle.*

Although equations (8-59) through (8-65) are vectorial in form, Z, X, X_L, X_C, and R are not vector quantities. These quantities have magnitude and position but do not have direction. A vector must have direction as well as magnitude and position. However, because of the quadrature relationship between R and X, vector analysis must be used to solve problems involving these quantities.

The numerical or absolute value of the impedance can be found from the relationship between the hypotenuse and the sides of a right angle triangle.

$$Z = \sqrt{R^2 + (X_L - X_C)^2} \quad (8\text{-}66)$$

In actual practice, however, equation (8-66) has very little value in solving a-c circuits, since not only must the value of the impedance be found but the angle θ between R and Z is very important. Therefore, trigonometry must be used for the solution of a-c circuit problems.

Example 8-13. A circuit contains a resistance of 25 ohms, an inductive reactance of 35 ohms, and a capacitive reactance of 10 ohms. What is the impedance?

Solution. Equations (8-64) and (8-65), solved by the methods explained in Sections 8-1, 8-2, and 8-3, will yield the desired results.

$$Z = R + j(X_L - X_C) = 25 + j(35 - 10)$$

$$= 25 + j25 = 35.4 \underline{/45^\circ} \text{ ohms}$$

8-9. Current and Voltage in a Series Circuit. If any impedance or component of impedance is multiplied by the current flowing through it, the result is the voltage across that impedance or component of impedance. The current in a circuit is always in phase with the resistance in that circuit, as indicated in Section 8-5.

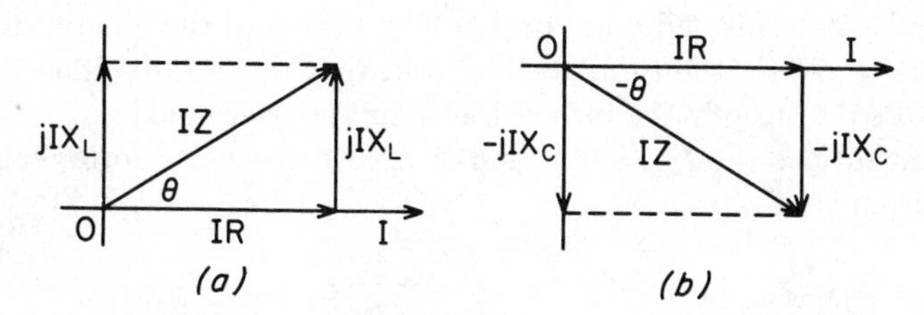

Fig. 8-10. Phasor diagrams for a series circuit.

If equation (8-59) is multiplied by the effective value I of the a-c circuit, we obtain the relationship

$$IZ = IR + jIX_L \tag{8-67}$$

where IZ is the voltage across the impedance. If Z is the total impedance of the circuit, then $IZ = E$, the effective value of the source voltage. If Z is the impedance of only a part of the circuit—such as a coil—then $IZ = V$, the voltage across that part of the circuit. IR is the voltage V_R across the resistance and IX_L is the voltage across the inductive reactance. These voltages have the same relative positions as the corresponding or related parts of the impedance triangle. The voltage relationships are shown in Fig. 8-10*a*.

If equation (8-61) is multiplied by the effective value I of the a-c circuit, we obtain the relationship

$$IZ = IR - jIX_C \tag{8-68}$$

These voltages are shown in Fig. 8-10*b*.

The vector diagrams shown in Fig. 8-10 are called *phasor diagrams*, since they show the phase relationships between current and voltage in the circuit. Since the current I is common to all parts of the series circuit, vector I is shown as the reference vector and for this reason is extended beyond the arrowhead representing the value of the voltage IR.

If equation (8-64) is multiplied by I, we have the relationship

$$IZ = IR + j(IX_L - IX_C) \tag{8-69a}$$

or

$$IZ = IR + jI(X_L - X_C) \tag{8-69b}$$

In a series a-c circuit involving a coil, part of the resistance R is the resistance of the coil itself. The method of solution requires that the resistance of the coil be determined from the current and voltage measurements or from any other information that may be available. This coil resistance is then added to the circuit resistance to obtain the total R, and from that the total voltage (IR) across the entire resistance of the circuit is determined.

Equations (8-67), (8-68), and (8-69), in the polar form, can be written

$$V = IZ \underline{/\pm\ \theta} \tag{8-70}$$

where V is the voltage across the circuit or any part of the circuit. The voltage thus obtained is in phase with the impedance Z. If the angle is $+\ \theta$, the current lags the voltage. If the angle is $-\ \theta$, the current leads the voltage.[||]

Example 8-14. The series circuit in Fig. 8-11*a* has a source voltage E of 250 volts, effective, and a current of 2 amperes, effective. If V_R—the voltage across the resistance R—is 200 volts, and V_L—the voltage across the coil—is 125 volts, find (a) the voltage V_{RL} across the resistance R_L of the coil, (b) the voltage V_{XL} across the inductive reactance X_L of the coil, (c) the impedance of the circuit, (d) the impedance of the coil, (e) the resistance of the coil, (f) the inductive reactance of the coil, (g) the angle

[||] Electrical engineers sometimes reverse the statement and say that if the angle is $+\ \theta$, the voltage leads, and if the angle is $-\ \theta$, the voltage lags. These statements mean exactly the same thing, because if the current lags the voltage, the voltage leads the current and when the current leads the voltage, the voltage lags the current.

θ_{LINE} between the current and the source voltage E, and (h) the angle θ_L between the current and the coil voltage V_L.

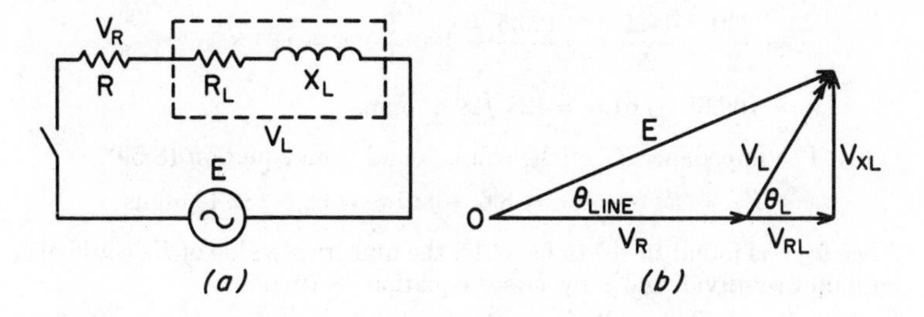

Fig. 8-11. Solving a series R-L circuit.

Solution. The circuit may be solved graphically as follows:

Set a pair of compasses for E to a convenient scale of perhaps 100 volts to the inch. With the point of the compasses at 0, strike an arc. Measure V_R to the same scale horizontally and to the right from 0, and draw an arrowhead. With the point of the compasses at the end of V_R and set for V_L to the same scale as for E, strike an arc. The two arcs—E and V_L—will cross at the apex of the voltage triangle in Fig. 8-11*b*. Now drop a line from this vertex perpendicular to V_R. This is the voltage V_{XL} to scale, and V_{RL} can be found as shown in the diagram. The values of V_{XL}, V_{RL}, θ_{LINE}, and θ_L can be found by measuring the voltage triangle. The impedances, resistances, and reactances can be determined by dividing E, V_R, V_L, V_{RL}, and V_{XL} by I.

The mathematical solution is as follows:

(h) The angle θ_L is the easiest quantity to find. By the law of cosines, we may write

$$\cos(180° - \theta_L) = \frac{V_L^2 + V_R^2 - E^2}{2V_L V_R} = \frac{(125)^2 + (200)^2 - (250)^2}{(2)(125)(200)}$$

$$= \frac{15{,}600 + 40{,}000 - 62{,}500}{50{,}000} = \frac{55{,}600 - 62{,}500}{50{,}000}$$

$$= -\frac{6{,}900}{50{,}000} = -0.138$$

$$\cos^{-1}(-0.138) = (180° - \theta_L) = (180° - 82.1°)$$

$$\theta_L = 82.1°$$

(a) By trigonometry, we obtain

$$V_{RL} = V_L \cos\theta_L = 125 \cos 82.1° = 17.2 \text{ volts}$$

(b) By trigonometry, we obtain

$$V_{XL} = V_L \sin\theta_L = 125 \sin 82.1° = 123.5 \text{ volts}$$

(c) The impedance of the circuit is found from equation (8-59).

$$Z = R_T + jX_L = R + R_L + jX_L = \frac{V_R}{I} + \frac{V_{RL}}{I} + j\frac{V_{XL}}{I}$$

$$= \frac{200}{2} + \frac{17.2}{2} + j\frac{123.5}{2} = 100 + 8.6 + j\,61.8$$

$$= 108.6 + j\,61.8 = 125\ \underline{/29.6^\circ} \text{ ohms}$$

(d) The impedance Z_L of the coil is found from equation (8-59).

$$Z_L = R_L + j\,X_L = 8.6 + j\,61.8 = 62.5\ \underline{/82.1^\circ} \text{ ohms}$$

Since θ_L was found in (h) to be 82.1°, the numerical value of Z_L could also be found by dividing V_L by I (see equation (8-70)):

$$Z_L = \frac{V_L \underline{/\theta_L}}{I} = \frac{125\ \underline{/82.1^\circ}}{2} = 62.5\ \underline{/82.1^\circ} \text{ volts}$$

(e) From equation (8-67), we may write

$$R_L = \frac{V_{RL}}{I} = \frac{17.2}{2} = 8.6 \text{ ohms}$$

This value was also obtained in (c).

(f) The inductive reactance of the coil can also be found from equation (8-67).

$$X_L = \frac{V_{XL}}{I} = \frac{123.5}{2} = 61.8 \text{ ohms}$$

This value was also obtained in (c).

(g) The angle θ_{LINE} was previously found in (c) to be 29.6°.

The complete solutions, therefore, are as follows:

(a) V_{RL} = 17.2 volts	(e) R_L = 8.6 ohms
(b) V_{XL} = 123.5 volts	(f) X_L = 61.8 ohms
(c) Z = $125\ \underline{/29.6^\circ}$ ohms	(g) θ_{LINE} = 29.6°
(d) Z_L = $62.5\ \underline{/82.1^\circ}$ ohms	(h) θ_L = 82.1°

8-10. Power in a Series A-C Circuit. In direct current, the power is equal to the current multiplied by the voltage. Because of the angle between the voltage and the current, power in alternating current cannot be calculated that way.

If θ is the angle of lag of the current behind the voltage, the equations of the current and the voltage may be written

$$i = I_m \sin \omega t \qquad \text{[see equation (8-17)]}$$

$$e = E_m \sin (\omega t + \theta) \tag{8-71}$$

If equations (8-17) and (8-71) are multiplied, the instantaneous power is obtained:

$$p = ei = I_m E_m \sin \omega t \sin (\omega t + \theta) \tag{8-72}$$

Equation (8-72) can be reduced by the use of trigonometric identities and solved as follows:

$$\begin{aligned} p &= I_m E_m \sin \omega t (\sin \omega t \cos \theta + \cos \omega t \sin \theta) \\ &= E_m I_m \sin^2 \omega t \cos \theta + E_m I_m \sin \omega t \cos \omega t \sin \theta \\ &= E_m I_m (\tfrac{1}{2} - \tfrac{1}{2} \cos 2 \omega t) \cos \theta + \tfrac{1}{2} E_m I_m \sin 2 \omega t \sin \theta \end{aligned}$$

$$p = \frac{E_m I_m}{2} \cos \theta - \frac{E_m I_m}{2} \cos 2 \omega t \cos \theta + \frac{E_m I_m}{2} \sin 2 \omega t \sin \theta \tag{8-73}$$

Equation (8-73) shows that the power curve consists of three components: a constant term and two double-frequency waves. If we multiply equations (8-51) and (8-52), we obtain

$$EI = \frac{E_m}{\sqrt{2}} \frac{I_m}{\sqrt{2}} = \frac{E_m I_m}{2} \tag{8-74}$$

From equation (8-74), we can see that all three terms of equation (8-73) contain the product of the effective values of the current and the voltage. Equation (8-73) may therefore be written

$$p = EI \cos \theta - EI \cos 2 \omega t \cos \theta + EI \sin 2 \omega t \sin \theta \tag{8-75}$$

The average power can be obtained by integrating equation (8-75) over one cycle, or between the limits $t = 0$ and $t = 2\pi/\omega$:

$$\begin{aligned} P = \int p\, dt &= \frac{\omega E I \cos \theta}{2 \pi} \int_{t=0}^{t=2\pi/\omega} dt \\ &\quad - \frac{\omega E I \cos \theta}{2 \pi} \int_{t=0}^{t=2\pi/\omega} \cos 2 \omega t\, dt \\ &\quad + \frac{\omega E I \sin \theta}{2 \pi} \int_{t=0}^{t=2\pi/\omega} \sin 2 \omega t\, dt \\ &= E I \cos \theta - \frac{E I \cos \theta}{4 \pi} \Big[\sin 2 \omega t \Big]_{t=0}^{t=2\pi/\omega} \\ &\quad - \frac{E I \sin \theta}{4 \pi} \Big[\cos 2 \omega t \Big]_{t=0}^{t=2\pi/\omega} \end{aligned}$$

When the limits are substituted in this equation, the second and third terms are found to equal zero, leaving only the constant term, which is the average power in an a-c system:

$$P = EI \cos \theta \tag{8-76}$$

If equation (8-76) is solved for $\cos \theta$, the result is

$$\cos \theta = \frac{P}{EI} = \frac{\text{true power}}{\text{volt-amperes}} \tag{8-77}$$

The factor $\cos \theta$ is therefore called the *power factor* of the circuit. It is calculated as a decimal but is referred to as a percentage of the volt-amperes# (as 75% instead of 0.75).

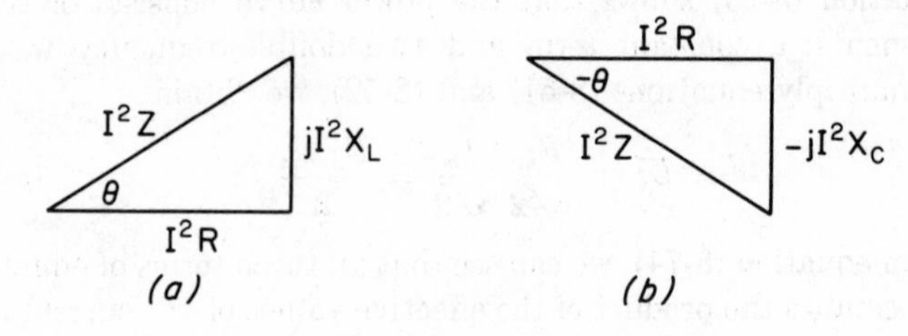

Fig. 8-12. The power triangle.

If the sides of the triangle in Fig. 8-10*a* are multiplied by the current I, we obtain a *power triangle* as shown in Fig. 8-12*a*. The sides of this triangle are

$$I\,(IZ) = I^2Z = EI \tag{8-78}$$

$$I\,(IR) = I^2R = EI \cos \theta \tag{8-79}$$

$$I\,(IX_L) = I^2X_L = EI \sin \theta \tag{8-80}$$

Equations (8-78) and (8-79) contain relationships that have already been introduced. Equation (8-80) introduces a new term called *reactive volt-amperes*, which has the unit *var*. The quantity $\sin \theta$ is called the reactive factor. Reactive volt-amperes are sometimes referred to as "reactive power," although they denote energy and not power. Reactive volt-amperes represent energy supplied to the circuit during part of a cycle and returned to the system during the time when the system inductance is discharging.

The quantity "volt-amperes" is sometimes called apparent power because it is calculated from the readings of the voltmeter and the ammeter. The term volt-amperes is more correct, however.

Although the equations developed in this section were derived on the basis of an RL circuit, they apply equally well to RC and RLC circuits. The derivation for these circuits would be almost identical to that given for the RL circuit. The power triangle for an RC circuit is shown in Fig. 8-12b.

Example 8-15. The current and voltage of a single phase a-c circuit are determined to be $E = 120 \underline{/75^\circ}$ and $I = 60 \underline{/40^\circ}$. Find the volt-amperes, power, and reactive volt-amperes of the circuit.

Solution. Since it is a series circuit and both current and voltage are identified by angles, the time $t = 0$ has been taken at an instant when neither the current nor the voltage is zero. From equation (8-76), we have determined that θ is the angle between the current and the voltage. Therefore,

$$\theta = \theta_E - \theta_I = 75^\circ - 40^\circ = 35^\circ$$

The power is found by use of equation (8-76).

$$P = EI \cos\theta = (120)\,(60)\,(\cos 35^\circ) = 5900 \text{ watts}$$

The reactive volt-amperes are found by use of equation (8-80).

$$EI \sin\theta = (120)\,(60)\,(\sin 35^\circ) = 4130 \text{ vars}$$

The volt-amperes of the circuit are found from equation (8-78).

$$VA = EI = (120)\,(60) = 7200 \text{ volt-amps}$$

8-11. Multiple Currents and Voltages. A single wire can be used to transmit currents and voltages of many different frequencies. This fact makes it possible in communications circuits to reduce the number of metallic conductors needed to convey messages.

The equation for a number of frequencies transmitted in this way may be written as follows:

$$i = I_{m1} \sin \omega t + I_{m3} \sin 3\,\omega t + \cdots + I_{mn-2} \sin (n-2)\,\omega t + I_{mn}\, n\,\omega t \tag{8-81}$$

Using equations (8-45) and (8-46) as guides, we may write

$$I_e^2 = \frac{\omega}{2\pi}\left[\int_{t=0}^{t=2\pi/\omega} I_{m1}^2 \sin^2 \omega t\,dt + \int_{t=0}^{t=2\pi/\omega} I_{m3}^2 \sin^2 3\,\omega t\,dt + \cdots + \int_{t=0}^{t=2\pi/\omega} I_{mn-2}^2 \sin^2 (n-2)\,\omega t\,dt + \int_{t=0}^{t=2\pi/\omega} I_{mn}^2 \sin^2 n\omega t\,dt\right] \tag{8-82}$$

$$I_e^2 = \frac{\omega}{2\pi}\left[I_{m1}^2 \int_{t=0}^{t=2\pi/\omega} (\tfrac{1}{2} - \tfrac{1}{2}\cos 2\,\omega t)\, dt \right.$$

$$+ I_{m3}^2 \int_{t=0}^{t=2\pi/\omega} (\tfrac{1}{2} - \tfrac{1}{2}\cos 6\,\omega t)\, dt + \cdots$$

$$+ I_{mn-2}^2 \int_{t=0}^{t=2\pi/\omega} (\tfrac{1}{2} - \tfrac{1}{2}\cos 2\,(n-2)\,\omega t)\, dt$$

$$\left. + I_{mn}^2 \int_{t=0}^{t=2\pi/\omega} (\tfrac{1}{2} - \tfrac{1}{2}\cos 2\,n\,\omega t)\, dt \right] \quad (8\text{-}83)$$

$$I_e^2 = \frac{\omega}{2\pi}\left[\frac{I_{m1}^2\, t}{2} + \frac{I_{m3}^2\, t}{2} + \cdots + \frac{I_{mn-2}^2\, t}{2} + \frac{I_{mn}^2\, t}{2} \right]_{t=0}^{t=2\pi/\omega}$$

$$+ \frac{\omega}{2\pi}\left[\frac{I_m^2}{2\,\omega}\sin 2\,\omega t + \frac{I_{m3}^2}{6\omega}\sin 6\,\omega t + \cdots \right.$$

$$+ \frac{I_{mn-2}^2}{2\,(n-2)\,\omega}\sin 2\,(n-2)\,\omega t$$

$$\left. + \frac{I_{mn}^2}{2\,n\,\omega}\sin 2\,n\,\omega t \right]_{t=0}^{t=2\pi/\omega} \quad (8\text{-}84)$$

By inserting the limits, we find that the second part of equation (8-84) equals zero, leaving only the following:

$$I_e^2 = \frac{I_{m1}^2}{2} + \frac{I_{m3}^2}{2} + \cdots + \frac{I_{mn-2}^2}{2} + \frac{I_{mn}^2}{2} \quad (8\text{-}85)$$

By extracting the square root of equation (8-85), we obtain the relationship

$$I = \sqrt{\frac{I_{m1}^2}{2} + \frac{I_{m3}^2}{2} + \cdots + \frac{I_{mn-2}^2}{2} + \frac{I_{mn}^2}{2}} \quad (8\text{-}86)$$

I_{m1}, etc., in equation (8-81) were maximum values as is indicated by the form of the original equation (8-81). The effective values are, therefore, from equation (8-51):

$$I_1^2 = \frac{I_{m1}^2}{2} \tag{8-87a}$$

$$I_2^2 = \frac{I_{m3}^2}{2} \tag{8-87b}$$

$$I_{n-2}^2 = \frac{I_{mn-2}^2}{2} \tag{8-87c}$$

$$I_n^2 = \frac{I_{mn}^2}{2} \tag{8-87d}$$

Substituting equations (8-87a), (8-87b), (8-87c), and (8-87d) in equation (8-86), we obtain the relationship

$$I = \sqrt{I_1^2 + I_3^2 + \cdots + I_{n-2}^2 + I_n^2} \tag{8-88}$$

Therefore, the total effective rms current is equal to the square root of the sum of the squares of the effective values of all the currents in the circuit. A derivation similar to that given for currents can be used to determine the effective value of the voltages.

$$E = \sqrt{E_1^2 + E_3^2 + \cdots + E_{n-2}^2 + E_n^2} \tag{8-89}$$

All of these equations are based on the presence of currents and voltages which are odd multiples (called odd *harmonics*) of the fundamental frequency. However, equations (8-88) and (8-89) are true for currents and voltages of all frequencies.

The power in a multiple current circuit can be found by adding the power contributed by the currents.

$$P_T = E_1 I_1 \cos \theta_1 + E_3 I_3 \cos \theta_3 + \cdots + E_{n-2} I_{n-2} \cos \theta_{n-2} + E_n I_n \cos \theta_n \tag{8-90}$$

The reactive volt-amperes can be found by an equation similar to (8-90) but using sin θ.

$$RVA_T = E_1 I_1 \sin \theta_1 + E_3 I_3 \sin \theta_3 + \cdots + E_{n-2} I_{n-2} \sin \theta_{n-2} + E_n I_n \sin \theta_n \tag{8-91}$$

The total volt-amperes is the product of equations (8-88) and (8-89).

$$\text{Volt-amperes}_T = EI \tag{8-92}$$

The power factor of such a circuit is found by the following equation, using the results of equations (8-90) and (8-92):

$$\cos \theta_T = \frac{P_T}{EI} \tag{8-93}$$

The reactive factor of the circuit is found by the following equation, using the results of equations (8-91) and (8-92):

$$\sin \theta_T = \frac{RVA_T}{EI} \tag{8-94}$$

Example 8-16. A circuit contains currents as follows: 15 sin ωt, 12 sin 3 ωt, -10 sin 5 ωt, and 6 sin 7 ωt. What is the total current?

Solution. This problem can be solved by use of equation (8-86).

$$I = \sqrt{\frac{I_{m1}^2 + I_{m3}^2 + I_{m5}^2 + I_{m7}^2}{2}} = \sqrt{\frac{(15)^2 + (12)^2 + (10)^2 + (6)^2}{2}}$$

$$= \sqrt{\frac{505}{2}} = \sqrt{252.5} = 15.9 \text{ amps}$$

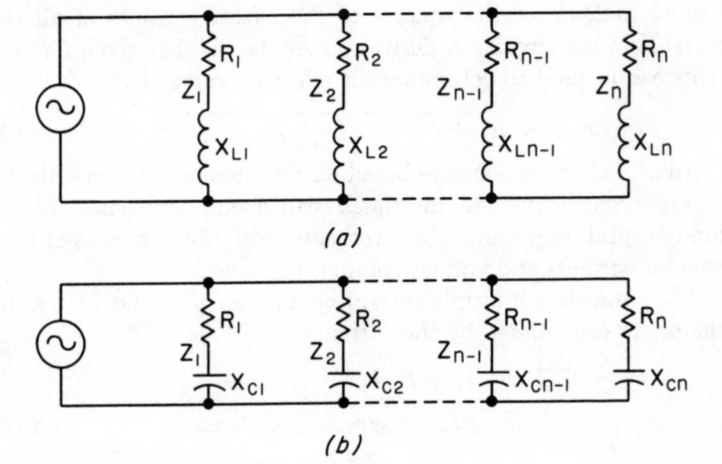

Fig. 8-13. Parallel a-c circuits.

8-12. Parallel Circuits. In the study of resistances in parallel in Section 1-7, the total resistance of the circuit was found to be the reciprocal of the sum of the reciprocals, that is,

$$\frac{1}{R_T} = \frac{1}{R_1} + \frac{1}{R_2} + \cdots + \frac{1}{R_{n-1}} + \frac{1}{R_n} \tag{8-95}$$

Equation (8-95) was found to represent the total conductance of the circuit in direct current, or in an alternating-current circuit containing only resistance. By the same method by which equation (8-95) was derived, we can prove that

$$\frac{1}{Z_T} = \frac{1}{Z_1} + \frac{1}{Z_2} + \cdots + \frac{1}{Z_{n-1}} + \frac{1}{Z_n} \tag{8-96}$$

In Fig. 8-13*a* is shown a parallel system containing the following inductances and resistances: $Z_1 = R_1 + jX_{L1}, Z_2 = R_2 + jX_{L2}, \cdots,$ $Z_{n-1} = R_{n-1} + jX_{Ln-1}$, and $Z_n = R_n + jX_{Ln}$. The value of $1/Z_1$ can be determined by substituting in an equation as follows:

$$\frac{1}{Z_1} = \frac{1}{R_1 + jX_{L1}} \tag{8-97}$$

The j operator in the denominator prevents the use of the equation in that form. However, the j can be moved to the numerator by multiplying both numerator and denominator by the conjugate of $R_1 + jX_{L1}$.

$$\frac{1}{Z_1} = \left(\frac{1}{R_1 + jX_{L1}}\right)\left(\frac{R_1 - jX_{L1}}{R_1 - jX_{L1}}\right) = \frac{R_1 - jX_{L1}}{R_1^2 + X_{L1}^2}$$

The quantity $1/Z$ can be called the admittance of the circuit and is given the symbol Y. The admittance Y_1 is, therefore,

$$Y_1 = \frac{1}{Z_1} = \frac{R_1}{R_1^2 + X_{L1}^2} - j\,\frac{X_{L1}}{R_1^2 + X_{L1}^2} \tag{8-98}$$

The admittance is composed of two quantities, as shown by equation (8-98). These quantities are called the *conductance* and the *susceptance*. The conductance is given the symbol G and the susceptance is given the symbol B.

$$G_1 = \frac{R_1}{R_1^2 + X_{L1}^2} \tag{8-99}$$

$$B_1 = \frac{X_{L1}}{R_1^2 + X_{L1}^2} \tag{8-100}$$

A complete mathematical analysis of equation (8-96) would show that the total admittance of all the parallel circuits in Fig. 8-13*a* is equal to the sum of all the conductances plus the sum of all the susceptances, according to the following equation:

$$Y_T = G_1 + G_2 + \cdots + G_{n-1} + G_n - j\,(B_1 + B_2 + \cdots + B_{n-1} + B_n) \tag{8-101}$$

In equation (8-101), the conductances G are all of the form indicated by equation (8-99) and the susceptances are all of the form indicated by equation (8-100). When the reactance is inductive, the susceptance is negative, as shown by equation (8-101). The unit for Y, G, and B is the mho (which is ohm spelled backward).

Fig. 8-13*b* shows a number of parallel circuits containing capacitors. An analysis of this system will yield an equation like (8-101), but the susceptances are positive. The equation is

$$Y_T = G_1 + G_2 + \cdots + G_{n-1} + G_n + j(B_1 + B_2 + \cdots + B_{n-1} + B_n) \qquad (8\text{-}102)$$

If a single circuit contains both an inductance and a capacitance, the total reactance of that circuit (or branch) is found by use of equation (8-64).

The relations of Y, G, and B for a single branch circuit can be shown by a triangle, called an *admittance triangle.*

The impedance triangle shown in Fig. 8-9*a* is reproduced in Fig. 8-14*a*. In polar form, the impedance is expressed by equation (8-60). The admittance, therefore, is

$$Y = \frac{1}{Z} = \frac{1}{Z\,\underline{/\,\theta}} = \frac{\underline{/-\theta}}{Z} = \frac{\underline{/-\theta}}{\sqrt{R^2 + X^2}} \qquad (8\text{-}103)$$

By substituting the value for Z, we obtain equation (8-97). If Y is multiplied by $\cos(-\theta)$, the equation becomes

$$Y\cos(-\theta) = \left(\frac{1}{\sqrt{R^2+X^2}}\right)\left(\frac{R}{\sqrt{R^2+X^2}}\right) = \frac{R}{R^2+X^2} \qquad (8\text{-}104)$$

which is the conductance G obtained in equation (8-99). By multiplying the admittance by $\sin(-\theta)$, we obtain

$$Y\sin(-\theta) = -\left(\frac{1}{\sqrt{R^2+X^2}}\right)\left(\frac{X}{\sqrt{R^2+X^2}}\right)$$

$$= -\frac{X}{\sqrt{R^2+X^2}} \qquad (8\text{-}105)$$

Equation (8-105) is the same as equation (8-100). The relations of admittance, conductance, and susceptance for an inductive circuit are shown in an admittance triangle in Fig. 8-14*b*. The admittance triangle for a capacitive circuit would be the inverse of

Fig. 8-14*b*. (See Fig. 8-9*b* for the impedance triangle of a capacitive circuit.)

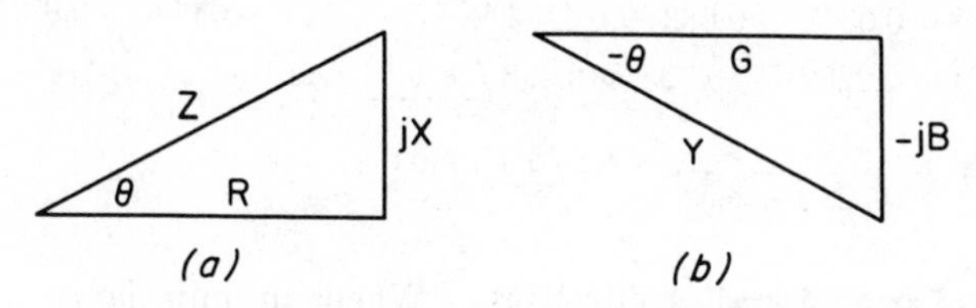

Fig. 8-14. Impedance and admittance triangles.

Example 8-17. The parallel a-c circuit shown in Fig. 8-15 contains impedances as follows: $Z_1 = 10 + j15$, $Z_2 = 5 - j6$, and $Z_3 = 6 + j(8 - 4)$. Find the total impedance of the system.

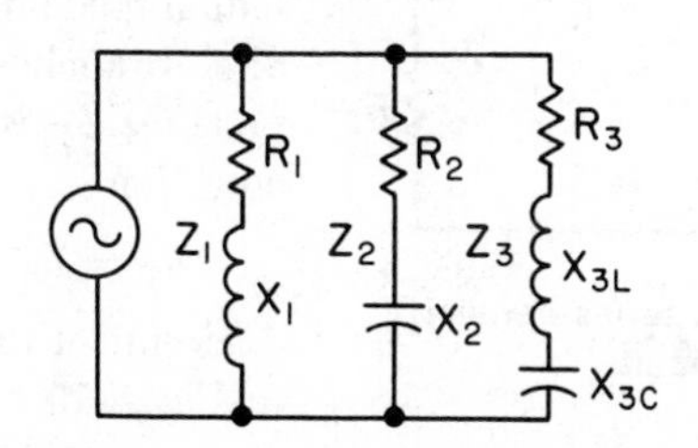

Fig. 8-15. A parallel circuit.

Solution. The conductances and susceptances are calculated from equations (8-104) and (8-105).

$$G_1 = \frac{R}{R^2 + X^2} = \frac{10}{(10)^2 + (15)^2} = \frac{10}{100 + 225} = \frac{10}{325} = 0.0308 \text{ mho}$$

$$jB_1 = -j\frac{X}{R^2 + X^2} = -j\frac{15}{325} = -j0.046 \text{ mho}$$

$$G_2 = \frac{R}{R^2 + X^2} = \frac{5}{5^2 + 6^2} = \frac{5}{25 + 36} = \frac{5}{61} = 0.082 \text{ mho}$$

$$jB_2 = j\frac{X}{R^2 + X^2} = j\frac{6}{61} = j0.098 \text{ mho}$$

$$G_3 = \frac{R}{R^2 + (X_L - X_C)^2} = \frac{6}{6^2 + (8 - 4)^2} = \frac{6}{36 + 16}$$

$$= \frac{6}{52} = 0.1154 \text{ mho}$$

$$jB_3 = -j\frac{X_L - X_C}{R^2 + (X_L - X_C)^2} = -j\frac{4}{52} = -j0.077 \text{ mho}$$

The total admittance is found from an equation in the form of (8-101).

$$
\begin{aligned}
Y_T &= G_1 + G_2 + G_3 + j\,(-B_1 + B_2 - B_3) \\
&= 0.0308 + 0.082 + 0.1154 + j\,(-0.046 + 0.098 - 0.077) \\
&= 0.2282 - j\,0.025 = 0.228\,\underline{/-6.5°}\text{ mho}
\end{aligned}
$$

$$Z_T = \frac{1}{0.228\,\underline{/-6.5°}} = 4.4\,\underline{/6.5°}\text{ ohms}$$

8-13. Series-Parallel Circuits. When an impedance is connected in series with a system of parallel circuits, the equivalent impedance of the parallel circuits is determined first and then added to the series impedance. If Z_S is the series impedance in ohms and Z_P is the equivalent impedance of all the parallel branches, the total impedance Z_T is found from the equation

$$Z_T = Z_S + Z_P \qquad (8\text{-}106)$$

A circuit of this type is shown in Fig. 8-16.

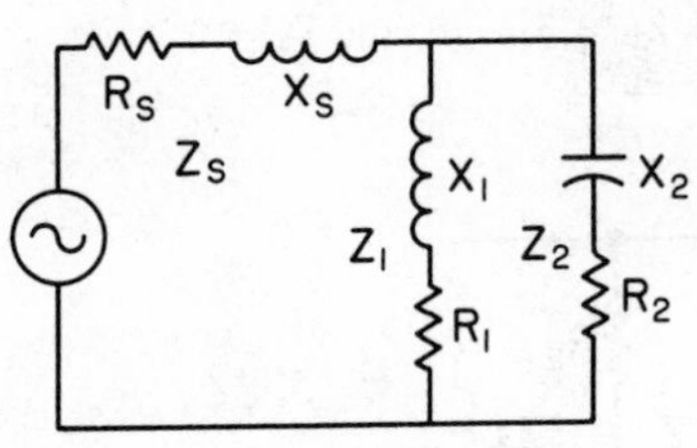

Fig. 8-16. A series-parallel circuit.

Example 8-18. In Fig. 8-16, $Z_S = 5 + j8$ ohms, $Z_1 = 8 + j12$, and $Z_2 = 10 - j6$. Find the total impedance of the system in both the polar and the complex forms.

Solution.

$$G_1 = \frac{R}{R^2 + X^2} = \frac{8}{(8)^2 + (12)^2} = \frac{8}{64 + 144} = \frac{8}{208} = 0.0385\text{ mho}$$

$$B_1 = -j\frac{X}{R^2 + X^2} = -j\frac{12}{208} = -j0.0577\text{ mho}$$

$$G_2 = \frac{R}{R^2 + X^2} = \frac{10}{100 + 36} = \frac{10}{136} = 0.0735\text{ mho}$$

$$B_2 = j\frac{X}{R^2 + X^2} = j\frac{6}{136} = j\,0.0441\text{ mho}$$

$$
\begin{aligned}
Y_P &= G_1 + G_2 + j\,(-B_1 + B_2) \\
&= 0.0385 + 0.0735 + j\,(-0.0577 + 0.0441) \\
&= 0.112 - j\,0.0136 = 0.113\,\underline{/-6.9°}\text{ mho}
\end{aligned}
$$

$$Z_P = \frac{1}{0.113\,\underline{/-6.9°}} = 8.85\,\underline{/6.9°}\text{ ohms}$$

Z_P can now be converted to the complex form by use of equation (8-9).

$$Z_P = 8.85\,(\cos 6.9^\circ + j \sin 6.9^\circ) = 8.79 + j\,1.06 \text{ ohms}$$

The total impedance is determined by use of equation (8-106).

$$Z_T = Z_S + Z_P = 5 + j8 + 8.79 + j\,1.06 = 5 + 8.79 + j\,(8 + 1.06)$$
$$= 13.79 + j9.06 \text{ ohms}$$

Z_T can be converted to the polar form by use of equation (8-10) as explained in Example 8-6.

$$\tan\theta = \frac{9.06}{13.79} = 0.656$$

$$\theta = 33.3^\circ$$

$$Z_T = 16.5\,\underline{/33.3^\circ} \text{ ohms}$$

8-14. Phasor Diagram for Parallel Circuits. In a system of parallel circuits, the voltage across the branches is the only vector common to all branches. The total current is the vector sum of all currents in the branches. Therefore, the voltage is the reference vector for the phasor diagram and all currents are identified with an angle θ with respect to the voltage.

Let a voltage, $E\,\underline{/0^\circ}$ volts, be applied to the parallel system in Fig. 8-15. The current in each branch would then be identified by the formula

$$I = \frac{E\,\underline{/0^\circ}}{Z\,\underline{/\theta}} = \frac{E}{Z}\,\underline{/-\theta} \qquad (8\text{-}107)$$

Equation (8-107) is for inductive circuits in which the current lags the voltage as indicated by the negative sign for the angle θ. The equation for capacitive circuits is

$$I = \frac{E\,\underline{/0^\circ}}{Z\,\underline{/-\theta}} = \frac{E}{Z}\underline{/\theta} \qquad (8\text{-}108)$$

The current obtained by use of equation (8-108) leads the voltage.

Equations (8-107) and (8-108) may also be written in terms of the admittance Y:

$$I = EY\,\underline{/-\theta} \qquad (8\text{-}109)$$

$$I = EY\,\underline{/\theta} \qquad (8\text{-}110)$$

The actual construction of the phasor diagram can best be explained by an example.

Example 8-19. Draw the phasor diagram for the circuit solved in Example 8-17 if the voltage source is 150 $\underline{/0^\circ}$ volts.

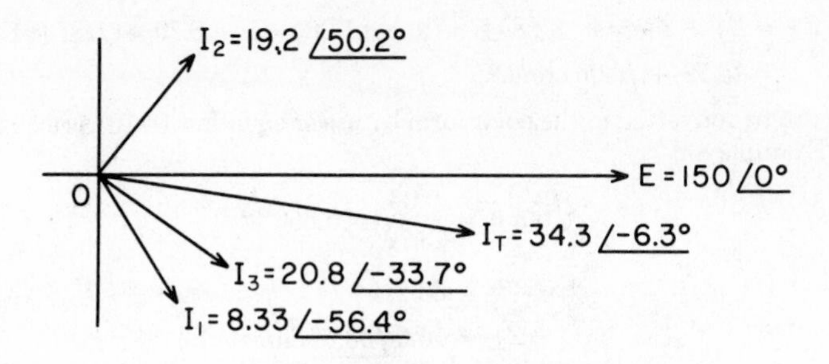

Fig. 8-17. Phasor diagram for parallel circuits.

Solution. The currents in Z_1, Z_2, and Z_3 are found by converting the impedance to the phasor form and dividing the result into the voltage. The phasor form is the polar form, since it gives the angle of lead or lag between the voltage and the current.

$$Z_1 = 10 + j\,15 = 18\,\underline{/56.4^\circ} \text{ ohms}$$

$$Z_2 = 5 - j\,6 = 7.8\,\underline{/-50.2^\circ} \text{ ohms}$$

$$Z_3 = 6 + j\,4 = 7.21\,\underline{/33.7^\circ} \text{ ohms}$$

$$I_1 = \frac{150\,\underline{/0^\circ}}{18\,\underline{/56.4^\circ}} = 8.33\,\underline{/-56.4^\circ} \text{ amps}$$

$$I_2 = \frac{150\,\underline{/0^\circ}}{7.8\,\underline{/-50.2^\circ}} = 19.2\,\underline{/50.2^\circ} \text{ amps}$$

$$I_3 = \frac{150\,\underline{/0^\circ}}{7.21\,\underline{/33.7^\circ}} = 20.8\,\underline{/-33.7^\circ} \text{ amps}$$

The three currents can now be added in the complex form to obtain the total current.

$$I_1 = 4.6 - j\,7 \text{ amps}$$

$$I_2 = 12.3 + j\,14.8 \text{ amps}$$

$$I_3 = 17.3 - j\,11.6 \text{ amps}$$

$$I_T = 4.6 + 12.3 + 17.3 + j\,(-7 + 14.8 - 11.6)$$

$$= 34.2 + j\,3.8 = 34.3\,\underline{/-6.3^\circ} \text{ amps}$$

This value for I_T can also be obtained by using either Y_T or Z_T in the polar form as determined in the example. The answers obtained by the several methods are slightly different and cannot be expected to be exactly alike because of the "rounding off" of values; however, the differences are negligible.

$$I_T = \frac{E}{Z_T} = \frac{150 \underline{/0^\circ}}{4.4 \underline{/6.5^\circ}} = 34.2 \underline{/-6.5^\circ} \text{ amps}$$

$$I_T = EY_T = (150 \underline{/0^\circ})(0.228 \underline{/-6.5^\circ}) = 34.2 \underline{/-6.5^\circ} \text{ amps}$$

These values are plotted on the phasor diagram in Fig. 8-17.

8-15. Phasor Diagram for Series-Parallel Circuits. In a system of series-parallel circuits, there is no vector common to all parts of the system. However, since some reference must be chosen, the voltage of the source is probably the most convenient to use.

The method of calculating the currents and voltages present in or across any particular part of the circuit has already been indicated. The actual construction of the phasor diagram can best be explained in an example.

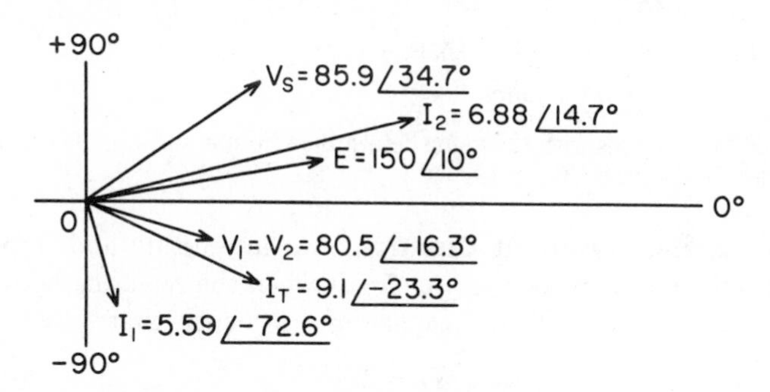

Fig. 8-18. Phasor diagram for series-parallel circuits.

Example 8-20. Draw the phasor diagram for the circuit solved in Example 8-18 if the voltage source is 150 $\underline{/10^\circ}$ volts.

Solution. The total current is found by dividing the impedance Z_T into the voltage E.

$$I_T = \frac{150 \underline{/10^\circ}}{16.5 \underline{/33.3^\circ}} = 9.1 \underline{/10 - 33.3^\circ} = 9.1 \underline{/-23.3^\circ} \text{ amps}$$

The voltage drop across Z_S, the series impedance, is found from the a-c form of Ohm's law, with Z_S in the polar form of vector notation.

$$V_S = I_T Z_S = (9.1 \underline{/-23.3^\circ})(9.45 \underline{/58^\circ}) = 85.9 \underline{/34.7^\circ} \text{ volts}$$

where $Z_S = 5 + j8 = 9.45 \underline{/58^\circ}$ ohms.

The voltage across the parallel circuits Z_1 and Z_2 is equal to $E - V_S$.

Converting E and V_S to the complex form, we have the values

$$E = 150\,\underline{/10^\circ} = 147.8 + j\,26.0 \text{ volts}$$

$$V_S = 85.9\,\underline{/34.7^\circ} = 70.6 + j\,48.9 \text{ volts}$$

$$V_1 = V_2 = E - V_S = 147.8 + j\,26.0 - 70.6 - j\,48.9 = 77.2 - j\,22.9$$
$$= 80.5\,\underline{/-16.3^\circ} \text{ volts}$$

The currents I_1 and I_2 in the parallel branches can be found by Ohm's law.

$$I_1 = \frac{V_1}{Z_1} = \frac{80.5\,\underline{/-16.3^\circ}}{14.4\,\underline{/56.3^\circ}} = 5.59\,\underline{/-72.6^\circ} \text{ amps}$$

$$I_2 = \frac{V_2}{Z_2} = \frac{80.5\,\underline{/-16.3^\circ}}{11.7\,\underline{/-31^\circ}} = 6.88\,\underline{/14.7^\circ} \text{ amps}$$

As a check, $I_T = I_1 + I_2$. If I_1 and I_2 are in the complex form,

$$I_1 = 5.59\,\underline{/-72.6^\circ} = 1.67 - j\,5.34 \text{ amps}$$

$$I_2 = 6.88\,\underline{/14.7^\circ} = 6.66 + j\,1.75 \text{ amps}$$

$$I_T = I_1 + I_2 = 1.67 - j\,5.34 + 6.66 + j\,1.75 = 8.33 - j\,3.59$$
$$= 9.1\,\underline{/-23.3^\circ} \text{ amps}$$

This value agrees with the value determined from E and Z_T. The phasor diagram is shown in Fig. 8-18.

8-16. Series Resonant Circuits. An interesting and important result occurs in a series a-c circuit when the relations between frequency, inductance, and capacitance are such that

$$X_L = X_C \tag{8-111}$$

When this condition exists, the impedance of the circuit is equal to the resistance and therefore has its lowest possible value. Substituting the appropriate values in equation (8-111), we obtain the relationship

$$2\,\pi f_R L = \frac{1}{2\,\pi f_R C} \tag{8-112}$$

where f_R is the resonant frequency in cycles per second and the other quantities are the same as those given in equations (8-24) and (8-32). If equation (8-112) is solved for the resonant frequency, we obtain the equation

$$f_R = \frac{1}{2\,\pi\sqrt{LC}} \tag{8-113}$$

Although series resonant circuits are of great value in electronics, they can be very dangerous if not carefully designed, as the voltages across the inductive reactance and across the capacitive reactance may reach values many times the applied voltage. This possible condition will be illustrated in Example 8-21.

The conditions that exist at series resonance are as follows:

1. $X_L = X_C$.
2. Z is a minimum and is equal to R.
3. Power Factor is unity.
4. The current from the voltage source is maximum and is determined by Ohm's law: $I = E/R$.
5. The voltage across the inductance is equal to the voltage across the capacitance.

Example 8-21. A 0.1-henry inductance, a 1-microfarad capacitor, and a 5-ohm resistor are connected across a 500-cycle 50-volt supply. Find the inductive and capacitive reactance, the impedance, and the voltage across every part of the circuit.

Solution. The inductive reactance is found by use of equation (8-24).

$$X_L = 2\pi f L = (2\pi)(500)(0.1) = 315 \text{ ohms}$$

The capacitive reactance is found from equation (8-32).

$$X_C = \frac{1}{2\pi f C} = \frac{10^6}{2\pi(500)(1)} = 315 \text{ ohms}$$

This is, therefore, a series resonant circuit.

The impedance is found by using equation (8-64).

$$Z = R + j(X_L - X_C) = 5 + j(315 - 315) = 5 \text{ ohms}$$

This computation shows that $Z = R$ for this circuit as predicted.

The current flowing in the circuit is found from Ohm's law.

$$I = \frac{E}{R} = \frac{50}{5} = 10 \text{ amps}$$

The voltage across the resistance is also found by Ohm's law.

$$V_R = IR = (10)(5) = 50 \text{ volts}$$

The voltages across the inductance and capacitance are found by multiplying the current by the respective reactances.

$$V_L = IX_L = (10)(315) = 3150 \text{ volts}$$

$$V_C = IX_C = (10)(315) = 3150 \text{ volts}$$

8-17. Parallel Resonant Circuits. The conditions defining resonance in a parallel circuit may be very different from those in a series circuit. The conditions for resonance require that the reactive current in the inductance be equal to the reactive current in the capacitance. That is,

$$I_L = I_C \tag{8-114}$$

If the circuit shown in Fig. 8-19 is in resonance, we may write

$$EB_L = EB_C \tag{8-115}$$

where E is the voltage of the source which is also the voltage across Z_L and Z_C, B_L is the susceptance of the inductive circuit,

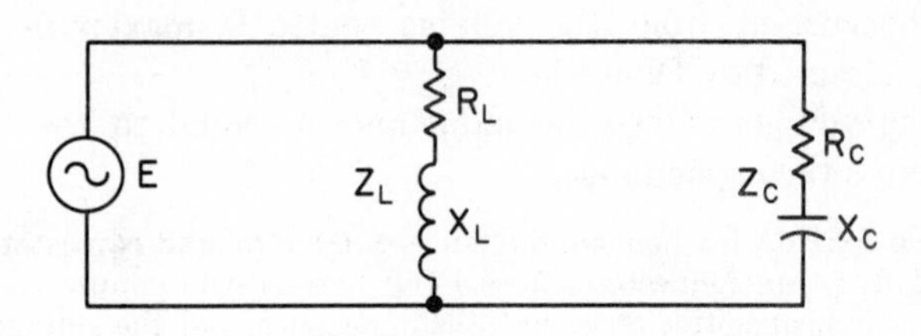

Fig. 8-19. A parallel resonant circuit.

and B_C is the susceptance of the capacitive circuit. Equation (8-100) indicates that equation (8-115) may be rewritten as follows:

$$\frac{X_L}{R_L^2 + X_L^2} = \frac{X_C}{R_C^2 + X_C^2} \tag{8-116}$$

By substituting the values of X_L and X_C from equations (8-24) and (8-32) in equation (8-116), we obtain the relationship

$$\frac{2\pi f_R L}{R_L^2 + (2\pi f_R L)^2} = \frac{\dfrac{1}{2\pi f_R C}}{R_C^2 + \left(\dfrac{1}{2\pi f_R C}\right)^2} \tag{8-117}$$

The equation for the determination of the resonant frequency f_R in cycles per second is obtained as follows:

$$\frac{2\pi f_R L}{R_L^2 + (2\pi f_R L)^2} = \frac{\dfrac{1}{2\pi f_R C}}{\dfrac{(2\pi R_C C f_R)^2 + 1}{(2\pi C f_R)^2}}$$

$$\frac{2\pi f_R L}{R_L^2 + (2\pi f_R L)^2} = \frac{2\pi f_R C}{(2\pi R_C C f_R)^2 + 1}$$

$$L\left[(2\pi R_C C f_R)^2 + 1\right] = C\left[R_L^2 + (2\pi L f_R)^2\right]$$

$$L\,(2\pi R_C C f_R)^2 + L = R_L^2 C + C\,(2\pi L f_R)^2$$

$$L\,(2\pi R_C C f_R)^2 - C\,(2\pi L f_R)^2 = R_L^2 C - L$$

$$(2\pi f_R)^2\,(R_C^2 C - L)\,LC = CR_L^2 - L$$

$$(2\pi f_R)^2 = \frac{R_L^2 C - L}{LC\,(R_C^2 C - L)}$$

$$f_R^2 = \frac{1}{(2\pi)^2 LC}\left[\frac{R_L^2 C - L}{R_C^2 C - L}\right]$$

$$f_R = \frac{1}{2\pi\sqrt{LC}}\left[\frac{R_L^2 C - L}{R_C^2 C - L}\right]^{\frac{1}{2}} \tag{8-118}$$

If the quantities $R_C^2 C$ and $R_L^2 C$ are equal, or if R_L and R_C are so near zero in value that they may be neglected, equation (8-118) reduces to

$$f_R = \frac{1}{2\pi\sqrt{LC}} \tag{8-119}$$

Equation (8-119) is identical with equation (8-113) for the series resonant circuit. In actual practice, R_L and R_C are designed to be extremely small so that equation (8-119) is nearly always sufficiently accurate for use with parallel resonant circuits.**

When R_L and R_C are both negligibly small, $Z_L = X_L = Z_C = X_C$. The total impedance as seen by the a-c voltage source is then found as follows:

$$\frac{1}{Z_T} = \frac{1}{X_L} - \frac{1}{X_C}$$

$$Z_T = \text{infinity}$$

With an infinite impedance, no current will flow from the a-c source, although large currents may be present in the parallel circuits at the resonant frequency.

Example 8-22. A parallel resonant circuit consists of a coil whose inductive reactance is 10 ohms and a capacitor whose capacitive reactance is

---

** If R_C and R_L are not sufficiently small, resonance may be impossible at any frequency. For a more complete discussion of parallel resonance, see books on alternating-current circuits such as *Alternating Current Circuits* by Russell M. Kerchner and George F. Corcoran (4th ed.; New York: John Wiley & Sons, Inc., 1960), pp. 162-68.

10 ohms. If the voltage of the a-c source is 100 volts, find the current delivered by the a-c source and the current flowing in the parallel branches.

Solution. The total impedance is found as follows:

$$\frac{1}{Z_T} = \frac{1}{10} - \frac{1}{10} = \text{zero}$$

$$Z_T = \text{infinity}$$

The current flowing from the source is, therefore,

$$I = \frac{E}{Z_T} = \frac{100}{\infty} = 0 \text{ amps}$$

The symbol ∞ represents infinity.

The current flowing in the inductance is

$$I_L = \frac{E}{X_L} = \frac{100}{10} = 10 \text{ amps}$$

The current flowing in the capacitance is

$$I_C = \frac{E}{X_C} = \frac{100}{10} = 10 \text{ amps}$$

8-18. Harmonics. Although an electrical voltage source is designed to deliver a sine wave of voltage and current at its terminals, induced voltages from nearby power lines, the presence of iron in electrical equipment, and other influences will alter the shape of the wave as indicated in Fig. 8-20.

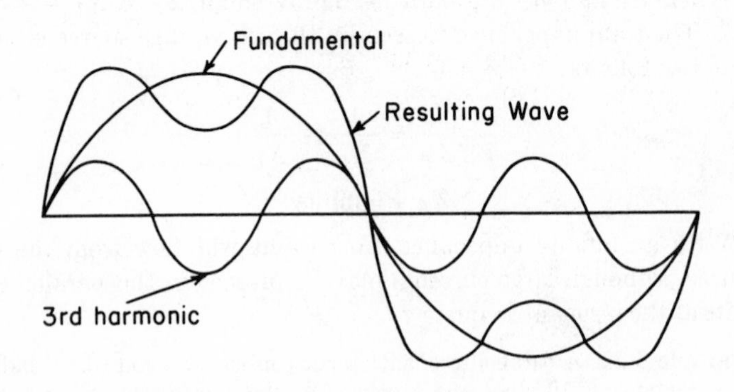

Fig. 8-20. Harmonic wave.

The equations of the principal wave—called the fundamental—may be given as

$$i_1 = I_{1m} \sin (\omega t + \theta_1) \qquad e_1 = E_{1m} \sin (\omega t + \psi_1)$$

The second harmonic, if present, may have the equations

$$i_2 = I_{2m} \sin (2\,\omega t + \theta_2) \qquad e_2 = E_{2m} \sin (2\,\omega t + \psi_2)$$

The third harmonic (shown in Fig. 8-20) might have the equations

$$i_3 = I_{3m} \sin (3\,\omega t + \theta_3) \qquad e_3 = E_{3m} \sin (3\,\omega t + \psi_3)$$

Other harmonics have similar equations.

All electrical waves, regardless of their shapes, are composed of a fundamental and one or more harmonic frequencies[††] if their shapes are irregular (not pure sine waves).

In power systems, both the positive and the negative alternations have the same appearance. Consequently, a power wave contains no even harmonics. A communications circuit, however, must carry all harmonics—odd and even—in order to convey voice, music, or other sound frequencies with a minimum amount of distortion.

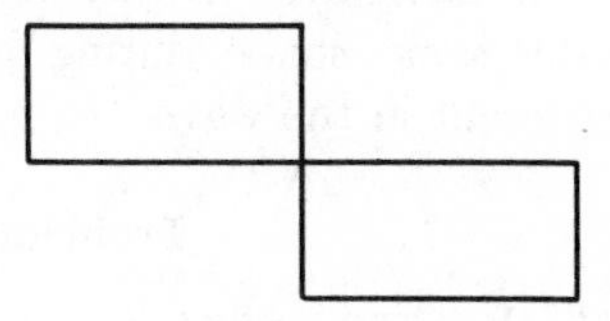

Fig. 8-21. Square wave.

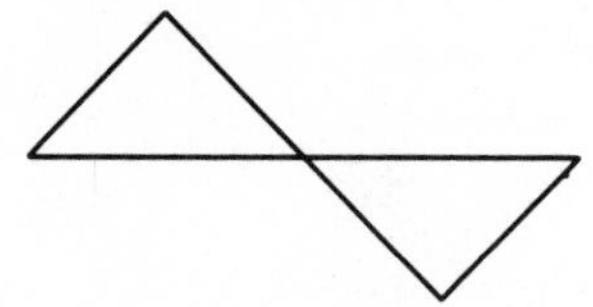

Fig. 8-22. Triangular wave.

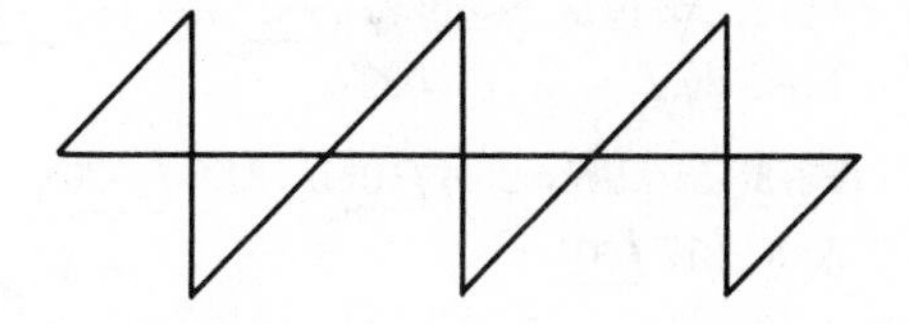

Fig. 8-23. Sawtooth wave.

Three waves often encountered in testing or other electrical work are shown in Figs. 8-21, 8-22, and 8-23. The equations that very closely approximate these waves are

Square Wave (Fig. 8-21):

$$e = E_1 \sin \omega t + \frac{1}{3} E_1 \sin 3\,\omega t + \frac{1}{5} E_1 \sin 5\,\omega t + \frac{1}{7} E_1 \sin 7\,\omega t + \cdots$$

Triangular Wave (Fig. 8-22):

$$e = E_1 \sin \omega t - \frac{1}{9} E_1 \sin 3\,\omega t + \frac{1}{25} E_1 \sin 5\,\omega t - \frac{1}{49} E_1 \sin 7\,\omega t + \cdots$$

[††] The method most generally used to determine the components of a wave is Fourier's Analysis. This method is explained in many good books on the subject of alternating current.

Sawtooth Wave (Fig. 8-23):

$$e = -E_1 \sin \omega t - \frac{1}{2}E_1 \sin 2\,\omega t - \frac{1}{3}E_1 \sin 3\,\omega t - \frac{1}{4}E_1 \sin 4\,\omega t$$

$$- \frac{1}{5}E_1 \sin 5\omega t - \cdots$$

The farther these expressions are carried out, the more nearly will the equations reproduce the actual waves. Since the square and rectangular waves have the same shape during the negative alternation that they have during the positive alternation, they contain no even harmonics. Since the sawtooth wave does not have the same shape during both alternations, even harmonics are present in the wave.

Problems Based on Chapter 8

P8-1. Three vectors, $3 + j5$, $12 - j3$, and $-6 + j14$, are to be added. Express the result in complex and polar forms.
Ans. $9 + j16 = 18.3 \underline{/60.6°}$.

P8-2. Add the vectors $15 \underline{/37°}$ and $18 \underline{/-17°}$.
Ans. $29.2 + j3.73 = 29.5 \underline{/7.3°}$.

P8-3. Multiply $25.6 \underline{/50°}$ by $31.9 \underline{/-20°}$.
Ans. $817 \underline{/30°}$.

P8-4. Divide $153 \underline{/40°}$ by $28.1 \underline{/-10°}$.
Ans. $5.42 \underline{/50°}$.

P8-5. What is the frequency of a 4-pole generator when running at 3000 rpm?
Ans. 100 cps.
At what speeds should an 8-pole a-c generator (also called an "alternator") run to deliver a frequency of 25 cps? 50 cps? 60 cps?
Ans. 375 rpm. 750 rpm. 900 rpm. (Note that one cycle is generated for every pair of poles in an a-c generator.)

P8-6. A 60-cycle voltage is at 10 volts when $t = 0$. If the maximum voltage E_m is 75 volts, write the equation for the voltage.
Ans. $e = 75 \sin (377t + 7.7°)$.

P8-7. A 50-cycle a-c generator has an output of 200 amps at an instant when $t = 0.011$ sec. What is the maximum value of the current if $i = 0$ when $t = 0$?
Ans. $200 = I_m \sin 198°$. $I_m = 648$ amps.

P8-8. In a series circuit, $R = 12$ ohms, $X_L = 5$ ohms, and $X_C = 7$ ohms. Find the instantaneous value of the voltage across the resistance, the inductive reactance, and the capacitive reactance, and across the entire circuit if $i = 3 \sin 157t$. What is the frequency of the circuit?

Ans. $e_R = 36 \sin 157t$. $e_L = 15 \sin (157t + 90°)$. $e_C = 21 \sin (157t - 90°)$. $e = 36.5 \sin (157t - 9.5°)$. $f = 25$ cps.

P8-9. The current and voltage in a circuit are expressed by the equations $i = 30 \sin \omega t$ and $e = 150 \sin (\omega t + 20°)$. What is the impedance? What is the resistance? What is the reactance? If the frequency is 60 cps, what is the inductance or capacitance responsible for the reactance?

Ans. $Z = 5 \underline{/20°}$. $R = 4.7$ ohms. $X_L = 1.7$ ohms. $L = 4.54 \times 10^{-3}$ henrys inductance.

P8-10. If the circuit of problem P8-9 includes a capacitor of 100 microfarads with no change in impedance, what would be the capacitive reactance, the inductive reactance, and the inductance?

Ans. $X_C = 27.2$ ohms. $X_L = 28.9$ ohms. $L = 76.5 \times 10^{-3}$ henrys.

P8-11. A 50-cycle circuit contains 8 ohms of resistance in series with a coil which has an inductance of 70 millihenrys (also written 70 mh or 70×10^{-3} henrys). What additional inductance would be required to make the inductive reactance 10 times as large as the resistance? What is the impedance under this condition?

Ans. 92.5 millihenrys. $Z = 80 \underline{/84.3°}$ ohms.

P8-12. A circuit has a current and a voltage whose equations are $i = 25 \sin \omega t$ and $e = 150 \sin (\omega t - 40°)$. What are the effective values of current and voltage in the circuit?

Ans. $I = 17.7$ amps. $E = 106$ volts.

P8-13. A voltmeter indicates that the supply to a building is 480 volts. If 25 amps are recorded on an ammeter in the same building, what are the maximum values of the voltage and the current?

Ans. $E_m = 677$ volts. $I_m = 35.5$ amps.

P8-14. The meter values of current and voltage in a circuit are 36 amps and 220 volts. What are the average values? Assume sine waves.

Ans. $I_{av} = 32.4$ amps. $E_{av} = 198$ volts.

P8-15. A voltage wave, when examined by use of an oscilloscope and analyzed, is found to have an average value of 185 volts when the voltmeter for the circuit indicates 300. What is the form factor?

Ans. 1.62.

P8-16. A series circuit contains a resistance of 30 ohms, an inductive reactance of 20 ohms, and a capacitive reactance of 12 ohms. What is the impedance? If a voltage of 250 volts is impressed on the circuit, what are the values across the resistance, the capacitive reactance, and the inductive reactance?

Ans. $Z = 31.3 \underline{/14.8°}$ ohms. $I = 8 \underline{/-14.8°}$ amps. $V_R = 240 \underline{/-14.8°}$

volts. $V_C = 96 \angle -104.8^\circ$ volts. $V_L = 160 \angle 75.2^\circ$ volts.

P8-17. A series circuit has a source voltage of 330 volts and a current of 5 amps as indicated by appropriate meters. Other meters indicate that the voltage across a resistance is 220 volts, and across a coil (including the resistance of the coil) is 200 volts. Find (a) the angle between the coil current and the voltage, (b) the voltage across the resistance of the coil, (c) the voltage across the inductive reactance of the coil, (d) the impedance of the circuit, (e) the impedance of the coil, (f) the inductive reactance of the coil, (g) the resistance of the coil, (h) the total resistance of the circuit (including that of the coil), and (i) the angle between line current and line voltage.

Ans. (a) $\theta_L = 76.9^\circ$. (b) $V_{RL} = 46$ volts. (c) $V_{XL} = 194$ volts. (d) $Z = 66 \angle 36.2^\circ$ ohms. (e) $Z_L = 40 \angle 76.9^\circ$ ohms. (f) $X_L = 38.8$ ohms. (g) $R_L = 9.2$ ohms. (h) $R = 33.2$ ohms. (i) $\theta_{\text{LINE}} = 36.2^\circ$.

P8-18. The impedance of a series circuit is found to be equal to $8 + j3$ ohms. If an a-c voltage of 120 volts is connected to the circuit, find the volt-amps, power, vars, power factor, and reactive factor.

Ans. 1690 volt-amps. 600 vars. $\cos \theta = 0.945$ so that power factor $= 94.5\%$. $\sin \theta = 0.355$ so that reactive factor $= 35.5\%$.

P8-19. The current and voltage in a series a-c circuit are found to be $15 \angle 30^\circ$ amps and $250 \angle 72^\circ$ volts. Find the impedance, the volt-amps, the power, and the vars of the circuit.

Ans. $Z = 16.7 \angle 42^\circ$ ohms $= 12.2 + j11$ ohms. 2500 volt-amps. 1830 watts. 1650 vars.

P8-20. An a-c circuit is found to contain the following currents and voltages at various frequencies: $I_1 = 10$ amps, $I_2 = 12$ amps, $I_3 = 9$ amps, $I_4 = 6$ amps, $E_1 = 150$ volts, $E_2 = 130$ volts, $E_3 = 120$ volts, $E_4 = 100$ volts. A wattmeter indicates that the power is equal to 3200 watts. Find the effective values of current and voltage, the power factor, and the total volt-amps.

Ans. $I = 19.1$ amps. $E = 253$ volts. PF $= 66.6\%$. 4740 volt-amps.

P8-21. The following voltages are found to be present in an a-c circuit: $830 \sin \omega t + 277 \sin 3\omega t - 166 \sin 5\omega t - 119 \sin 7\omega t + 92 \sin 9\omega t$. Find the effective value of the voltage.

Ans. 637 volts.

P8-22. A coil having an inductance of 0.053 henry and 3 ohms resistance is in parallel with a resistance of 12 ohms across a 120-volt 60-cycle source. What is the total impedance of the circuit? What is the total current and the current in each of the parallel branches?

Ans. $Z_T = 9.7 \angle 28.3^\circ$ ohms. $I_T = 12.4 \angle -28.3^\circ$ amps $= 10.9 - j5.9$ amps. $I_1 = 5.9 \angle -81.5^\circ$ amps $= 0.9 - j5.8$ amps. $I_2 = 10 \angle 0^\circ = 10 + j0$ amps.

P8-23. In Fig. P8-23, $Z_1 = 8 + j3$ ohms but the total impedance Z_T is $5 + j3$ ohms. Find Z_2.

Ans. $Z_2 = 16.4 \angle 51.4^\circ$ ohms $= 10.3 + j12.8$ ohms.

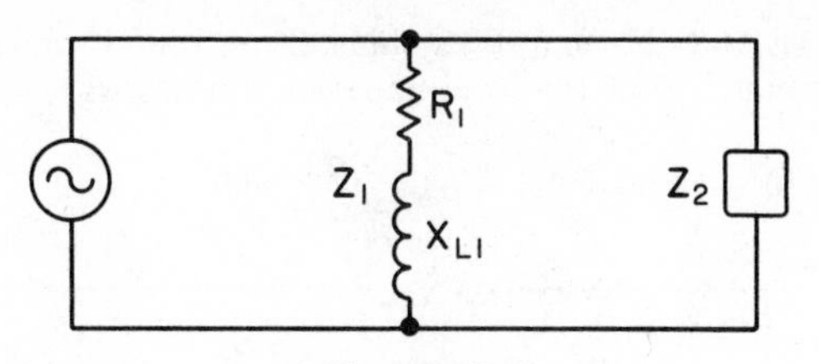

Fig. P8-23.

P8-24. The impedances in a parallel a-c circuit are: $Z_1 = 12 + j8$, $Z_2 = 9 - j3$, and $Z_3 = 15 - j9$ ohms. Find Z_T.

Ans. $Z_T = 4.8\,\underline{/-6.7^\circ}$ ohms $= 4.76 - j0.56$ ohms.

P8-25. In Fig. 8-16 (page 170), $Z_S = 0.5 + j0.3$, $Z_1 = 15 + j7$, and $Z_2 = 20 - j7$. Find the total impedance of the system.

Ans. $Z_T = 10.45 + j1.31$ ohms $= 10.55\,\underline{/7.1^\circ}$ ohms.

P8-26. An a-c device, when connected to a 120-volt 60-cycle circuit, draws 10 amps current. The power factor of the device is 85%, lagging. Find the impedance, the resistance, the inductive reactance, and the inductance of the device.

Ans. $Z = 12\,\underline{/32^\circ}$ ohms. $R = 10.2$ ohms. $X_L = 6.36$ ohms. $L = 0.0168$ henry.

P8-27. In Fig. P8-27, $Z_1 = 10 + j6$ ohms and $Z_2 = 10 + j10$ ohms. What series resistance R_S is required if the power factor is to be brought up to 90%?

Ans. $R_S = 2.86$ ohms.

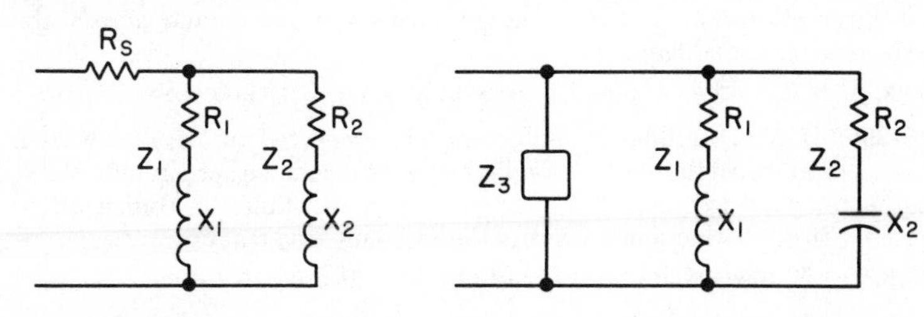

Fig. P8-27. Fig. P8-28.

P8-28. In Fig. P8-28, $Z_1 = 3 + j8$ ohms and $Z_2 = 6 - j18$ ohms. Find Z_3 to make the power factor equal to 87% lagging.

Ans. $Z_3 = 3.92\,\underline{/-90^\circ}$ ohms (pure capacitance).

P8-29. If the circuit in problem P8-23 is connected across a 480-volt source, find the current, the power, the power factor, and the reactive factor. What is the apparent power?

Ans. $I = 82.5\,\underline{/-31^\circ}$ amps. $P = 33{,}900$ watts. PF $= 51.5\%$. $VA =$ 39,600 volt-amps.

P8-30. In Fig. P8-30, $Z_1 = 5 + j8$ ohms, $Z_2 = 3 + j10$ ohms, and $Z_S = 0.05 + j0.08$ ohm. Find the total impedance measured across terminals *A-B*.

Ans. $Z_T = 2.10 + j4.58$ ohms $= 5.06 \underline{/65.3°}$ ohms.

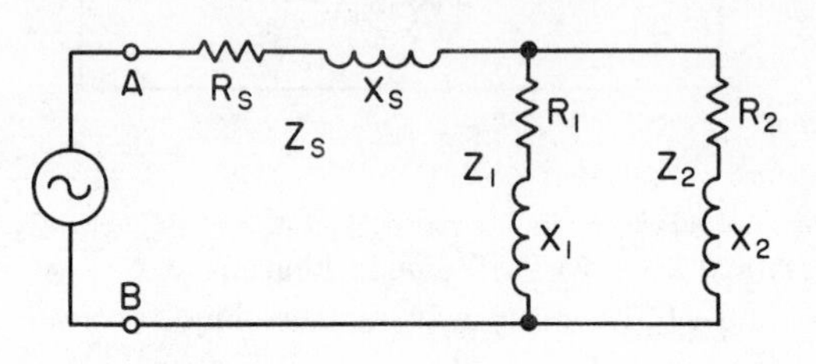

Fig. P8-30.

P8-31. What pure capacitance should be connected across terminals *A-B* in Fig. P8-30 if the system is to have a power factor of 85% and the frequency is 60 cycles?

Ans. $X_C = 3.5$ ohms. $C = 758$ microfarads.

P8-32. A 0.1-henry coil is connected in series with a 0.0063-microfarad capacitor. What is the resonant frequency?

Ans. 2000 cps.

P8-33. A 10-henry coil is connected in series with a capacitor for a resonant frequency of 200 cps. What is the value of the capacitor?

Ans. $C = 0.063$ microfarad.

P8-34. If the circuit of problem P8-32 includes a 5-ohm resistance and the current is 0.5 amp, find the voltage across the circuit and across the resistance, coil, and capacitor.

Ans. $E = 2.5$ volts. $V_R = 2.5$ volts. $V_C = V_L = 19{,}900$ volts.

P8-35. (a) A 0.1-millihenry inductance is connected in parallel with a 0.1-$\mu\mu$ farad capacitance with negligible resistance in either circuit. What is the resonant frequency? (b) If a 15-ohm resistance is connected in series with the inductance, what is the resonant frequency?

Ans. (a) 50 megacycles. (b) Is not resonant at any frequency.

9 THREE-PHASE CIRCUITS

9-1. Polyphase Systems. Single-phase systems are inefficient and unsatisfactory for power applications. To increase the amount of power transmitted over a given set of cables or wires, experiments were made with two or more single-phase systems operating together but out of phase with each other.

If two single-phase systems are connected together, the windings of the generator are arranged so that the output phases are 90 electrical degrees apart. This system is indicated in Fig. 9-1.

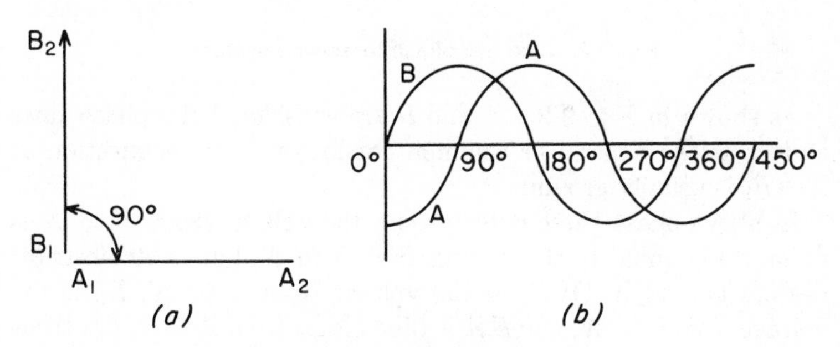

Fig. 9-1. The two-phase system.

If A_1-A_2 of Fig. 9-1*a* is a vector at zero electrical degrees and B_1-B_2 is a vector at 90° counterclockwise from A_1-A_2, then these vectors represent the effective values of the voltages of a two-phase system. The actual output will appear as two sine waves, A and B, as shown in Fig. 9-1*b*.

The two-phase system can be operated with four conductors, two for B phase and two for A phase. In a perfectly balanced system of this kind, the voltages and currents of both windings are equal. In equation form, this condition can be expressed as follows:

$$I_A = I_B \tag{9-1a}$$

$$E_A = E_B \tag{9-1b}$$

In practice, two-phase four-wire systems have never been generally accepted, even where two-phase systems were used. Since the two phases are electrically isolated from each other, a voltmeter will not register a difference in potential between them. Since two points that have the same potential (or are not at different potentials) can be connected, points A_1 and B_1 can be tied together, as shown in Fig. 9-2*a*. When this connection is made, only three conductors are required, since B_1 and A_1 are electrically identical.

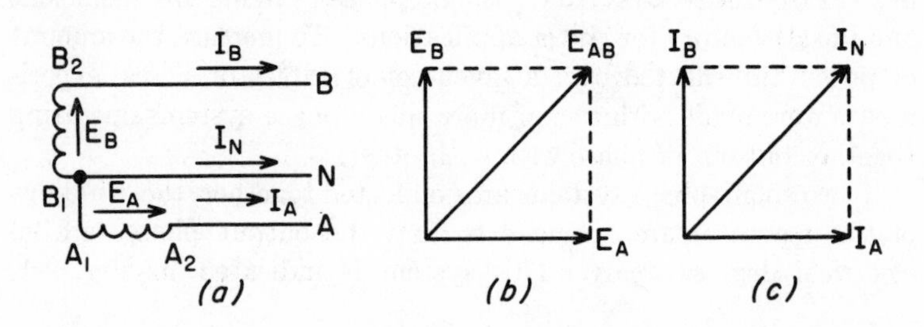

Fig. 9-2. The two-phase three-wire system.

As shown in Fig. 9-2*a*, A and B are considered the phase lines and N is the neutral or common conductor. The connection at A_1–B_1 is usually grounded.

In a two-phase three-wire system, the voltage from A to N is numerically equal to the voltage from B to N, but is 90 electrical degrees behind it. If E_A is the voltage from A to N, E_B is the voltage from B to N, and E_{AB} is the voltage from A to B, the three voltages have the vector relationships shown in Fig. 9-2*b*. From this figure, we may write the equations for the voltages. If the system is balanced, the relationships are expressed as follows:

$$E_A = E_B \tag{9-2a}$$

$$E_{AB} = E_A \sqrt{2} \tag{9-2b}$$

$$E_{AB} = E_B \sqrt{2} \tag{9-2c}$$

In the balanced two-phase three-wire system shown in Fig. 9-2*c*, the currents in the two outside conductors are equal but the current in the center or neutral conductor is the vector sum of the phase currents. These relationships are shown by the following equations:

$$I_A = I_B \tag{9-3a}$$

$$I_N = I_A \sqrt{2} \tag{9-3b}$$

$$I_N = I_B\sqrt{2} \tag{9-3c}$$

The two-phase system has the disadvantage of unbalanced voltages and currents because of E_{AB} and I_N. Consequently, its use has been limited to a few local areas, many of which have been changed over to the more advantageous three-phase system. The two-phase system is now obsolete or very nearly so.

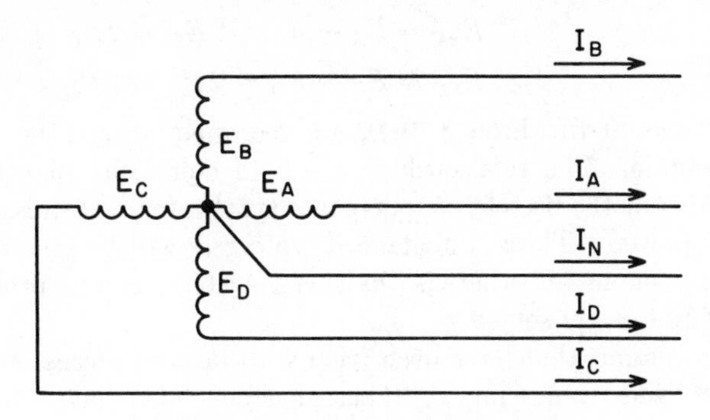

Fig. 9-3. The two-phase five-wire system (also called the four-phase system).

Another system that has been tried is the two-phase five-wire system (also called the four-phase system) which consists of two two-phase systems.* In this system, the neutral conductor is the fifth wire which may be grounded. A schematic diagram of the two-phase five-wire system is shown in Fig. 9-3. Although in a balanced system the phase voltages and currents are balanced, the voltages across adjacent phases are not. The equations for this system are

$$E_A = E_B = E_C = E_D \tag{9-4a}$$

$$\bar{I}_A + \bar{I}_B + \bar{I}_C + \bar{I}_D + \bar{I}_N = 0 \tag{9-4b}$$

$$\bar{E}_{AB} = \bar{E}_A + \bar{E}_B \tag{9-4c}$$

$$\bar{E}_{BC} = \bar{E}_B + \bar{E}_C \tag{9-4d}$$

$$\bar{E}_{CD} = \bar{E}_C + \bar{E}_D \tag{9-4e}$$

* In a four-wire two-phase system, the neutral is generally grounded. If the fifth wire is taken out as a conductor, it is strictly a four-phase five-wire system, although custom considers it as a two-phase system. If the neutral is not taken out as a conductor, the connection is a type of two-phase four-wire system.

$$\overline{E}_{DA} = \overline{E}_D + \overline{E}_A \tag{9-4f}$$

$$E_{AB} = E_A\sqrt{2} = E_B\sqrt{2} \tag{9-4g}$$

$$E_{BC} = E_B\sqrt{2} = E_C\sqrt{2} \tag{9-4h}$$

$$E_{CD} = E_C\sqrt{2} = E_D\sqrt{2} \tag{9-4i}$$

$$E_{DA} = E_D\sqrt{2} = E_A\sqrt{2} \tag{9-4j}$$

$$E_{AC} = E_A + E_C = 2E_A = 2E_C \tag{9-4k}$$

$$E_{BD} = E_B + E_D = 2E_B = 2E_D \tag{9-4l}$$

Equations (9-4b) through (9-4f) are vector equations; the others are algebraic. The relationships given in equations (9-4k) and (9-4l) prevent the use of the four-phase system for transmission of electric power. These unbalanced voltages which are always present, even in an otherwise balanced system, create problems that are not easily solved.

Other systems that have been tried with limited success are the six-phase and twelve-phase. These systems also have the unbalanced voltage problem and are used almost exclusively for rectification to direct current for special loads such as electrified railroads and electroplating. In this type of loading, the power is transmitted to the using plant in a three-phase three-wire system and converted to six-phase or twelve-phase in a substation at or near the using equipment.

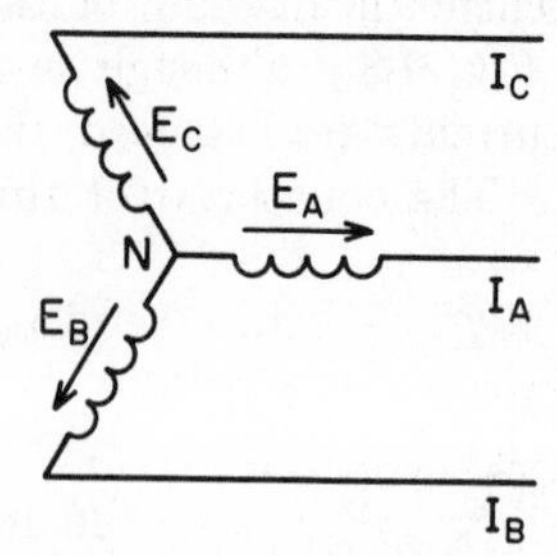

Fig. 9-4. A three-phase system.

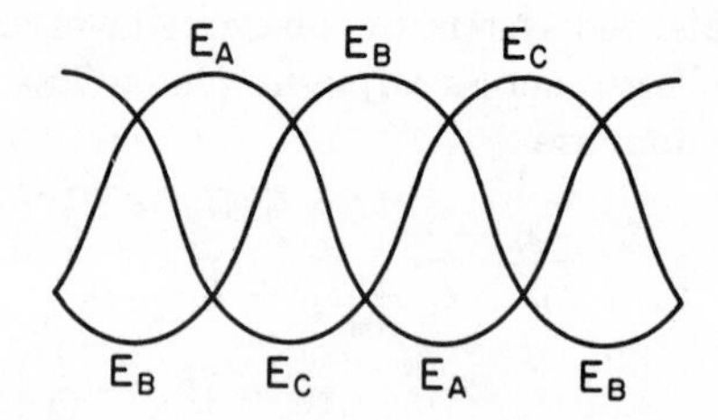

Fig. 9-5. The three-phase sine wave.

9-2. The Three-Phase Wye Connection. The windings of a three-phase generator are spaced 120 electrical degrees apart, as shown schematically in Fig. 9-4. In the connection shown, all three windings are tied together at one point—as N—and the phase voltages E_A, E_B, and E_C are measured with respect to that point. When the windings are connected as shown in Fig. 9-4, they are shaped, schematically, in the form of the letter Y. For this reason, this connection is called the wye (or star†) connection.

The three-phase voltages are actually three single-phase voltages spaced 120 electrical degrees apart. The sine curves or waves for this system are shown in Fig. 9-5.

In a balanced three-phase three-wire wye-connected system, the relationships are as follows:

$$\overline{E}_{AB} = \overline{E}_A + \overline{E}_B \tag{9-5a}$$

$$\overline{E}_{BC} = \overline{E}_B + \overline{E}_C \tag{9-5b}$$

$$\overline{E}_{CA} = \overline{E}_C + \overline{E}_A \tag{9-5c}$$

where $\overline{E}_{AB}$, $\overline{E}_{BC}$, and $\overline{E}_{CA}$ are line voltages which may be designated as $\overline{E}_{\text{LINE}}$, and $\overline{E}_A$, $\overline{E}_B$, and $\overline{E}_C$ are phase voltages. The equation for the currents is

$$\overline{I}_A = \overline{I}_B = \overline{I}_C = \overline{I}_{\text{LINE}} \tag{9-6}$$

where $\overline{I}_A$, $\overline{I}_B$, and $\overline{I}_C$ are the currents in the phase windings. These currents are, consequently, equal to the line current $\overline{I}_{\text{LINE}}$ in every one of the three line conductors. Equations (9-5a), (9-5b), and (9-5c) are vector relationships, as indicated by the line drawn above the E. The actual values of the line voltages must be determined by vector addition.

The vector diagram for the wye system is shown in Fig. 9-6*a*. It is customary to indicate voltage directions by arrows pointing outward from the central point shown in the diagram. The voltage across lines A to B is found from equation (9-5a), which means that we must trace the connection from the point of the arrow at E_A to the neutral point N, and then out toward the end of the arrow E_B. This means we have traced E_A in reverse. Therefore, we may write

$$\overline{E}_{AB} = \overline{E}_{AN} + \overline{E}_{NB} = -\overline{E}_{NA} + \overline{E}_{NB} \tag{9-7}$$

If $\overline{E}_{NA}$ is at zero degrees, it may be designated $E_{NA}\underline{/0^\circ}$. Since $\overline{E}_{AN}$ is a negative $\overline{E}_{NA}$, we must write the voltage as $-E_{NA}\underline{/0^\circ}$ or $E_{AN}\underline{/180^\circ}$. $\overline{E}_{NB}$ is at 240° and may be written $E_{NB}\underline{/240^\circ}$. With

† The term "star" refers to any polyphase connection that has one common point—as N—regardless of the number of phases. Present practice is to use the term "star" for six-phase and twelve-phase systems and "wye" specifically for the three-phase connection discussed in this section.

these substitutions, equation (9-5a) may be written

$$\overline{E}_{AB} = E_{AN} \underline{/180°} + E_{NB} \underline{/240°} \tag{9-8a}$$

The values in equation (9-8a) can be converted to complex notation by the method given in Chapter 8.

$$\overline{E}_{AB} = - E_{NA} + j0 - 0.5\, E_{NB} - j0.866\, E_{NB} \tag{9-9a}$$

But $E_{NA} = E_{NB}$ except for the angle. Therefore,

$$\overline{E}_{AB} = - 1.5\, E_{NA} - j\frac{\sqrt{3}}{2}E_{NA} \tag{9-10a}$$

where $\sqrt{3}/2 = 0.866$. Equation (9-10a) can now be changed into the polar form:

$$\overline{E}_{AB} = E_{AN}\sqrt{3}\, \underline{/210°} \tag{9-11a}$$

The actual value of the line voltage is, therefore, $\sqrt{3}$ times the phase voltage. The graphical addition is shown in Fig. 9-6*b*.

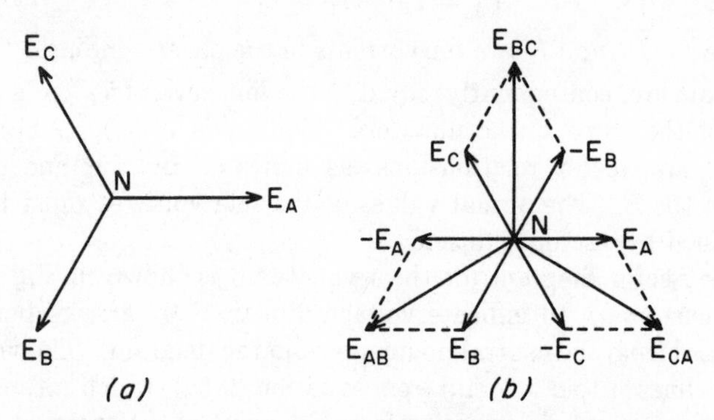

Fig. 9-6. Vector diagrams for three-phase wye connection.

Line voltages $\overline{E}_{BC}$ and $\overline{E}_{CA}$ can be found by the analysis given for $\overline{E}_{AB}$. The corresponding equations will then be

$$\overline{E}_{BC} = E_{BN} \underline{/60°} + E_{NC} \underline{/120°} \tag{9-8b}$$

$$\overline{E}_{CA} = E_{CN} \underline{/300°} + E_{NA} \underline{/0°} \tag{9-8c}$$

$$\overline{E}_{BC} = 0.5\, E_{BN} + j\frac{\sqrt{3}}{2} E_{BN} + 0.5\, E_{CN} - j\frac{\sqrt{3}}{2} E_{BN} \tag{9-9b}$$

$$\overline{E}_{CA} = 0.5\, E_{CN} - j\frac{\sqrt{3}}{2} E_{CN} + E_{AN} \tag{9-9c}$$

$$\overline{E}_{BC} = 0 + jE_{BN}\sqrt{3} \tag{9-10b}$$

$$\overline{E}_{CA} = 1.5\,E_{CN} - j\,\frac{\sqrt{3}}{2}\,E_{CN} \tag{9-10c}$$

$$\overline{E}_{BC} = E_{BN}\,\sqrt{3}\,\underline{/90^\circ} \tag{9-11b}$$

$$\overline{E}_{CA} = E_{CN}\,\sqrt{3}\,\underline{/330^\circ} \tag{9-11c}$$

The vector diagram showing the phase relations of the three line voltages is shown in Fig. 9-6*b*.

In actual practice, when line voltages are referred to, usually only one letter is used, as *A*-phase voltage (or $\overline{E}_A$) for $\overline{E}_{AB}$, *B*-phase voltage (or $\overline{E}_B$) for $\overline{E}_{BC}$, and *C*-phase voltage (or $\overline{E}_C$) for $\overline{E}_{CA}$.

From equations (9-11a), (9-11b), and (9-11c), we may write the general relationships for three-phase three-wire wye-connected system voltages:

$$E_{\text{LINE}} = \sqrt{3}\,E_{\phi} \tag{9-12}$$

where E_{LINE} is any of the line voltages and E_{ϕ} is any voltage to neutral (phase voltage). Equation (9-6) can be rewritten in the same form for currents.

$$I_{\text{LINE}} = I_{\phi} \tag{9-13}$$

Whenever phase currents and voltages are used, the symbol ϕ (phi) is used as the subscript for identification.

The wye-connected system can be operated as a four-wire transmission or distribution line by bringing out the neutral (*N*) connection as the fourth line. This is the system most generally used in distribution systems in residential neighborhoods.

Example 9-1. The line voltage of a three-phase four-wire distribution system is 4800 volts. What is the voltage from line to neutral?

Solution. The voltage from line to neutral is the phase voltage which can be found from equation (9-12).

$$E_{\phi} = \frac{E_{\text{LINE}}}{\sqrt{3}} = \frac{4800}{1.732} = 2770 \text{ volts}$$

Example 9-2. The currents in a three-phase four-wire wye-connected system are: $I_A = 100$ amps, $I_B = 115$ amps, $I_C = 110$ amps. What current is carried in the neutral conductor? Assume a resistive load.

Solution. From the information already given in this book, we may write the following vector equation:

$$\overline{I}_A + \overline{I}_B + \overline{I}_C + \overline{I}_N = 0 \tag{9-14}$$

When the three line currents are equal and spaced exactly 120° apart, or if there is no neutral conductor, $I_N = 0$. Since the unbalance in this problem is relatively small, we may assume the following phase relationships:

$$\bar{I}_A = 100 \underline{/0^\circ} \qquad \bar{I}_B = 115 \underline{/240^\circ} \qquad \bar{I}_C = 110 \underline{/120^\circ}$$

These expressions may be converted to the complex form as follows:

$$\begin{aligned} I_A &= 100.0 + j0.0 \\ I_B &= -57.7 - j99.6 \\ I_C &= -55.0 + j95.3 \\ \hline \bar{I}_A + \bar{I}_B + \bar{I}_C &= -12.7 - j4.3 \end{aligned}$$

Equation (9-14) is then solved for I_N. Notice that I_N is reversed in phase with respect to the sum of the three line currents.

$$I_N = 12.7 + j4.3 = 13.4 \underline{/18.7^\circ} \text{ amps}$$

9-3. The Three-Phase Delta Connection. Since the three windings in a three-phase generator are completely isolated from each other, electrically, until some connection is made, the start of one winding can be connected to the finish of another for all three windings, as shown in Fig. 9-7. The resulting connection has a schematic form that looks like an equilateral triangle or the Greek letter delta (Δ). Consequently, this connection is called the three-phase, three-wire delta connection, the line wires being taken from the junction point between two adjacent phase windings.

In Fig. 9-7, $\bar{E}_{BA}$ is at zero electrical degrees, $\bar{E}_{AC}$ is at 120 degrees, and $\bar{E}_{CB}$ is at 240 degrees. Since the line connections are made across the phase windings, we may write

$$E_{\text{LINE}} = E_\phi \tag{9-15}$$

where the subscripts have the same significance as in equation (9-12).

An inspection of Fig. 9-7 shows that the following current relationships exist in the delta connection:

$$\bar{I}_A = \bar{I}_{BA} + \bar{I}_{AC} \tag{9-16a}$$

$$\bar{I}_B = \bar{I}_{CB} + \bar{I}_{BA} \tag{9-16b}$$

$$\bar{I}_C = \bar{I}_{AC} + \bar{I}_{CB} \tag{9-16c}$$

By an analysis similar to that made for the voltages in the wye connection, we find that the line currents and phase currents have the relative values

$$I_{\text{LINE}} = I_\phi \sqrt{3} \tag{9-17}$$

for a balanced delta system in which $I_A = I_B = I_C$.

There is no proper way to ground a delta system, as there is no point in the delta which is at an equal potential with respect to

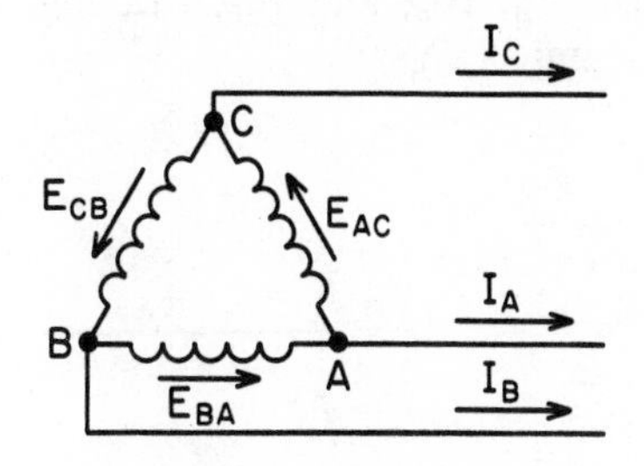

Fig. 9-7. The three-wire delta connection.

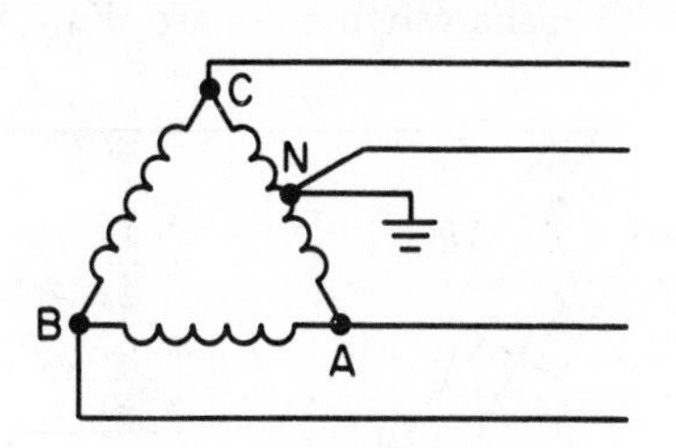

Fig. 9-8. The four-wire delta connection.

all three line voltages. In some small installations, former practice was to ground one winding, as *AC*, at the center, as indicated in Fig. 9-8. This point was then taken off as a fourth conductor. All single-phase 120-volt circuits for lighting and small appliances were connected either between *A* and *N* or between *C* and *N*. The voltages for these branches are indicated by the equations

$$\overline{E}_{AC} = \overline{E}_{AN} + \overline{E}_{NC} \tag{9-18a}$$

$$\overline{E}_{AN} = \overline{E}_{NC} = \tfrac{1}{2} E_{AC} \tag{9-18b}$$

The four-wire delta system is considered dangerous because of the voltage from the third line to ground:

$$E_{BN} = E_{AN}\sqrt{3} = E_{NC}\sqrt{3} \tag{9-19}$$

Another disadvantage of the four-wire delta system is the fact that winding *AC* must carry a power current equal to that in windings *BA* and *CB* plus the additional single-phase loads for *AN* and *NC*. This connection is now illegal in some localities and is being replaced by other systems based on the wye connection.

Example 9-3. The line current in a balanced three-phase delta-connected system is 108 amperes. What is the phase current?

Solution. Equation (9-17) can be solved for I_ϕ.

$$I_\phi = \frac{I_{\text{LINE}}}{\sqrt{3}} = \frac{108}{1.732} = 62.4 \text{ amps}$$

9-4. Measurement of Power. Power in every phase of a polyphase system can be measured just as it is in a single-phase system, and the meter readings can then be added to give the total power in the system. The connection for the wattmeters with this method is given in Fig. 9-9 for both wye and delta connections. In Fig. 9-9*a*, the wattmeters are designated W_A, W_B, and W_C. In Fig. 9-9*b*, the wattmeters are W_{AC}, W_{CB}, and W_{BA}.

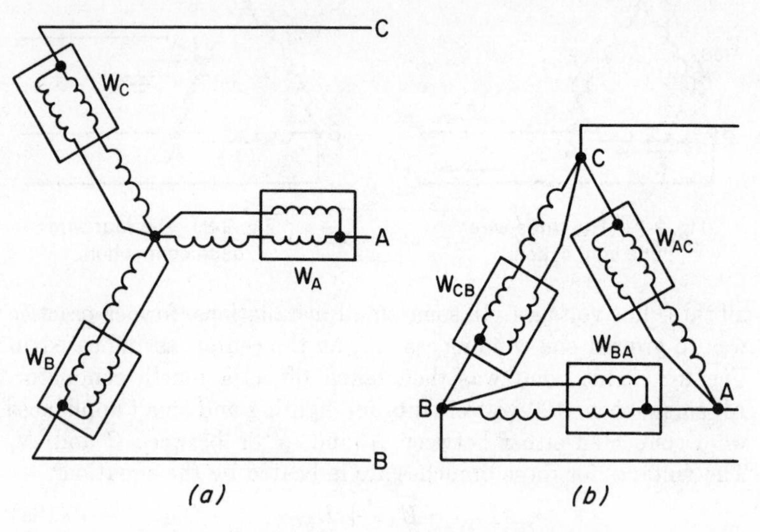

Fig. 9-9. Measurement of three-phase power.

The single-phase measurement of three-phase power is generally unsatisfactory because phase currents and phase voltages cannot be tapped in locations where the power is to be measured. Some power companies simplify their problem by assuming that all currents and voltages are balanced. On the basis of this assumption, they use one single-phase wattmeter connected as shown in

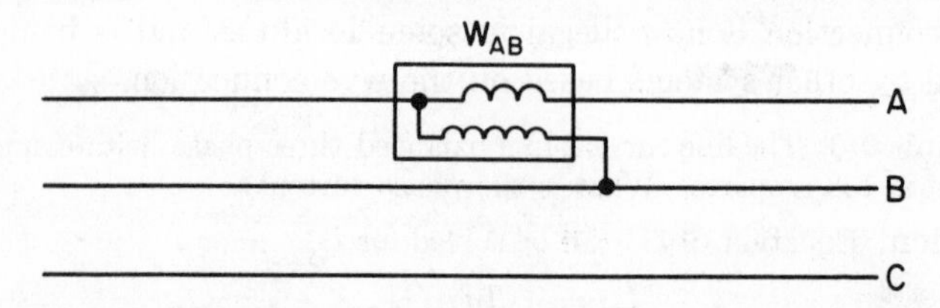

Fig. 9-10. Single-phase measurement of three-phase power.

Fig. 9-10. This meter W_{AB} actually reads the line voltage from phase A to phase B and the line current in phase A. The meter is then calibrated to read the entire power in the three-phase system, although no measurements are taken of conditions in reference to phase C. This method of power measurement can be used for either a wye or a delta system.

As has been shown in Section 8-10, the power in an a-c system is found by the equation

$$P = E_\phi I_\phi \cos \theta \tag{9-20}$$

In applying equation (9-20) to three-phase systems, only phase voltages and currents can be used. Since the phase voltage in a wye and the phase current in a delta are not available except within the generator windings, equation (9-20) cannot be applied directly to three-phase systems.

The total power in a three-phase system is found by multiplying equation (9-20) by 3:

$$P = 3E_\phi I_\phi \cos \theta \tag{9-20a}$$

For the wye connection, the values of E_{LINE} and I_{LINE} can be substituted from equations (9-12) and (9-13) in equation (9-20a). From this substitution the following relationship is obtained:

$$P = \frac{3}{\sqrt{3}} E_{\text{LINE}}\, I_{\text{LINE}} \cos \theta$$

or

$$P = \sqrt{3}\, E_{\text{LINE}}\, I_{\text{LINE}} \cos \theta \tag{9-21a}$$

A similar substitution from equations (9-15) and (9-17) in equation (9-20a) shows that equation (9-21a) applies to both the wye and the delta systems. The wattmeter in Fig. 9-10, therefore, would be calibrated to read $\sqrt{3}$ times the power that actually flows through its windings.

Because most work in polyphase measurements requires line currents and voltages, the subscript *LINE* may be omitted. Equation (9-21a) can therefore be written

$$P = \sqrt{3}\, EI \cos \theta \tag{9-21b}$$

Equation (9-21b) is one of the most important equations in three-phase system studies. The quantity $\sqrt{3}\, EI$ is the so-called "apparent power" and is measured in volt-amperes. The power P is in watts.

Example 9-4. The power in a balanced three-phase system is found to be 10,000 kw (kilowatts, or watts × 1000) when the current is 250 amperes at 33 KV (kilovolts, or volts × 1000). What are the apparent power and the power factor?

Solution. The apparent power is found from the readings of the voltmeter and the ammeter when the system is balanced.

$$VA = \sqrt{3}\,EI = (\sqrt{3})\,(33{,}000)\,(250) = 14{,}300{,}000 \text{ volt-amps}$$

or 14,300 kva (kilovolt-amps)

The power factor, which is equal to the cos θ, is found from equation (9-21b).

$$\text{PF} = \cos\theta = \frac{\text{true power}}{\text{apparent power}} = \frac{P}{\sqrt{3}\,EI} = \frac{10{,}000}{14{,}300} = 0.700$$

Since the power factor is usually expressed as a percentage, the answer is 70.0%.

9-5. The Two-Wattmeter Method of Measuring Three-Phase Power. Not all three-phase systems are balanced. When they are not, the methods of measuring three-phase power already discussed are not sufficiently accurate for use. Perhaps the most accurate method of measuring three-phase power in any system, balanced or unbalanced, is the two-wattmeter method shown in Fig. 9-11.

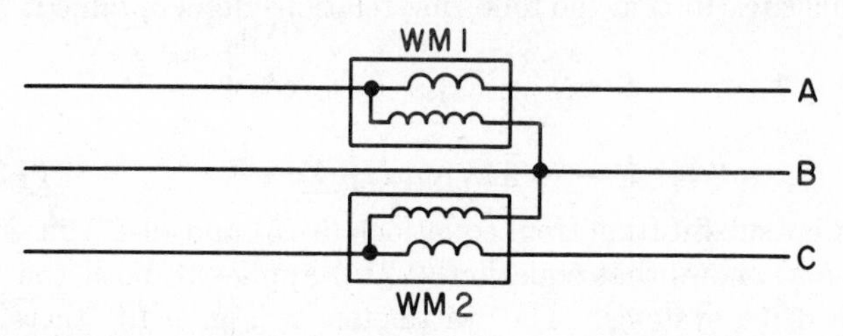

Fig. 9-11. The two-wattmeter method of measuring three-phase power.

In Fig. 9-11, WM1 (wattmeter number 1) reads A-phase current and B-A voltage, while WM2 (wattmeter number 2) reads C-phase current and C-B voltage. If we assume that the voltages E_A, E_B, and E_C are 120 electrical degrees out of phase with each other and that the current in each line lags its respective voltage by an angle θ, the electrical conditions in this three-phase three-wire system are as shown in Fig. 9-12.

The vector diagram for the two-wattmeter connection is shown in Fig. 9-13. Since WM1 is connected to read the voltage from B to A, the vector representing phase voltage E_B is reversed. Wattmeter WM1, therefore, according to Fig. 9-13, reads the quantity

$$P_1 = E_{BA} I_A \cos\,(30° + \theta) \qquad (9\text{-}22)$$

Since WM2 is connected to read the voltage from B to C and the current in C, Fig. 9-13 shows that wattmeter WM 2 reads the quantity

$$P_2 = E_{BC} I_C \cos (30° - \theta) \tag{9-23}$$

The total power in the system is the sum of the two wattmeter readings:

$$P_T = P_1 + P_2 \tag{9-24}$$

Proof that equation (9-24) is true involves adding equations

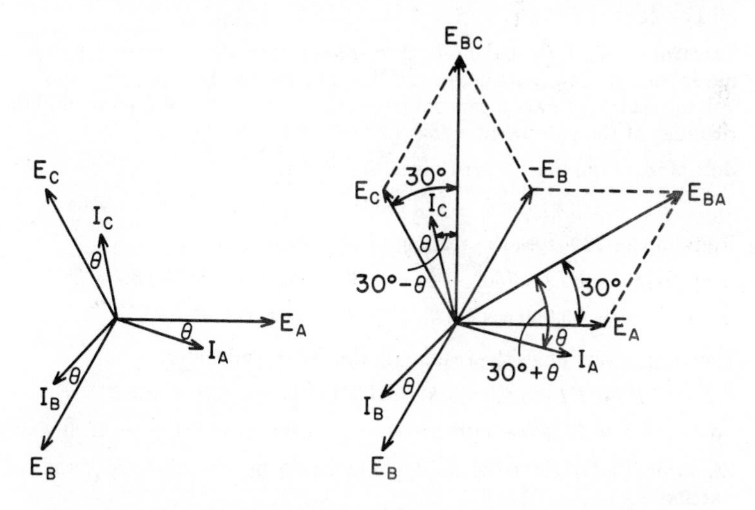

Fig. 9-12. Current and voltage relationships in a three-phase system.

Fig. 9-13. Vector diagram for two-wattmeter power measurement.

(9-22) and (9-23). Since E_{BA} and E_{BC} are both equal to E_{LINE} (or E) and I_A and I_C are equal to I_{LINE} (or I), we can write

$$P_1 + P_2 = EI \cos (30° + \theta) + EI \cos (30° - \theta) \tag{9-25}$$

From trigonometry we learn the following identities:

$$\cos (30° + \theta) = \cos 30° \cos \theta - \sin 30° \sin \theta$$

$$\cos (30° - \theta) = \cos 30° \cos \theta + \sin 30° \sin \theta$$

Adding these two quantities gives the following result:

$$\cos (30° + \theta) + \cos (30° - \theta) = 2 \cos 30° \cos \theta$$

But $\cos 30° = \sqrt{3}/2$, or 0.866. Therefore, the above quantity may be written

$$\cos (30° + \theta) + \cos (30° - \theta) = \sqrt{3} \cos \theta$$

Substituting this value in equation (9-25) gives equation (9-21b) for the total power in a three-phase system.

An examination of equation (9-22) shows that when $\theta = 60°$, $30° + \theta = 90°$, and P_1 is then equal to zero. The power factor when $\theta = 60°$ is equal to 50 per cent ($\cos 60° = 0.500$). Wattmeter WM1, therefore, will give positive readings when the power factor is greater than 50 per cent, zero when the power factor is exactly 50 per cent, and negative when the power factor is less than 50 per cent.

Example 9-5. In a balanced three-phase three-wire system, power is measured by two wattmeters. If the current is 125 amperes and the voltage is 600 volts at 45 per cent power factor, find the total power and the readings of the two wattmeters.

Solution. Equation (9-21b) gives the power.

$$P_T = \sqrt{3}\, EI \cos\theta = \sqrt{3}\,(600)\,(125)\,(0.45) = 58{,}600 \text{ watts}$$

Equation (9-23) gives the reading of one wattmeter.

$$P_2 = EI\cos(30° - \theta) = (600)\,(125)\cos(30° - 63.2°)$$
$$= 75{,}000\cos(-33.2°) = 62{,}800 \text{ watts}$$

Equation (9-22) gives the reading of the other wattmeter.

$$P_1 = EI\cos(30° + \theta) = (600)\,(125)\cos(30° + 63.2°)$$
$$= 75{,}000\cos(93.2°) = -\,75{,}000\cos(86.8°) = -\,4200 \text{ watts}$$

Equation (9-24) gives the total power based on the readings of the two wattmeters.

$$P_T = P_1 + P_2 = 62{,}800 + (-4200) = 62{,}800 - 4200$$
$$= 58{,}600 \text{ watts}$$

9-6. Measurement of Reactive Volt-Amperes. The measurement of reactive volt-amperes (vars) is of extreme importance to a power station. Since a system viewed from the station is always well balanced, sufficiently accurate results can be obtained with a single meter, called a var-meter.

If the current coil of a wattmeter is connected for *A*-phase current and the voltage coil is connected across *B-C* voltage as shown in Fig. 9-14*a*, the meter will read I_A and E_{BC}. At unity power factor, these two quantities are exactly 90° out of phase with each other, since $\theta = 0°$. Under any condition, Fig. 9-14*b* shows that the reading will be

$$R = EI\cos(90° + \theta) \qquad \text{(9-26a)}$$

where R simply means the reading of the meter.

But $\cos(90° + \theta) = \sin(-\theta)$. Therefore,

$$R = -EI \sin \theta \tag{9-27a}$$

Equation (9-27a) is based on Fig. 9-14*b* which shows that the current is lagging the voltage. The negative sign in equation (9-27a) indicates a lagging (or inductive) power factor. If the current leads the voltage, the meter reads

$$R = EI \cos(90° - \theta) \tag{9-26b}$$

But $\cos(90° - \theta) = \sin \theta$. Therefore,

$$\text{Vars} = EI \sin \theta \tag{9-27b}$$

Equation (9-27b) indicates a leading (or capacitive) power factor. Var-meters are supplied with a scale having a zero point at the center and reading plus to the right (for leading power factor) and negative to the left (for lagging power factor). The scale would actually be calibrated to read

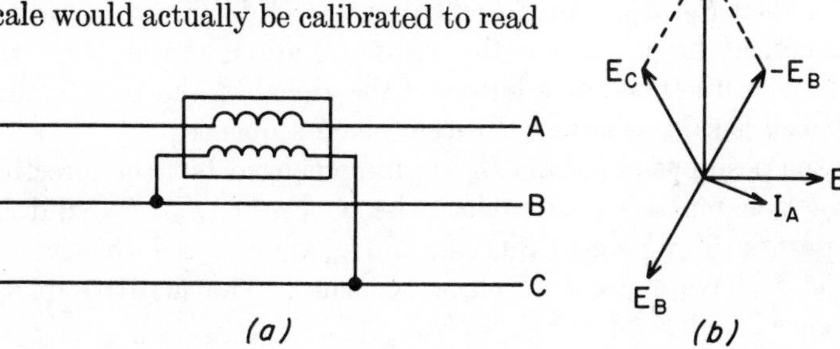

Fig. 9-14. Measuring reactive volt-amperes.

$\sqrt{3}$ times the value obtained by use of equations (9-27a) or (9-27b). Therefore,

$$\text{Total vars} = \pm \sqrt{3} EI \sin \theta \tag{9-28}$$

The reactive volt-amperes can be determined from the readings of the two wattmeters in the two-wattmeter method of measuring power.

$$P_2 - P_1 = EI \cos(30° - \theta) - EI \cos(30° + \theta)$$

Using the trigonometric identities given in Section 9-5, we may transform this equation to read

$$P_2 - P_1 = EI \sin \theta$$

Multiplying this equation by $\sqrt{3}$ gives the following expression:

$$\sqrt{3}(P_2 - P_1) = \sqrt{3} EI \sin \theta \tag{9-28a}$$

The right side of equation (9-28a) is identical with that of equation (9-28). Equation (9-28a), therefore, gives a means of obtaining the reactive volt-amperes—and, of course, the power factor—directly from the readings of the two wattmeters.

Example 9-6. Find the reactive volt-amperes of the system in Example 9-5.

Solution. From equation (9-28) we obtain the reactive volt-amperes.

$$\text{Vars} = -\sqrt{3}EI \sin\theta = -\sqrt{3}\,(600)\,(125) \sin 63.2° = -116{,}000 \text{ vars}$$

The negative sign indicates a lagging power factor. As a check, the vars and power (watts) should add vectorially to equal the volt-amperes.

$$VA = \sqrt{3}EI = 130{,}000 \text{ volt-amps}$$

$$VA = \overline{P} + \overline{\text{vars}} = 58{,}600 - j116{,}000 = 130{,}000 \text{ volt-amps}$$

9-7. Phase Sequence. If the vectors in Fig. 9-6*a* are assumed to rotate counterclockwise and the position of E_A is considered to be 0°, then E_A, E_B, and E_C will pass the 0° reference in proper alphabetical order. Since the phase rotation agrees with the sequence of the first three letters of the alphabet, the system thus described is said to have a positive phase sequence.

If the positions of E_B and E_C are interchanged but the direction of rotation remains counterclockwise as before, E_A, E_C, and E_B will pass the 0° reference. Since E_C and E_B are reversed, this system is said to have a negative phase sequence. The negative phase sequence is indicated in Fig. 9-15*a*.

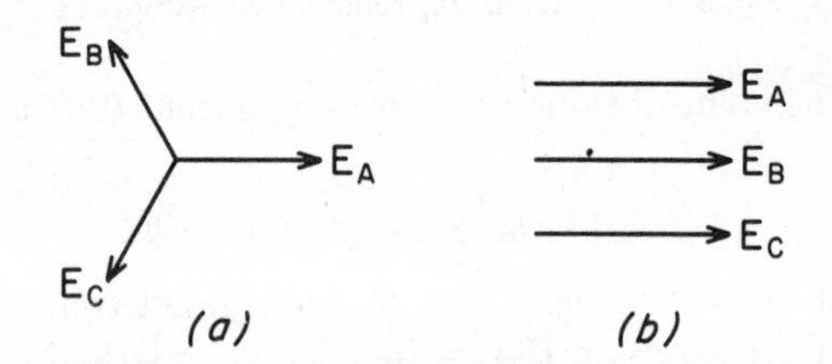

Fig. 9-15. Negative and zero phase sequence.

If E_A, E_B, and E_C are all in phase with each other, their vectors assume the positions indicated in Fig. 9-15*b*. If these voltages were the only ones present in a three-phase four-wire wye-connected system, they would produce a current in the neutral conductor equal numerically to the sum of the three line currents. Because all three voltages differ in phase by 0° (all are in phase), this system is said to have a zero phase sequence.

Even in a system that is designed as a positive phase sequence system, voltages of all three sequences may be present at the same time. Zero phase sequence voltages are very large when the system has a ground fault. Any unbalanced system can be shown to contain voltages of all three sequences. As will be shown in Section 9-8, harmonic currents and voltages also cause all three voltages and currents to be present.

9-8. Harmonics in a Three-Phase System. Just as in single-phase a-c systems, three-phase voltages and currents can be written in the sine wave form. Using Fig. 9-6*a* as a guide, we may write the voltage equations in the following form:

$$E_A = E_m \sin \omega t \tag{9-29a}$$

$$E_B = E_m \sin (\omega t + 240°) \tag{9-29b}$$

$$E_C = E_m \sin (\omega t + 120°) \tag{9-29c}$$

Equations of the currents corresponding to these voltages have the same form except that the phase angle θ appears:

$$I_A = I_m \sin (\omega t - \theta) \tag{9-30a}$$

$$I_B = I_m \sin (\omega t + 240 - \theta) \tag{9-30b}$$

$$I_C = I_m \sin (\omega t + 120 - \theta) \tag{9-30c}$$

In power systems, generators are designed so that positive and negative alternations of both current and voltage waves have the same shape. Therefore, only odd harmonics need be considered in any power system. (Even harmonics are present in electronic circuits which are single phase circuits.)

The first odd harmonic voltage is the third harmonic. If the angles in equations (9-29a), (9-29b), and (9-29c) are multiplied by 3, these equations become

$$E_{3A} = E_{3m} \sin 3\,\omega t \tag{9-31a}$$

$$\begin{aligned} E_{3B} &= E_{3m} \sin 3(\omega t + 240) = E_{3m} \sin (3\,\omega t + 720) \\ &= E_{3m} \sin 3\,\omega t \end{aligned} \tag{9-31b}$$

$$\begin{aligned} E_{3C} &= E_{3m} \sin 3(\omega t + 120) = E_{3m} \sin (3\,\omega t + 360) \\ &= E_{3m} \sin 3\,\omega t \end{aligned} \tag{9-31c}$$

Equations (9-31a), (9-31b), and (9-31c) show that the third harmonic voltages are all in phase (zero phase sequence). In these equations, the figure "3" in the subscripts indicates third harmonic voltage values.

If the angles in equations (9-29a), (9-29b), and (9-29c) are multiplied by 5, the equations are converted to fifth harmonic voltages:

$$E_{5A} = E_{5m} \sin 5\,\omega t \tag{9-32a}$$

$$E_{5B} = E_{5m} \sin 5(\omega t + 240) = E_{5m} \sin (5\,\omega t + 1200)$$
$$= E_{5m} \sin (5\,\omega t + 120) \tag{9-32b}$$

$$E_{5C} = E_{5m} \sin 5(\omega t + 120) = E_{5m} \sin (5\,\omega t + 600)$$
$$= E_{5m} \sin (5\,\omega t + 240) \tag{9-32c}$$

Equations (9-32a), (9-32b), and (9-32c) show that phases B and C are reversed for fifth harmonic voltages (negative phase sequence).

If the angles are multiplied by 7, the equations are converted to seventh harmonic voltages:

$$E_{7A} = E_{7m} \sin 7\,\omega t \tag{9-33a}$$

$$E_{7B} = E_{7m} \sin 7(\omega t + 240) = E_{7m} \sin (7\,\omega t + 240) \tag{9-33b}$$

$$E_{7C} = E_{7m} \sin 7(\omega t + 120) = E_{7m} \sin (7\,\omega t + 120) \tag{9-33c}$$

The seventh harmonic voltages have the same sequence as the fundamental voltages (positive phase sequence).

The phase sequence of higher harmonics rotates in the same manner as those already considered. All triple harmonics (third, ninth, etc.) have zero phase sequence. The fifth, eleventh, etc., harmonic voltages have negative phase sequence. Seventh, thirteenth, etc., harmonic voltages have positive phase sequence.

9-9. Voltage Drop in Three-Phase Systems. A metallic transmission line (wires or cables) consists of two or more cables which are approximately parallel to each other and which are separated by an insulator or dielectric. Overhead transmission lines are separated by air and underground lines are separated by the insulation around the conductor. A transmission line, therefore, is in effect a giant capacitor whose capacitance is proportional to the length of the line.

A transmission line conducts current in two directions at the same time and, in effect, is a giant one-turn coil of wire whose inductance is proportional to the length of the line. The inductance—and sometimes the capacitance—of a transmission line, therefore, must be considered in addition to the resistance in computing the voltage drop in a line if the line is more than 2 miles in length. For shorter lines, the capacitance can be neglected.

The vector diagram for short transmission lines less than 40 miles in length looks much like the diagram for any other electrical equipment. The resistance voltage drop IR in the line is added vectorially to the inductive reactance voltage drop IX to equal the actual line voltage drop IZ. This relationship is shown in

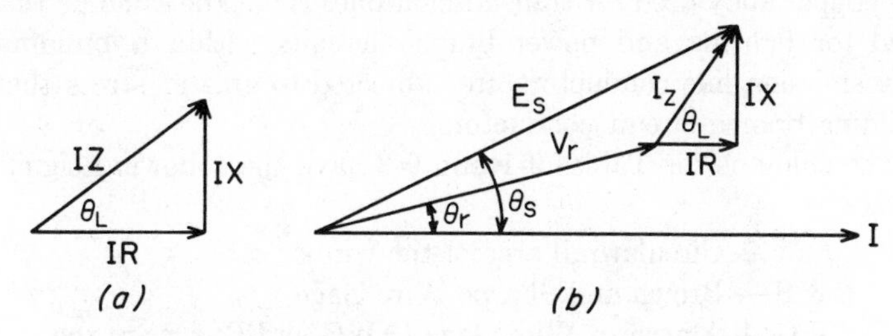

Fig. 9-16. Voltage drop in short transmission line.

Fig. 9-16*a*. The IZ drop is then added to the receiving end phase voltage V_r to obtain the sending end phase voltage E_S. If the load has a lagging power factor, the current I lags the receiving end voltage by the angle θ_r and therefore lags the sending end voltage by the angle θ_S. These vector relationships are shown in Fig. 9-16*b*.

From Fig. 9-16*b* we can write the relationship

$$\overline{E_S} = \overline{V_r} + \overline{IZ} \tag{9-34}$$

Equation (9-34) is a vector equation which can also be written in the following form:

$$E_S \underline{/ \theta_S} = V_r \underline{/ \theta_r} + IZ \underline{/ \theta_L} \tag{9-35}$$

The angle θ_L is the power factor angle of the line.

The magnitude of the sending end voltage, therefore, can be determined from the equation

$$E_S = \sqrt{(V_r \cos \theta_r)^2 + (V_r \sin \theta_r \pm IX)^2} \tag{9-36}$$

In equation (9-36), the quantity IX is positive if X is predominantly inductive and negative if X is predominantly capacitive. The phase angle θ_S can be determined from the equation

$$\theta_S = \tan^{-1} \frac{V_r \sin \theta \pm IX}{V_r \cos \theta + IR} \tag{9-37}$$

The reactance of a line depends on the length and spacing of the line as well as on the circular mil area of the conductors. Tables

9-1, 9-2, 9-3, and 9-4 give the appropriate values for cable sizes generally used for transmitting power. Table 9-1 is for hard drawn copper conductors of 97.3 per cent conductivity. Table 9-2 is for aluminum cable steel reinforced. Values of resistance in these tables do not generally agree with those given previously because the copper alloy used for transmission lines is not the same as that used for lighting and power branch circuits within a building. Transmission line conductors are subjected to greater stress than building branch circuit conductors.

The columns for Tables 9-1 and 9-2 have the following significance:

CM — Circular mil area of the wire or cable.
B & S — Brown and Sharpe Wire Gage.
AWG — American Wire Gage (AWG and B & S are the same).
Capacity — Current carrying capacity in amperes.
x'_a — Shunt capacitive reactance at 1 foot spacing in megohms per mile.
r_a — Resistance in ohms per conductor per mile at 50° C.
x_a — Inductive reactance at 1 foot spacing in ohms per conductor per mile.

Table 9-3 is based on the values of inductive reactance to be added to or subtracted from x_a when the spacing between conductors is greater or less than one foot. Table 9-4 is based on the values of capacitive reactance to be added to or subtracted from x'_a when the spacing is greater or less than one foot.

For a given spacing of conductors and length of line, the inductive reactance is found from the equation

$$x_L = L(x_a + x_d) \tag{9-38}$$

where L is the length of the line in miles, and x_a and x_d are values taken from Table 9-1 (or Table 9-2) and Table 9-3. The value x_L is the total inductive reactance of the line.

The capacitive reactance for the same condition is

$$x_C = \frac{(x'_a + x'_d)\ 1{,}000{,}000}{L} \tag{9-39}$$

where L is the length of the line in miles, and x'_a and x'_d are values taken from Table 9-1 (or Table 9-2) and Table 9-4. The value x_C is the total capacitive reactance of the line.

The resistance does not depend on the spacing. For a given

Table 9-1. Characteristics of Copper Conductors

(Conductors at 75° C; air at 25° C; wind 1.4 mph or 2 fps; frequency 60 cycles.)

CM	B & S or AWG	Capacity, amperes	x_a' *	r_a †	x_a ‡
1,000,000	....	1,300	0.0901	0.0685	0.400
900,000	....	1,220	.0916	.0752	.406
800,000	....	1,130	.0934	.0837	.413
750,000	....	1,090	.0943	.0888	.417
700,000	....	1,040	.0954	.0947	.422
600,000	....	940	.0977	.109	.432
500,000	....	840	.1004	.130	.443
450,000	....	780	.1020	.144	.451
400,000	....	730	.1038	.162	.458
350,000	....	670	.1058	.184	.466
300,000	....	610	.1080	.215	.476
250,000	....	540	.1108	.257	.487
211,600	4/0	480	.1136	.303	.503
167,800	3/0	420	.1171	.382	.518
133,100	2/0	360	.1205	.481	.532
105,500	1/0	310	.1240	.607	.546
83,690	1	270	.1274	.765	.560
66,370	2	240	.1281	.955	.571
52,630	3	200	.1315	1.20	.585
41,740	4	180	.1349	1.52	.599
33,100	5	150	.1384	1.91	.613
26,250	6	120	.1483	2.39	.637
20,800	7	110	.1517	3.01	.651
16,510	8	90	1552	3.80	.665

* x_a' – Shunt capacitive reactance at 1 foot spacing in megohms per mile.
† r_a – Resistance in ohms per conductor per mile at 50° C.
‡ x_a – Inductive reactance at 1 foot spacing in ohms per conductor per mile.

Courtesy of Westinghouse Electric Corporation.

length L of the line in miles, the resistance is simply

$$R = Lr_a \tag{9-40}$$

where L is the length of the line in miles, and r_a is the resistance value from Table 9-1 (or Table 9-2). The value R is the total resistance of the line. In equations (9-38), (9-39), and (9-40), x_L, x_C, and R are in ohms for the total length of the line.

Tables 9-1, 9-2, 9-3, and 9-4 are based on symmetrical spacing of the conductors. If the spacing between conductors is not symmetrical, the effective spacing can be taken as the cube root of the product of the three spacings for a three-phase transmission line.

Table 9-2. Characteristics of Aluminum Cable Steel Reinforced (ACSR) (Conductor at 75° C; air at 25° C; wind 1.4 mph or 2 fps; frequency 60 cycles.)

Size of Conductor CM or AWG	Copper Equivalent CM or AWG	Capacity, amperes	x_a' *	r_a †	x_a ‡
1,590,000	1,000,000	1,380	0.0814	.0684	.359
1,510,000	950,000	1,340	.0821	.0720	.362
1,431,000	900,000	1,300	.0830	.0760	.365
1,351,000	850,000	1,250	.0838	.0803	.369
1,272,000	800,000	1,200	.0847	.0851	.372
1,192,500	750,000	1,160	.0857	.0906	.376
1,113,000	700,000	1,110	.0867	.0969	.380
1,033,500	650,000	1,060	.0878	.104	.385
954,000	600,000	1,010	.0890	.113	.390
900,000	566,000	970	.0898	.119	.393
874,500	550,000	950	.0903	.123	.395
795,000	500,000	900	.0917	.138	.401
666,000	419,000	800	.0943	.160	.412
636,000	400,000	770	.0950	.169	.414
605,000	380,500	750	.0957	.178	.417
556,500	350,000	730	.0965	.186	.420
477,000	300,000	670	.0988	.216	.430
397,500	250,000	590	.1015	.259	.441
336,400	4/0	530	.1039	.306	.451
266,800	3/0	460	.1074	.385	.465
4/0	2/0	340	.1113	.592	.581
3/0	1/0	300	.1147	.723	.621
2/0	1	270	.1182	.895	.641
1/0	2	230	.1216	1.12	.656
1	3	200	.1250	1.38	.665
2	4	180	.1285	1.69	.665
4	6	140	.1355	2.57	.659

* x_a' – Shunt capacitive reactance at 1 foot spacing in megohms per mile.

† r_a – Resistance in ohms per conductor per mile at 50° C.

‡ x_a – Inductive reactance at 1 foot spacing in ohms per conductor per mile.

Courtesy of Westinghouse Electric Corporation.

Table 9-3. Inductive Reactance Spacing Factors
(Bar over number indicates negative value.)

x_d – Separation, Feet

Feet	0	1	2	3	4	5	6	7	8	9
0	....	0	.084	.133	.168	.195	.217	.236	.252	.267
10	.279	.291	.302	.311	.320	.329	.336	.344	.351	.357
20	.364	.369	.375	.380	.386	.391	.395	.400	.404	.409
30	.413	.417	.421	.424	.428	.431	.435	.438	.441	.445

x_d – Separation, Inches

In.	0	1	2	3	4	5	6	7	8	9
0	....	$\overline{.302}$	$\overline{.217}$	$\overline{.169}$	$\overline{.134}$	$\overline{.107}$	$\overline{.085}$	$\overline{.066}$	$\overline{.050}$	$\overline{.035}$
10	$\overline{.023}$	$\overline{.011}$	0	.010	.019	.027	.035	.042	.049	.056
20	.062	.068	.074	.079	.084	.089	.094	.098	.103	.107
30	.111	.115	.119	.123	.126	.130	.133	.137	.140	.143
40	.146	.149	.152	.155	.158	.160	.163	.166	.168	.171

Courtesy of Westinghouse Electric Corporation.

Example 9-7. A 60-cycle transmission line 26 miles in length consists of three conductors in a vertical arrangement. The spacing between adjacent conductors is 3 feet from A to B, 3 feet from B to C, and 6 feet from C to A. The power factor of the load is 75 per cent. If the voltage across the load is 100,000 volts at a current of 100 amperes, and No. 4/0 aluminum cable steel reinforced (ACSR) is used, find (a) the voltage at the sending end of the line, and (b) the power loss in the line.

Solution. The resistance r_a of 4/0 ACSR cable as given in Table 9-2 is 0.592 ohm per mile. The total resistance is obtained by use of equation (9-40).

$$R = Lr_a = (26)(0.592) = 15.4 \text{ ohms}$$

The effective spacing of the conductors is found by extracting the cube root of the product of the three actual spacings.

$$\text{Spacing} = \sqrt[3]{(3)(3)(6)} = 3\sqrt[3]{2} = (3)(1.26) = 3.78 \text{ ft}$$

The inductive reactance is found from Tables 9-2 and 9-3. Since 3.78 feet is approximately 3 feet 9.35 inches, or 45.35 inches, we use the value 0.581 ohm from Table 9-2 for one-foot spacing and add a value from Table 9-3 to obtain the total inductive reactance in accordance with equation (9-38).

At 45 inches the inductive reactance is 0.160 ohm, and at 46 inches the inductive reactance is 0.163 ohm. The value for this line is, therefore,

$$x_d = 0.160 + (0.35)(0.003) = 0.161 \text{ ohm}$$

The total inductive reactance, therefore, is

$$x_L = L(x_a + x_d) = 26(0.581 + 0.161) = 26(0.742) = 19.3 \text{ ohms}$$

Table 9-4. Capacitive Reactance Spacing Factors

(Bar over number indicates negative value.)

x_d' – Separation, Feet

Feet	0	1	2	3	4	5	6	7	8	9
0	....	0	.0206	.0326	.0411	.0478	.0532	.0577	.0617	.0652
10	.0683	.0711	.0737	.0761	.0783	.0804	.0823	.0841	.0858	.0874
20	.0889	.0903	.0917	.0930	.0943	.0955	.0967	.0978	.0989	.0999
30	.1010	.1020	.1030	.1040	.1050	.1060	.1060	.1070	.1080	.1090

x_d' – Separation, Inches

In.	0	1	2	3	4	5	6	7	8	9
0	....	$\overline{.0737}$	$\overline{.0532}$	$\overline{.0411}$	$\overline{.0326}$	$\overline{.0260}$	$\overline{.0206}$	$\overline{.0160}$	$\overline{.0120}$	$\overline{.009}$
10	$\overline{.0050}$	$\overline{.0030}$	0	.0023	.0045	.0066	.0085	.0103	.0120	.0136
20	.0151	.0166	.0180	.0193	.0206	.0218	.0229	.0240	.0251	.0262
30	.0272	.0281	.0291	.0300	.0309	.0317	.0326	.0334	.0342	.0349
40	.0357	.0364	.0371	.0378	.0385	.0392	.0398	.0405	.0411	.0417

Courtesy of Westinghouse Electric Corporation.

The capacitive reactance can be found in a similar manner from Tables 9-2 and 9-4 and equation (9-39).

$$x_C = \frac{(x_a' + x_d')\,1{,}000{,}000}{L}$$

$$= \frac{0.1113 + 0.0392 + (0.0006)\,(0.35)}{26}\,(1{,}000{,}000)$$

$$= \frac{(0.1113 + 0.0394)\,(1{,}000{,}000)}{26} = 5800 \text{ ohms}$$

Since this reactance is across the line, the current flowing through it is a charging current and not the 100-ampere load current. This charging current is found from the equation

$$I_C = \frac{E_S}{x_C} \tag{9-41}$$

where E_S is the phase voltage at the sending end of the line and x_C is the capacitive reactance. The value of E_S for this line is not known, but the charging current can be estimated by assuming a value for E_S such as 15 per cent higher than the receiving end phase voltage. This estimate is, therefore,

$$I_C = \frac{(100{,}000)\,(1.15)}{(\sqrt{3})\,(5800)} = 1.4 \text{ amps}$$

Since the charging current is such a small fraction of the line current, capacitive reactance can be neglected. The sending end voltage can therefore be found from equation (9-36), using the resistance and inductive reactance of the line. Since $\cos \theta_r = 0.75$, $\theta_r = 41.5°$. The phase voltage V_r is $100{,}000/\sqrt{3}$, or 57,700 volts.

$$E_S = \sqrt{(V_r \cos \theta_r + IR)^2 + (V_r \sin \theta_r + IX)^2}$$

$$= \sqrt{[(57{,}700)(0.75) + (100)(15.4)]^2 + [(57{,}700)(0.662) + (100)(19.3)]^2}$$

$$= \sqrt{(43{,}300 + 1504)^2 + (38{,}300 + 1930)^2}$$

$$= \sqrt{(44{,}804)^2 + (40{,}230)^2} = 60{,}300 \text{ volts}$$

The line voltage at the sending end is, therefore,

$$E_S = (60{,}300)(\sqrt{3}) = 104{,}500 \text{ volts}$$

This value can be checked directly from Fig. 9-16. The resistance loss IR is found to be

$$IR = (100)(15.4) = 1540 \text{ volts}$$

The inductive reactance voltage drop is

$$IX = (100)(19.3) = 1930 \text{ volts}$$

The power component of the load is

$$V_r \cos \theta_r = (57{,}700)(0.75) = 43{,}300 \text{ volts}$$

The reactive component of the load is

$$V_r \sin \theta_r = (57{,}700)(0.662) = 38{,}300 \text{ volts}$$

$$\overline{V}_r = (43{,}300 + 1540) + j(38{,}300 + 1930)$$
$$= 44{,}840 + j\,40{,}230 = 60{,}300 \underline{/42°} \text{ volts}$$

The power loss in the line is simply the I^2R value for the line. Since there are three lines in a three-phase system, the power loss is

$$P_L = 3I^2R = (3)(100)^2(15.4) = 462{,}000 \text{ watts}$$

This answer can be checked. The total power taken by the load is

$$P_r = \sqrt{3}\,VI \cos \theta_r = \sqrt{3}\,(100{,}000)(100)(0.75) = 13{,}010{,}000 \text{ watts}$$

The power at the sending end of the line is

$$P_S = \sqrt{3}\,EI \cos \theta_S = \sqrt{3}\,(104{,}500)(100)(0.745) = 13{,}470{,}000 \text{ watts}$$

The difference between P_S and P_r is the line loss:

$$P_L = P_S - P_r = 13{,}470{,}000 - 13{,}010{,}000 = 460{,}000 \text{ watts}$$

9-10. Unbalanced Delta-Connected System. Although large power systems are kept balanced by design and operation, a smaller system or subsystem may be unbalanced. Even such an unbalanced system will usually be fed by balanced voltages, the unbalance being in the magnitude and phase relations of the currents in the line and in the phase windings or load.

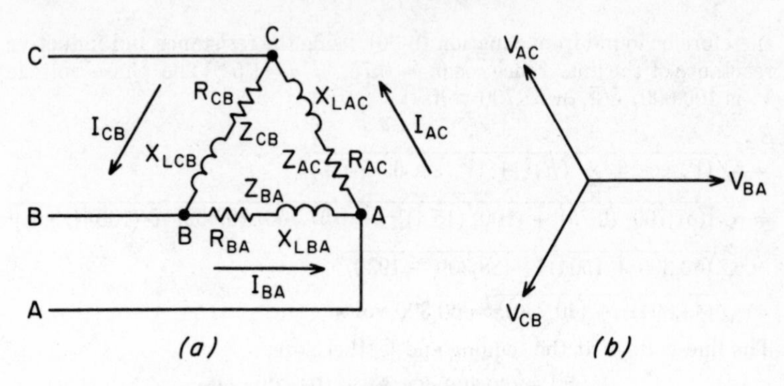

Fig. 9-17. Unbalanced delta-connected system.

An unbalanced delta-connected system is shown in Fig. 9-17. The loading is shown schematically in Fig. 9-17*a* where R_{AC}, R_{CB}, and R_{BA} are the load resistances which may or may not be equal, and X_{LAC}, X_{LCB}, and X_{LBA} are the load reactances which may or may not be equal.

Even in an unbalanced delta system, the following line current relationships are true by Kirchhoff's laws:

$$\bar{I}_A + \bar{I}_B + \bar{I}_C = 0 \tag{9-42}$$

but

$$\bar{I}_{AC} + \bar{I}_{CB} + \bar{I}_{BA} \neq 0^{\ddagger} \tag{9-43}$$

Equation (9-42) refers to the vector relationship of line currents and equation (9-43) refers to the vector relationship of phase currents. The values of the phase currents can be determined from Fig. 9-17*a*.

$$I_{AC} = \frac{V_{AC}}{Z_{AC}} \tag{9-44a}$$

$$I_{CB} = \frac{V_{CB}}{Z_{CB}} \tag{9-44b}$$

$$I_{BA} = \frac{V_{BA}}{Z_{BA}} \tag{9-44c}$$

From the same figure, the line currents are found to be

$$\bar{I}_A = \bar{I}_{BA} - \bar{I}_{AC} \tag{9-45a}$$

$$\bar{I}_B = \bar{I}_{CB} - \bar{I}_{BA} \tag{9-45b}$$

‡ Although the sum of the line currents in an unbalanced delta-connected three-phase system equals zero in accordance with equation (9-42), the sum of the phase currents is not equal to zero, as the symbol ≠ in equation (9-43) indicates.

$$\bar{I}_C = \bar{I}_{AC} - \bar{I}_{CB} \qquad (9\text{-}45c)$$

Equations (9-45a), (9-45b), and (9-45c) show vector relationships.

Since Z_{AC}, Z_{CB}, and Z_{BA} are not equal in magnitude or direction, the currents and voltages in the three phases are out of phase by the unequal angles θ_{AC}, θ_{CB}, and θ_{BA}. The power factor of this load, therefore, is merely a ratio between the apparent power and the true power and does not represent the cosine of an actual angle of lead or lag. However, for convenience, it is customary, even in an unbalanced system, to refer to "power factor angle" and "cos θ." Thus, the angle θ in an unbalanced system is considered to be in the nature of a composite or effective power factor angle.

Example 9-8. The impedances in a delta-connected load are $Z_{AC} = 3 + j5$, $Z_{CB} = 4 - j3$, and $Z_{BA} = 3 + j3$. If the voltages across the loads are balanced and are equal to 480 volts, find the three phase currents, the three line currents, the angles of lead or lag, the total power, and the power factor.

Solution. Since the voltages are balanced, their values are

$$\bar{V}_{BA} = 480 \underline{/0^\circ} \text{ volts}$$

$$\bar{V}_{AC} = 480 \underline{/120^\circ} \text{ volts}$$

$$\bar{V}_{CB} = 480 \underline{/240^\circ} \text{ volts}$$

The three impedances are

$$\bar{Z}_{AC} = 3 + j5 = 5.83 \underline{/59^\circ} \text{ ohms}$$

$$\bar{Z}_{CB} = 4 - j3 = 5 \underline{/-36.7^\circ} \text{ ohms}$$

$$\bar{Z}_{BA} = 3 + j3 = 4.25 \underline{/45^\circ} \text{ ohms}$$

The phase currents are found by use of equations (9-44a), (9-44b), and (9-44c):

$$I_{AC} = \frac{V_{AC}}{Z_{AC}} = \frac{480 \underline{/120^\circ}}{5.83 \underline{/59^\circ}} = 82.3 \underline{/61^\circ} \text{ amps}$$

$$I_{CB} = \frac{V_{CB}}{Z_{CB}} = \frac{480 \underline{/240^\circ}}{5 \underline{/-36.7^\circ}} = 96 \underline{/276.7^\circ} \text{ amps}$$

$$I_{BA} = \frac{V_{BA}}{Z_{BA}} = \frac{480 \underline{/0^\circ}}{4.25 \underline{/45^\circ}} = 113 \underline{/-45^\circ} \text{ amps}$$

The three line currents are found by use of equations (9-45a), (9-45b), and (9-45c).

$$\begin{aligned}\bar{I}_A = \bar{I}_{BA} - \bar{I}_{AC} &= 113 \underline{/-45^\circ} - 82.3 \underline{/61^\circ} \\ &= (79.9 - j79.9) - (40 + j72) = 39.9 - j151.9 \\ &= 157 \underline{/-75.4^\circ} \text{ amps}\end{aligned}$$

$$\bar{I}_B = \bar{I}_{CB} - \bar{I}_{BA} = 96 \underline{/276.7°} - 113 \underline{/-45°}$$
$$= (11.2 - j95) - (79.9 - j79.9)$$
$$= -68.7 - j15.1 = 70 \underline{/192.4°} \text{ amps}$$
$$\bar{I}_C = \bar{I}_{AC} - \bar{I}_{CB} = 82.3 \underline{/61°} - 96 \underline{/276.7°}$$
$$= (40 + j72) - (11.2 - j95)$$
$$= 28.8 + j167 = 169 \underline{/80.2°} \text{ amps}$$

The angles of lead or lag are

Between V_{AC} and I_{AC}: $120° - 61° = 59°$

Between V_{CB} and I_{CB}: $240° - 276.7° = -36.7°$

Between V_{BA} and I_{BA}: $0° - (-45°) = 45°$

Between V_{AC} and I_C: $120° - 80.2° = 39.8°$

Between V_{CB} and I_B: $240° - 192.4° = 47.6°$

Between V_{BA} and I_A: $0° - (-75.4°) = 75.4°$

The total power is found by calculating the I^2R for every phase:

$$P_{AC} = I_{AC}^2 R_{AC} = (82.3)^2 (3) = 20{,}200 \text{ watts}$$
$$P_{CB} = I_{CB}^2 R_{CB} = (96)^2 (4) = 37{,}000 \text{ watts}$$
$$P_{BA} = I_{BA}^2 R_{BA} = (113)^2 (3) = 38{,}400 \text{ watts}$$

The total apparent power is found by calculating the I^2Z or VA for every phase:

$$VA_{AC} = I_{AC}^2 Z_{AC} = (82.3)^2 (5.83) = 39{,}400 \text{ volt-amps}$$
$$VA_{CB} = I_{CB}^2 Z_{CB} = (96)^2 (5) = 46{,}100 \text{ volt-amps}$$
$$VA_{BA} = I_{BA}^2 Z_{BA} = (113)^2 (4.25) = 54{,}200 \text{ volt-amps}$$

or

$$VA_{AC} = V_{AC} I_{AC} = (480)(82.3) = 39{,}400 \text{ volt-amps}$$
$$VA_{CB} = V_{CB} I_{CB} = (480)(96) = 46{,}100 \text{ volt-amps}$$
$$VA_{BA} = V_{BA} I_{BA} = (480)(113) = 54{,}200 \text{ volt-amps}$$

The power in the three phases can be represented in terms of the volt-amperes and the cosine of the power factor angle.

$$P_{AC} = 39{,}400 \cos 59° = 20{,}200 \text{ watts}$$
$$P_{CB} = 46{,}100 \cos(-36.7°) = 37{,}000 \text{ watts}$$
$$P_{BA} = 54{,}200 \cos 45° = 38{,}300 \text{ watts}$$

The reactive volt-amperes in the three phases can be represented in terms of the volt-amperes and the sine of the power factor angle.

$$\text{Vars}_{AC} = 39{,}400 \sin 59° = 33{,}800 \text{ vars}$$
$$\text{Vars}_{CB} = 46{,}100 \sin(-36.7°) = -27{,}600 \text{ vars}$$
$$\text{Vars}_{BA} = 54{,}200 \sin 45° = 38{,}300 \text{ vars}$$

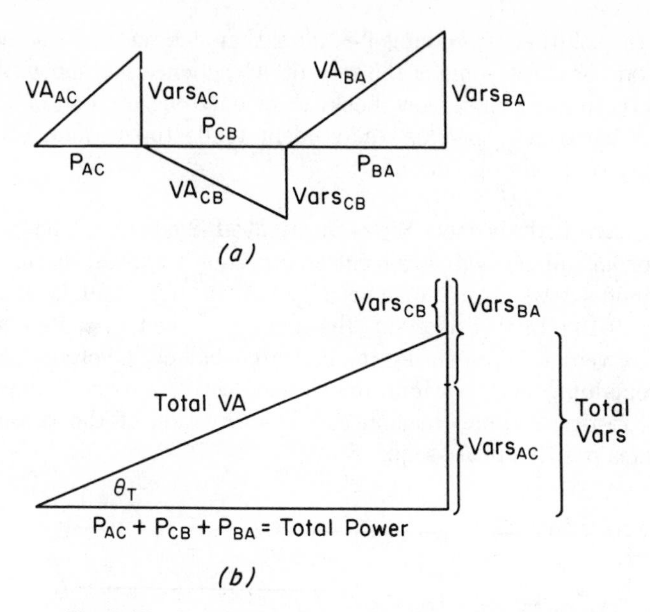

Fig. 9-18. Total volt-amperes in a three-phase system.

The vars can be added together and the power can be added together, and from their total values the total volt-amperes can be determined. The volt-amperes of apparent power cannot be found by direct algebraic addition. The vector relationships are shown in Fig. 9-18. Fig. 9-18*a* shows the power, vars, and volt-amperes as they are drawn for vector addition. Fig. 9-18*b* shows all the power components added together and all the vars components added together. The method of addition is indicated in the figure. The three quantities—power, vars, and volt-amperes—are added vectorially because they have magnitude and position, although they are not vectors because they do not have direction.

The total power is

$$P_T = 20{,}200 + 37{,}000 + 38{,}300 = 95{,}500 \text{ watts}$$

The total vars are

$$\text{Vars}_T = 33{,}800 + 38{,}300 - 27{,}600 = 44{,}500 \text{ vars}$$

The total apparent power is

$$VA_T = \sqrt{(95{,}500)^2 + (44{,}500)^2} = 105{,}500 \text{ volt-amps}$$

The power factor angle is

$$\cos\theta = \frac{\text{true power}}{\text{apparent power}} = \frac{95{,}500}{105{,}500} = 0.905$$

$$\theta = 25^\circ$$

The power factor is 90.5%.

In the solution of Example 9-8, more than one method was used to obtain or check some of the results. Experience has shown that when textbooks or reference books show only one method of solution of electrical problems, the student tends to overlook other, possibly more simple, methods.

9-11. An Unbalanced Wye-Connected System. The solution of an unbalanced wye-connected system requires the use of Kirchhoff's laws. An unbalanced system of this kind is shown in Fig. 9-19. In this diagram, the arrows marked V_{CA}, V_{BC}, and V_{AB} are vectors representing the indicated balanced voltages, and the remaining symbols indicate the respective currents, impedances, resistances, and reactances. The direction of the voltages indicates positive phase sequence.

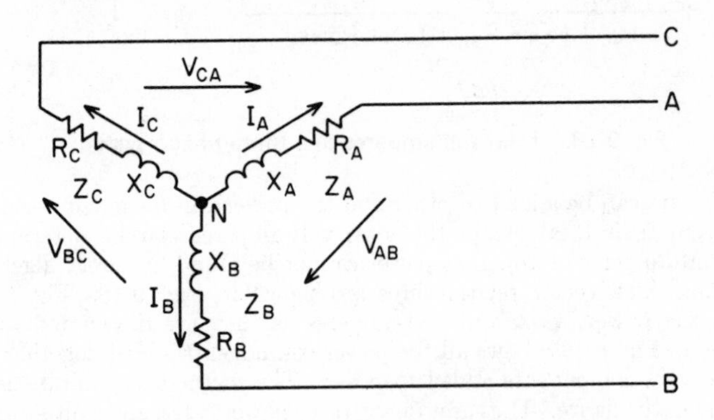

Fig. 9-19. An unbalanced wye-connected system.

The five Kirchhoff's law equations are as follows:

$$\bar{I}_A + \bar{I}_B + \bar{I}_C = 0 \tag{9-46}$$

$$\overline{V}_{CA} + \overline{V}_{BC} + \overline{V}_{AB} = 0 \tag{9-47}$$

$$\overline{V}_{CA} = \bar{I}_A Z_A - \bar{I}_C Z_C \tag{9-48}$$

$$\overline{V}_{BC} = \bar{I}_C Z_C - \bar{I}_B Z_B \tag{9-49}$$

$$\overline{V}_{AB} = \bar{I}_B Z_B - \bar{I}_A Z_A \tag{9-50}$$

The solution of these equations will give the magnitude and phase relations of the three line currents and the three phase voltages.

The currents can most easily be solved by use of equations (9-47), (9-48), and (9-49) by the method of determinants.

The determinant D of the denominator of the solution is

$$D = \begin{vmatrix} 1 & 1 & 1 \\ Z_A & 0 & -Z_C \\ 0 & -Z_B & Z_C \end{vmatrix} = (Z_A)(-Z_B) - Z_A Z_C - (-Z_C)(-Z_B)$$

$$= -(Z_A Z_B + Z_B Z_C + Z_C Z_A)$$

The solution for I_A is

$$\bar{I}_A = \frac{\begin{vmatrix} 0 & 1 & 1 \\ \bar{V}_{CA} & 0 & -Z_C \\ \bar{V}_{BC} & -Z_B & Z_C \end{vmatrix}}{D} = \frac{-Z_C \bar{V}_{BC} - Z_B \bar{V}_{CA} - Z_C \bar{V}_{CA}}{D}$$

$$= \frac{Z_C(\bar{V}_{BC} + \bar{V}_{CA}) + Z_B \bar{V}_{CA}}{Z_A Z_B + Z_B Z_C + Z_C Z_A}$$

But, from equation (9-47),

$$\bar{V}_{BC} + \bar{V}_{CA} = -\bar{V}_{AB}$$

Therefore,

$$\bar{I}_A = \frac{\bar{V}_{CA} Z_B - \bar{V}_{AB} Z_C}{Z_A Z_B + Z_B Z_C + Z_C Z_A} \tag{9-51}$$

Solution by determinants gives the following values for the other two currents:

$$\bar{I}_B = \frac{\bar{V}_{AB} Z_C - \bar{V}_{BC} Z_A}{Z_A Z_B + Z_B Z_C + Z_C Z_A} \tag{9-52}$$

$$\bar{I}_C = \frac{\bar{V}_{BC} Z_A - \bar{V}_{CA} Z_B}{Z_A Z_B + Z_B Z_C + Z_C Z_A} \tag{9-53}$$

Equations (9-51), (9-52), and (9-53) should be solved in the complex form. Using the polar form for multiplication and the complex form only for addition can introduce small errors which may become significant in the final solution.

Example 9-9. The impedances in a wye-connected load are $Z_A = 3 + j5$, $Z_B = 4 - j3$, and $Z_C = 3 + j3$. If the voltages across the lines are equal to 480 volts and are balanced, find the three line currents and the phase voltages.

Solution. Since the voltages are balanced, their values are

$$\bar{V}_{CA} = 480 \underline{/0^\circ} = 480 + j0 \text{ volts}$$

$$\bar{V}_{BC} = 480 \underline{/120^\circ} = -240 + j415 \text{ volts}$$

$$\bar{V}_{AB} = 480 \underline{/240^\circ} = -240 - j415 \text{ volts}$$

The impedance relations are

$$Z_A = 3 + j5 = 5.83 \underline{/59^\circ} \text{ ohms}$$

$$Z_B = 4 - j3 = 5 \underline{/-36.7^\circ} \text{ ohms}$$

$$Z_C = 3 + j3 = 4.25 \underline{/45^\circ} \text{ ohms}$$

Inserting appropriate values in equation (9-51) gives the current in line A.

$$\bar{I}_A = \frac{(480 + j0)(4 - j3) - (-240 - j415)(3 + j3)}{(3 + j5)(4 - j3) + (4 - j3)(3 + j3) + (3 + j3)(3 + j5)}$$

$$= \frac{1920 - j1440 - 525 + j1965}{27 + j11 + 21 + j3 - 6 + j24} = \frac{(1395 + j525)(42 - j38)}{(42 + j38)(42 - j38)}$$

$$= \frac{78{,}540 - j30{,}960}{1764 + 1444} = \frac{78{,}540 - j30{,}960}{3208}$$

$$= 24.5 - j9.6 = 26.3 \underline{/-21.4^\circ} \text{ amps}$$

$$\bar{I}_B = \frac{(-240 - j415)(3 + j3) - (-240 + j415)(3 + j5)}{42 + j38}$$

$$= 20.3 - j65.6 = 69 \underline{/-72.9^\circ} \text{ amps}$$

$$\bar{I}_C = \frac{(-240 + j415)(3 + j5) - (480 + j0)(4 - j3)}{42 + j38}$$

$$= -45.6 + j75.2 = 87.9 \underline{/121.3^\circ} \text{ amps}$$

The phase voltages can be found by Ohm's law.

$$V_A = I_A Z_A = (26.3 \underline{/-21.4^\circ})(5.83 \underline{/59^\circ}) = 153.3 \underline{/37.6^\circ} \text{ volts}$$

$$V_B = I_B Z_B = (69 \underline{/-72.9^\circ})(5 \underline{/-36.7^\circ}) = 345 \underline{/-109.6^\circ} \text{ volts}$$

$$V_C = I_C Z_C = (87.9 \underline{/121.3^\circ})(4.25 \underline{/45^\circ}) = 374 \underline{/166.3^\circ} \text{ volts}$$

The power can be found by the same method as in the unbalanced delta system.

9-12. Power Factor Correction. In Fig. 9-18, the total reactive volt-amperes (sometimes called "reactive power") in vars is shown 90° from the total power. Since the position of this representative line is above the horizontal reference, it is inductive. This inductive component of the apparent power can be reduced, as far as the transmission line is concerned, by introducing a capacitive reactance in parallel with the inductive load so that the power factor from the line will be closer to unity than it would be without the capacitive reactance.

Fig. 9-20*a* shows a load connected to power lines A, B, and C. Since this load has a low power factor, it is decided to connect a capacitive load at points 1, 2, and 3, so that the power factor to the left of these points will be improved, thereby reducing the power loss in the transmission line. However, the conditions between points 1, 2, and 3 and the load cannot be changed and will act as if the capacitive load were not present.

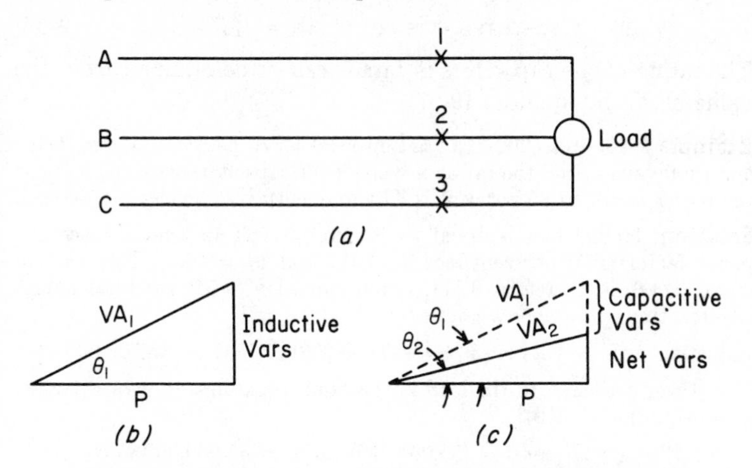

Fig. 9-20. Power factor correction in a three-phase system.

Fig. 9-20*b* shows the power triangle for the load without the power factor correction, and Fig. 9-20*c* shows the result of adding the capacitive load. The amount of capacitive load required can be found by use of the sine of the power factor angle.

$$\text{Inductive vars} = VA_1 \sin \theta_1 \tag{9-54}$$

$$\text{Net vars} = VA_2 \sin \theta_2 \tag{9-55}$$

$$\text{Capacitive vars} = \text{inductive vars} - \text{net vars} \tag{9-56a}$$

or

$$\text{Capacitive vars} = VA_1 \sin \theta_1 - VA_2 \sin \theta_2 \tag{9-56b}$$

Equations (9-54), (9-55), and (9-56b) are true for either the wye- or delta-connected capacitors,§ since the quantities are in vars. The capacitor ratings in farads per phase can be determined from

§ Power factor improvement can be accomplished in any one of three ways:

1. By adding a load which operates at unity power factor.
2. By use of static capacitors (sometimes called static condensers) connected in either wye or delta.
3. By use of synchronous motors whose power factor can be adjusted. If the motor is used only for power factor correction and is not driving any mechanical load, it is called a "synchronous condenser."

the rating in vars. Since there are three phases, the capacitive vars per phase are equal to the total capacitive vars divided by 3.

From Ohm's law for a-c circuits, the following relationship is obtained:

$$\text{Capacitive vars per phase} = I_C^2 X_C \tag{9-57}$$

The rating of the capacitors in farads can be determined from the value of X_C in equation (9-57).

Example 9-10. A 50,000-kva load operates at 70 per cent power factor and 2400 volts. Find the rating in vars of the capacitors required to raise the power factor to 85 per cent. The frequency is 60 cycles per second.

Solution. 50,000 kva is equal to 50,000,000 volt-amperes. Since the power factor is 70 per cent, $\cos \theta_1 = 0.7$ and $\theta_1 = 45.5°$. The reactive factor ($\sin \theta$) is, therefore, 0.714. From equation (9-54) the total inductive reactive volt-amperes can be found.

$$\text{Inductive vars} = VA_1 \sin \theta_1 = (50{,}000{,}000)\ (0.714) = 35{,}700{,}000 \text{ vars}$$

The power delivered to the load is the same, regardless of power factor. From equation (9-21b),

$$P = \sqrt{3}\,EI \cos \theta = (50{,}000{,}000)\ (0.70) = 35{,}000{,}000 \text{ watts}$$

Note that $\sqrt{3}\,EI$ is equal to the volt-amperes. (See also Example 9-4.)

Since the power factor is to be raised to 85 per cent, $\cos \theta_2 = 0.85$ and $\theta_2 = 31.8°$. The reactive factor is 0.527. The new apparent power is

$$VA_2 = \frac{P}{\cos \theta} = \frac{35{,}000{,}000}{0.85} = 41{,}200{,}000 \text{ volt-amps}$$

The net vars are determined from equation (9-55).

$$\text{Net vars} = VA_2 \sin \theta_2 = (41{,}200{,}000)\ (0.527) = 21{,}700{,}000 \text{ vars}$$

The rating of the capacitors in vars is found from equation (9-56b).

$$\text{Capacitive vars} = 35{,}700{,}000 - 21{,}700{,}000 = 14{,}000{,}000 \text{ vars}$$

Example 9-11. What additional capacitors would be required to raise the power factor of Example 9-10 from 85 per cent to 90 per cent?

Solution. The steps used in this solution are the same as those used in Example 9-10 except that we can use the results already obtained.

The new power factor angle is 26°. The reactive factor for this angle is 0.439.

The new apparent power is

$$\frac{35{,}000{,}000}{0.9} = 38{,}900{,}000 \text{ volt-amps}$$

The new net vars are

$$(38{,}900{,}000)\ (0.439) = 17{,}000{,}000 \text{ vars}$$

The capacitors required would have the rating

$$21{,}700{,}000 - 17{,}000{,}000 = 4{,}700{,}000 \text{ vars}$$

Example 9-12. What is the rating in farads of the capacitors in Example 9-10 if the capacitors are connected (a) in delta, (b) in wye?

Solution. (a) The capacitive current in this system is found as follows (see Example 9-4), where the vars of the capacitors are used in place of volt-amperes.

$$I_C = \frac{\text{vars}}{\sqrt{3}\,E} = \frac{14{,}000{,}000}{(\sqrt{3})\,(2400)} = 3360 \text{ amps}$$

This is the line current to the capacitors. The phase current in the delta is found as follows:

$$I_{\phi C} = \frac{3360}{\sqrt{3}} = 1935 \text{ amps}$$

The vars per phase rating is

$$\text{Vars per phase} = \frac{14{,}000{,}000}{3} = 4{,}670{,}000 \text{ vars}$$

$$\text{Vars} = I^2 X_C$$

Therefore,

$$X_C = \frac{\text{vars}}{I^2} = \frac{4{,}670{,}000}{(1935)^2} = \frac{4{,}670{,}000}{3{,}750{,}000} = 1.25 \text{ ohms}$$

The capacitance at 60 cycles in a delta connection is, therefore,

$$C = \frac{1}{2\,\pi f X_C} = \frac{1}{(377)\,(1.25)} = \frac{1}{471} = 0.00212 \text{ farad}$$

$$= 2120 \text{ microfarads per phase}$$

(b) The 3360-ampere line current found in part (a) is the phase current in the wye connection. The vars per phase rating of the capacitors is 4,670,000 vars for the wye as well as for the delta. The capacitive reactance is found by the same equation as before:

$$X_C = \frac{\text{vars}}{I^2} = \frac{4{,}670{,}000}{(3360)^2} = \frac{4{,}670{,}000}{11{,}250{,}000} = 0.416 \text{ ohm}$$

The capacitance at 60 cycles in a wye connection is

$$C = \frac{1}{(377)\,(0.416)} = \frac{1}{157} = 0.00637 \text{ farad}$$

$$= 6370 \text{ microfarads per phase}$$

9-13. Table of Power Factor Correction Multipliers. The vars or kvars (kilovars) of either static or synchronous condensers or capacitors can be determined quickly and fairly accurately by use of a table such as Table 9-5. The existing power factor from 50 to 95 per cent is shown in the left hand column of Table 9-5. The desired power factor is shown in columns 2 through 7. When the power factor of a load is to be improved, the known power

Table 9-5. Power Factor Correction Multipliers

Existing Power Factor %	Corrected Power Factor					
	100%	95%	90%	85%	80%	75%
50	1.732	1.403	1.247	1.112	0.982	0.850
52	1.643	1.314	1.158	1.023	0.893	0.761
54	1.558	1.229	1.073	0.938	0.808	0.676
55	1.518	1.189	1.033	0.898	0.768	0.636
56	1.479	1.150	0.994	0.859	0.729	0.597
58	1.404	1.075	0.919	0.784	0.654	0.522
60	1.333	1.004	0.848	0.713	0.583	0.451
62	1.265	0.936	0.780	0.645	0.515	0.383
64	1.201	0.872	0.716	0.581	0.451	0.319
65	1.168	0.839	0.683	0.548	0.418	0.286
66	1.139	0.810	0.654	0.519	0.389	0.257
68	1.078	0.749	0.593	0.458	0.328	0.196
70	1.020	0.691	0.535	0.400	0.270	0.138
72	0.964	0.635	0.479	0.344	0.214	0.082
74	0.909	0.580	0.424	0.289	0.159	0.027
75	0.882	0.553	0.397	0.262	0.132	
76	0.855	0.526	0.370	0.235	0.105	
78	0.802	0.473	0.317	0.182	0.052	
80	0.750	0.421	0.265	0.130		
82	0.698	0.369	0.213	0.078		
84	0.646	0.317	0 161			
85	0.620	0.291	0.135			
86	0.594	0.265	0.109			
88	0.540	0.211	0.055			
90	0.485	0.156				
92	0.426	0.097				
94	0.363	0.034				
95	0.329					

Courtesy of Westinghouse Electric Corporation.

factor is found in the left column, as, for example, 60 per cent. If this power factor is to be improved to 90 per cent, the decimal 0.848 is found in the same row and under the proper column. This decimal from the table is multiplied by the power in watts or kilowatts of the existing load to obtain the vars or kvars of the capacitors to be installed.

Example 9-13. Solve Examples 9-10 and 9-11 by use of Table 9-5.

Solution. The power load in these examples was found to be 35,000 kw.

The multiplier in Table 9-5 corresponding to an existing power factor of 70 per cent and a desired power factor of 85 per cent is 0.400. Therefore, the var rating of the capacitors is found to be

$$(35{,}000)\ (0.400) = 14{,}000 \text{ kilovars} = 14{,}000{,}000 \text{ vars}$$

The multiplier in Table 9-5 corresponding to an increase in power factor from 85 per cent to 90 per cent is 0.135. Therefore, the var rating of the capacitors is found to be

$$(35{,}000)\ (0.135) = 4720 \text{ kilovars} = 4{,}720{,}000 \text{ vars}$$

Problems Based on Chapter 9

P9-1. Lines A and B of a balanced two-phase three-wire system carry 175 amps each. What is the current in the neutral conductor?

Ans. 248 amps.

P9-2. The impedances of the load in problem P9-1 are $2 + j5$ in each phase. What are the voltages across each winding and between lines A and B?

Ans. $V_A = 943\ \underline{/68.2^\circ}$ volts. $V_B = 943\ \underline{/158.2^\circ}$ volts. $V_{AB} = 1335\ \underline{/113.2^\circ}$ volts. In complex form: $V_A = 350 + j875$ volts. $V_B = -875 + j350$ volts. $V_{AB} = -525 + j1225$ volts.

Table 9-6. Standard and Commonly Used Line Voltages for Three-Phase Systems

120/208Y	4,800	34,500
240	6,900	46,000
480	12,000	69,000
600	13,200	115,000
2,400	13,800	132,000
4,160	23,000	187,000

P9-3. Table 9-6 shows some of the standard and commonly used line voltages. Make a table showing the corresponding line-to-neutral voltages for all except the 120/208Y system.

Ans. See Table 9-7 (page 224).

P9-4. The current in the line of a balanced three-phase system is 125 amps. What is the phase current if the load is connected in delta?

Ans. 72.1 amps.

P9-5. The currents in a three-phase four-wire wye-connected system are: $I_A = 25\ \underline{/-10^\circ}$, $I_B = 30\ \underline{/215^\circ}$, and $I_C = 18\ \underline{/130^\circ}$. What is the current in the neutral wire?

Ans. Since $I_A = 24.6 - j4.25$, $I_B = -24.6 - j17.2$, and $I_C = -11.6 + j13.8$, $I_N = 11.6 + j7.65 = 13.86\ \underline{/33.4^\circ}$ amps.

P9-6. A balanced three-phase load draws 300 amps at 600 volts and 80% power factor. Find the apparent power, the true power, and the reactive power.

Ans. 312,000 volt-amps. 250,000 watts. 187,000 vars.

P9-7. The power in a three-phase three-wire 480-volt system is measured by two wattmeters which read $P_1 = +30{,}000$ and $P_2 = +20{,}000$. If the system is balanced and the line current is 100 amps, find the power factor by use of equation (9-28a).

Ans. $P = 50{,}000$ watts. RVA = 17,320 vars. PF = cos 19.1° = 94.5%.

P9-8. The power in a three-phase three-wire 600-volt system is measured by two wattmeters. If the total power is 100,000 watts at 48% power factor, what will be the readings of the two wattmeters?

Ans. $P_1 = -3000$ watts. $P_2 = +103{,}000$ watts.

P9-9. A 100-hp three-phase 480-volt motor operates at 85% efficiency and 85% power factor, lagging. Find the current in the line. If two wattmeters are used to measure the power, what will be the indication on each of the meters? (1 hp at 100% efficiency and unity power factor = 746 watts.)

Ans. 124 amps. $P_1 = 28{,}000$ watts. $P_2 = 61{,}000$ watts.

P9-10. When two wattmeters are used to measure the input to a balanced three-phase delta-connected system, the meter readings are 1800 and 2700 watts. The terminal emf is 600 volts. Determine the power factor and the line and phase currents.

Ans. $\theta = 19.1°$. PF = 94.3%. 4.57 amps. 2.64 amps.

P9-11. If two wattmeters used to determine the power in a three-phase system show identical readings, what is the power factor?

Ans. $P_1 + P_2 = 2\,P_1 = 2\,P_2$. $\sqrt{3}\,(P_2 - P_1) = 0$. Therefore, PF = 100%.

P9-12. Two wattmeters are used to indicate the power in a three-phase system. If $P_1 = 2900$ and $P_2 = 4500$, find the reactive power. Is the power factor leading or lagging?

Ans. 2780 vars. PF is lagging.

P9-13. If the readings of the wattmeters in problem P9-12 are reversed, find the reactive power. Is the power factor leading or lagging?

Ans. −2780 vars. PF is leading.

P9-14. Two wattmeters are connected to read the power in a three-phase system. The voltage, current, and power factor are 480 volts, 50 amps, 75% leading. Find the readings of the two wattmeters.

Ans. $\theta = -41.4°$. $P_1 = 23{,}500$ watts. $P_2 = 7700$ watts.

P9-15. A three-phase line consists of three 300-MCM copper cables with symmetrical spacing of 3 ft between conductors. If the line is 15 miles long and carries 200 amps at 23,000 volts between conductors at the receiving end, find the voltage drop in the line. Ignore the capacitance as being negligible. What is the total power lost in the line?

Ans. 1940 volts. $3I^2R = 386{,}000$ watts.

P9-16. Three neoprene-jacketed cables in an underground duct are used as a three-phase transmission line. The spacing between conductors is one inch. If the cables are 3/0 copper, the sending end emf is 4200 volts, and the line is 6 miles in length, find the charging current.

Ans. $x_a' = 7230$ ohms. $I_C = 0.58$ amp.

P9-17. An overhead transmission line is 32 miles long. ACSR cable whose area is 336,400 CM is used as the conductor. The spacing between conductors is 5 ft between adjacent cables and 10 ft between the two outside conductors. The receiving end voltage is 69,000 volts between conductors when the current is 450 amps. The load operates at 80% power factor. Find the sending end voltage if capacitance is neglected.

Ans. $x_a = 32(0.451 + 0.222) = 21.536$ ohms. Effective spacing = 6.3 ft. $V_\phi = 49{,}400$ volts. $V_S = 85{,}500$ volts line-to-line.

P9-18. The impedances in a delta-connected load are $Z_{AC} = 2 + j1$, $Z_{CB} = 3 + j2$, and $Z_{BA} = 2 + j7$ ohms. The voltages are balanced and are equal to 600 volts, line-to-line. Find the three phase currents, the three line currents, the power factor, and the total power.

Ans. $I_{AC} = 268 \underline{/93.5°} = -16.4 + j268$ amps. $I_{CB} = 167 \underline{/206.3°} = -150 - j74$ amps. $I_{BA} = 82.5 \underline{/-74.1°} = 22.6 - j79.5$ amps. $I_A = 49 - j347.5$ amps. $I_B = -172.6 + j5.5$ amps. $I_C = 133.6 + j342$ amps. $P = 143{,}000 + 83{,}500 + 13{,}600 = 240{,}100$ watts. PF = 45.3%.

P9-19. The impedances in a wye-connected load are $Z_A = 2 + j1$, $Z_B = 3 + j2$, and $Z_C = 2 + j2$ ohms. The line voltages are balanced and are equal to 1000 volts. Find the three line currents.

Ans. $I_A = 214 - j24.1 = 216 \underline{/353.5°}$ amps. $I_B = -118.6 - j154.2 = 195 \underline{/232.5°}$ amps. $I_C = -95.4 + j178.3 = 201 \underline{/118.3°}$ amps.

P9-20. The impedances in a wye-connected load are $Z_A = 3 + j0$, $Z_B = 2 + j0$, and $Z_C = 5 + j0$ ohms. The line voltages are balanced and are equal to 480 volts. Find the three line currents and the phase voltages.

Ans. $I_A = 69.7 - j67.1 = 97 \underline{/316.1°}$ amps. $I_B = -15.5 + j107 = 108 \underline{/98.2°}$ amps. $I_C = -54.2 - j40 = 67.5 \underline{/216.4°}$ amps. $V_A = 209 - j201$ volts. $V_B = -31 + j214$ volts. $V_C = -271 - j200$ volts. (Note that although the power factor is 100%, the line currents are not in phase with the line voltages. They are in phase with the phase voltages, however.)

P9-21. Power in a three-phase three-wire system is measured by two wattmeters. If the readings of the wattmeters are $P_2 = 40{,}000$ and $P_1 = -13{,}000$, find the power factor. Find the rating in vars of the capacitors required to raise the power factor to 90%.

Ans. PF=29.4%. 78,900 vars.

P9-22. A 75,000 volt-amp load operates at 65% power factor. (a) Find the rating in vars of the capacitors required to raise the power factor to 90%. (b) Find the rating in vars of the capacitors required to raise the power factor from 90 to 95%. (c) What is the volt-amp load at 90% and

95% power factor if the actual power is the same as it is at 65%?

Ans. (a) 33,400 vars. (b) 7600 vars. (c) 54,100 volt-amps and 51,300 volt-amps.

P9-23. A load of 50,000 watts is supplied at 70% power factor. What additional load in watts at 100% power factor must be added to bring the total power factor to 80%?

Ans. 18,000 watts.

P9-24. If the power factor of problem P9-23 were increased by the use of capacitors without changing the load in watts, find the capacitive vars required.

Ans. 13,500 vars.

P9-25. If 68,000 capacitive vars were added to the system described in problem P9-23, what change in the power factor would result?

Ans. PF would go to 95% lead.

Table 9-7. Line and Line-to-Neutral Three-Phase Voltages

240/138.5	4,800/2,770	34,500/19,800
480/277	6,900/3,980	46,000/26,500
600/340	12,000/6,910	69,000/39,800
2,400/1,385	13,200/7,610	115,000/66,300
4,160/2,400	13,800/7,950	132,000/76,100
	23,000/13,250	187,000/108,000

10 MAGNETISM

10-1. Electromagnetic Induction. In 1819, the Danish scientist, Hans Christian Oersted, found that a pivoted magnet (magnetic compass) was always deflected when near a wire carrying an electric current. In 1831, Michael Faraday discovered that when a conductor was moved in a magnetic field, an electric current flowed in the conductor. Further investigation showed that because of forces existing between stationary or moving electrical charges and magnetic fields, energy could be converted from the mechanical to the electrical form (electrical generators) and from the electrical to the mechanical (motors).

The nature of magnetism is not known, but its characteristics have been rather accurately determined. For example, if a magnetic field is held to a constant value and an electrical charge is brought within the field, there is no force exerted between the magnetic field and the electrical field surrounding the charge. If the charge is now caused to move, the force exerted on the charge is proportional to the magnitude of the electrical charge and the velocity at which the charge is moving through the field. The relationship is given by the equation

$$F = Bqv \sin \phi \tag{10-1}$$

The explanation depends on reference to Fig. 10-1*a* and *b*. F is the magnitude of the force in newtons, B is the flux density of the magnetic induction (or magnetic field) in webers per square meter, q is the electrical charge in coulombs, v is the velocity of the moving charge in meters per second, and ϕ is the angle between the direction of the magnetic field and the direction of the motion of the charge. The directions shown in Fig. 10-1 are based on a positive electrical charge. The direction of the force F is reversed if the charge is negative.

The direction of the force on a positive charge can be determined by the left hand rule as indicated in Fig. 10-1*b*. If the first (or index) finger of the left hand points in the direction of the magnetic field and the second (longest) finger points in the direction of v sin

ϕ, the thumb will point in the direction of the force if the charge is positive. The direction of the force F is reversed if the charge is negative. To find the direction of the force for a negative charge, the right hand can be used, with the first and second fingers representing the direction of the magnetic field and the motion of the electrical charge. The thumb again indicates the direction of the force. The right hand rule for negative charges is illustrated in Fig. 10-1c.

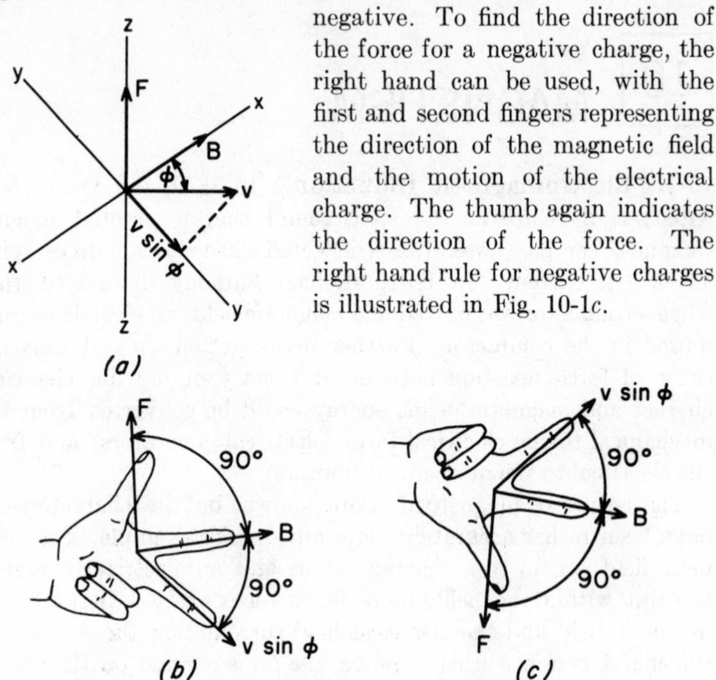

Fig. 10-1. Magnetic force on an electrical charge.

The unit of the magnetic field is based on the assumption that one weber per square meter is equal to one line of magnetic flux per square meter. In reality, a magnetic field does not consist of "lines of flux," but magnetic theory and computations can be more conveniently explained and understood on the basis of this assumption.

If equation (10-1) is solved for the magnetic flux density, we obtain the relationship

$$B = \frac{F}{qv \sin \phi} \tag{10-2}$$

The two sides of equation (10-2) have the units as follows:

$$\frac{\text{weber}}{\text{meter}^2} = \frac{\text{newton}}{\text{coulomb} \cdot \dfrac{\text{meter}}{\text{second}}}$$

Since one ampere is equal to one coulomb per second, the unit for flux has the equivalent

$$\frac{\text{weber}}{\text{meter}^2} = \frac{\text{newton}}{\text{ampere} \cdot \text{meter}}$$

This relationship between units is of importance in electrical engineering.

When an electric current flows in a wire, a magnetic field builds up around the conductor. If we take the conventional direction of current flow (not electron flow) as being from positive to negative, we may use a right hand rule for determining the direction of the magnetic field. By this rule, if we grasp the conductor with the fingers of the right hand so that the thumb points along the wire in the direction of current flow, the fingers point in the direction of the magnetic field.

We may assume that a rectangular coil of wire is placed in a magnetic field as indicated in Fig. 10-2*c*. The stationary magnetic field is perpendicular to the axis of the coil in the position shown. The X's in this view indicate that the magnetic field is directed into the paper (away from the viewer). The coil is pivoted along axis 0-0′ and is free to rotate around that axis. The current flows in the direction indicated by the arrows. The coil has a length l perpendicular to the 0-0′ axis, and a width w parallel to 0-0′.

If we now mentally cut this coil along axis Y-Y′ and look at the coil in the direction of the double arrows, we obtain the view shown in Fig. 10-2*a*. In this view, the current in the bottom of the coil is flowing toward the viewer (away from the page) as indicated by the dot* at that end of the coil. The current in the top of the coil is flowing away from the viewer (into the page) as indicated by the X at that end of the coil.

The force obtained from equation (10-1) is the force F shown in Fig. 10-2*a*. The current in amperes is equal to the charge in coulombs passing a given point in a second. The quantity qv in equation (10-1) is coulombs times meters per second, or the charge in coulombs passing along a conductor of length l meters in a second.

---

* The dot represents the point of an arrow. If an arrow was fired at a person, he would see the point of the arrow coming toward him. On the other hand, if he shot the arrow, he would see the X position of the feathers as the arrow went away from him. The direction of the arrow has been adopted to indicate the direction of current flow in a diagram drawn perpendicular to the page.

Dividing qv by l gives the current:

$$i = \frac{qv}{l} \text{ amperes} \tag{10-3}$$

From equation (10-3) we see that $il = qv$. Substituting this value in equation (10-1) gives the relationship

$$F = Bil \sin \phi \tag{10-4}$$

In a motor, the coils consist of more than one turn. For a coil of N turns, the force equation is

$$F = NBil \sin \phi \tag{10-5}$$

In Fig. 10-2*a*, the coil is shown in three positions. When the coil is parallel to the magnetic field, ϕ is 90° and the force is maximum.

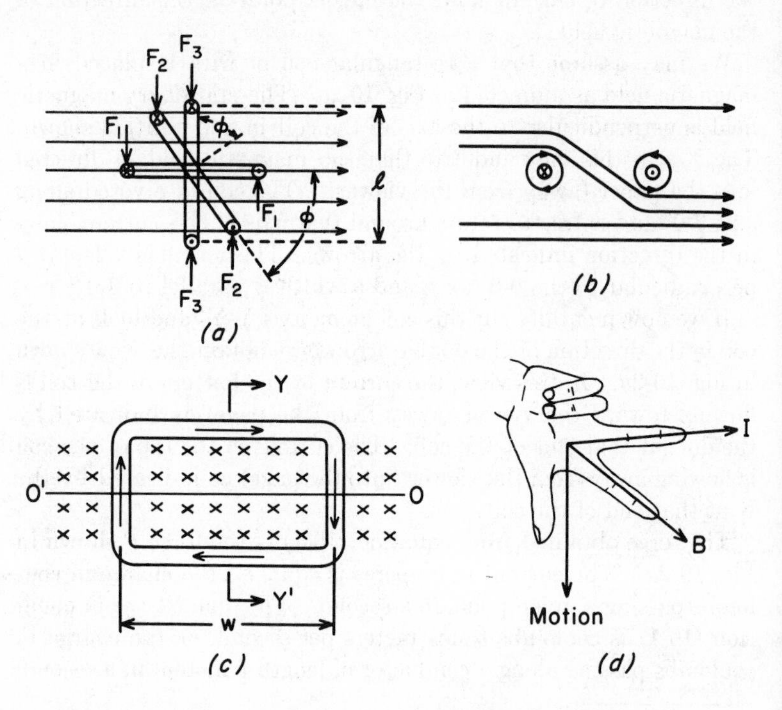

Fig. 10-2. Magnetic force on an electrical conductor.

Therefore, the force on each coil side is found from equation (10-4), with $\sin \phi = 1$:

$$F = Bil \tag{10-4a}$$

As the coil moves counterclockwise, the force on each coil side for a one-turn coil is found by use of equation (10-4). The force F_2, therefore, is somewhat less than F_1. When the coil is perpendicular to the field, ϕ is 0° and the force F_3 is zero. In an actual motor, when the coil reaches this position, either the current is reversed in the coil—by use of a commutator—or the magnetic field is reversed as in an a-c motor, thereby maintaining the same direction of rotation.

Although the direction of rotation has been specified in this discussion, it can be determined or checked by use of Fig. 10-2*b*. In this figure, the flux moves from left to right as indicated by the arrows, and current flows into the page in the wire at the left and out of the page in the wire at the right as indicated by the symbols. The field around the left hand wire is shown by the right hand rule to be directed clockwise, and that around the right hand wire by the same rule is counterclockwise.

The field flux finds the path across the coil easier if it follows the direction of the flux around the wire. The field flux, then, becomes more dense above the left side of the coil and below the right side. Since magnetic flux prefers the shortest path, the flux from the external field attempts to straighten, and in so doing rotates the coil in a counterclockwise direction.

A right hand rule can be applied to determine the direction of motion. As shown in Fig. 10-2*d*, if the index finger of the right hand points in the direction of the field flux B and the middle finger points in the direction of the current, the thumb will point in the direction of motion of the conductor. Applying this rule to either side (or both sides) of the coil in Fig. 10-2*a* shows that the coil rotates counterclockwise in agreement with the discussion of Fig. 10-2*b*.

The letter B represents the flux per unit area. The symbol Φ (Greek letter phi) is used to designate the total flux present in the field. The relationship between B and Φ is indicated in the equation

$$\Phi = BA \tag{10-6}$$

The quantity Φ is in webers.

Example 10-1. The total flux threading an area of 40 square centimeters is 2 webers. A one-turn coil of wire 5 centimeters long lies in the field with its plane parallel to the direction of the flux. If the coil carries a current of 3 amperes, find the flux density B and the maximum force on one side of the coil.

Solution. From equation (10-6), we find the flux density.

$$B = \frac{\Phi}{A} = \frac{2}{(0.4)^2} = \frac{2}{0.16} = 12.5 \text{ webers/cm}^2$$

Equation (10-4) gives the force on one side of the coil.

$$F = Bi\,l \sin\phi = (12.5)\,(3)\,(0.05) = 1.875 \text{ newtons}$$

10-2. Force and Torque. The force exerted on the sides of a coil is independent of the width of the coil w. In an actual motor, this width is important in that it determines how much torque is available in the motor. Horsepower depends on torque. Torque in a motor is also called the moment of a couple.

Two equal and opposite (parallel) forces not in the same line of action are called a *couple.* The *moment of a couple* can be shown to be equal to the product of one of the equal forces and the distance between them.† If w is the width of the coil, and therefore the distance between the forces, the moment M of the couple is

$$M = Fw \tag{10-7}$$

where F is defined by equation (10-4). The moment M is in meter-newtons. The complete equation for the moment is

$$M = Bil\,w \sin\phi \tag{10-8}$$

The product lw is the area of the coil. Equation (10-8) can therefore be written

$$M = BAi \sin\phi \tag{10-9}$$

Substituting equation (10-6) in equation (10-9) gives the relationship

$$M = \Phi\, i \sin\phi \tag{10-10}$$

The torque in meter-newtons, therefore, is proportional to the total flux threading the coil and the current flowing in the coil. The total current flowing in the coil is the current in one turn multiplied by the number N of turns per coil. The total torque is, therefore,

$$M = N\,\Phi\, i \sin\phi \tag{10-11}$$

Equation (10-11) can be converted to the engineering unit, foot-pound (ft-lb). To change newtons to pounds, the number of

† See, for example, Chapter 5 of *Elementary Engineering Mechanics* by Eugene George Key (New York: John Wiley & Sons, Inc., 1960).

newtons is multiplied by 0.2248. To change meters to feet, the number of meters is multiplied by 3.281. If these two constants are multiplied together, we obtain the product 0.7376. Therefore, the torque or moment of the couple in foot-pounds is obtained from meter-newtons by multiplying equation (10-11) by 0.7376, or

$$M = 0.7376\, N\, \Phi\, i \sin \phi \text{ ft-lbs} \qquad (10\text{-}12)$$

Example 10-2. If the coil in Example 10-1 is 5 centimeters wide, find the torque in meter-newtons and in foot-pounds.

Solution. The torque is found from equation (10-8) or equation (10-9).

$$M = Bi\, lw \sin \phi = (12.5)\,(3)\,(0.05)^2 = 0.09375 \text{ m-n}$$

The torque in foot-pounds is obtained by multiplying this result by 0.7376.

$$M = (0.09375)\,(0.7376) = 0.0692 \text{ ft-lb}$$

10-3. Magnetic Field Around a Long Straight Conductor. The magnetic field around a long straight conductor was determined by actual experiment and the equation for the field intensity was derived from the experimental results. The equation is

$$B = \frac{\mu_0}{4\pi} \frac{2i}{a} \qquad (10\text{-}13)$$

where B is the field density in webers per square meter, μ_0 is $4\pi \times 10^{-7}$ or 12.57×10^{-7}, i is the current in amperes, and a is the distance from the center of the wire to the point at which the field strength is B.

Equation (10-13), known as the Biot-Savart law, is named after the men who derived it from experimental data. This equation was later derived analytically by the use of calculus.‡

Although most equations in the mks system use the constant μ_0, equation (10-13) can be simplified by using the value for this constant:

$$B = \frac{2i}{a} \times 10^{-7} \qquad (10\text{-}14)$$

In equation (10-14), the 4π disappears.

‡ A derivation and explanation of the analytical development of equation (10-13) can be found in Chapter 32 of *University Physics* by Francis W. Sears and Mark W. Zemansky (3rd ed.; Reading, Mass.: Addison-Wesley Publishing Co., Inc., 1964). A slightly different approach is used in *Principles of Electrical Engineering* by William H. Timbie and Vannevar Bush (4th ed.; New York: John Wiley & Sons, Inc., 1951).

Equations (10-13) and (10-14) are used only when the radius or distance a is small compared to the length of the wire.

Fig. 10-3 shows a portion of a wire carrying a current in the direction indicated. The direction of the magnetic field around the wire is found by use of the right hand rule explained in Section 10-1 in which the conductor is grasped by the right hand with the thumb pointing in the direction of current flow.

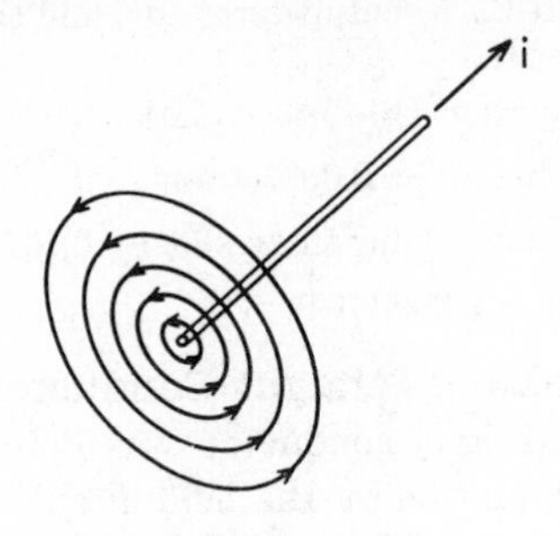

Fig. 10-3. Magnetic field around a conductor.

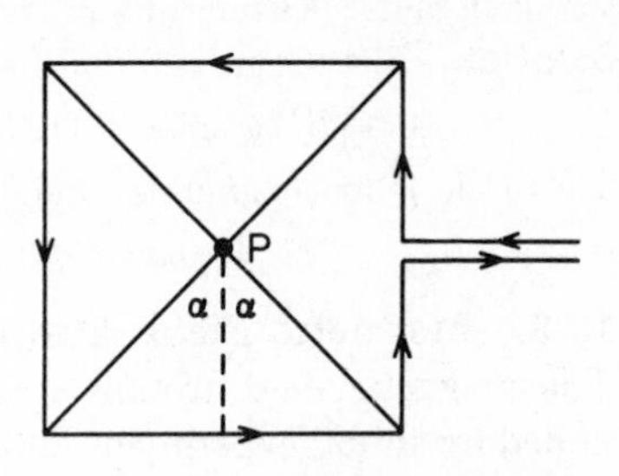

Fig. 10-4. Field within a closed square loop.

If the flux density at some point opposite the center of the long straight conductor is desired, equation (10-14) is multiplied by the sine of the angle α measured between the point and the end of the wire as indicated in Fig. 10-4. The equation then has the form

$$B = \frac{2i}{a} \times 10^{-7} \times \sin \alpha \tag{10-15}$$

When α is less than 5.8°, the results obtained by equations (10-14) and (10-15) are so nearly identical that $\sin \alpha$ can be ignored. The error is so small that it cannot be determined by use of a slide rule.[§]

Example 10-3. Find the flux density at the center of a loop consisting of a closed square of wire if the loop is 30 centimeters on a side and the wire is carrying 45 amperes of current. The contribution of the lead-in wires is to be considered negligible. See Fig. 10-4.

Solution. In this problem, α is 45°. The field at P is the total contributed

[§] For angles smaller than 5.8°, $\sin \alpha = \tan \alpha$ with an error of 0.0005 or less, so that the hypotenuse and the side opposite the angle are essentially equal. Even at 9°, the sine and tangent functions are different by only 0.002.

by the four wires, or four times the result obtained by use of equation (10-15).

$$B = \frac{8\,i}{a} \times 10^{-7} \times \sin \alpha = \frac{(8)\,(45)\,(\sin 45^\circ)\,(10^{-7})}{(0.15)}$$

$$= 1.70 \times 10^{-4} \text{ webers/m}^2$$

If the field were to be calculated at any point other than the center, the angle α would have to be determined. Since the angles are not the same size, we may designate them as α_1 and α_2. Equation (10-15) can then be written

$$B = \frac{i}{a}(\sin \alpha_1 + \sin \alpha_2) \times 10^{-7} \qquad (10\text{-}16)$$

In a problem such as Example 10-3, when the point P is not at the center, the contribution of flux by every wire must be determined and the four results added.

10-4. Force Between Parallel Conductors. When two parallel conductors are carrying currents i_1 and i_2, the magnetic field at one conductor caused by current in the other is given by equation (10-14). At the conductor carrying current i_2, the field is, therefore,

$$B = \frac{2\,i_1}{a} \times 10^{-7} \qquad (\text{A})$$

The current i_2 does not appear in equation (A), since the distance from the center of the wire carrying that current to the field is zero. The force on this conductor is found from equation (10-4a):

$$F = B i_2 l \qquad (\text{B})$$

Substituting equation (A) in equation (B) gives the equation for the force between conductors:

$$F = \frac{2\,i_1\,i_2\,l}{a} \times 10^{-7} \qquad (10\text{-}17)$$

Equation (10-17) is the same for either conductor. The symbols i_1 and i_2 represent the current in amperes in wires 1 and 2, l is the length of the conductors, and a is the distance between the conductors. The current is in amperes and the distances are in meters. The force F is therefore in newtons. The force per unit length is obtained by dividing equation (10-17) by l:

$$\frac{F}{l} = \frac{2\,i_1\,i_2}{a} \times 10^{-7} \qquad (10\text{-}18)$$

If the currents in the two conductors are equal, the equation becomes simply

$$\frac{F}{l} = \frac{2\,i^2}{a} \times 10^{-7} \tag{10-19}$$

If the force in dynes (cgs system) is desired, l and a are in centimeters and equation (10-17) has the form

$$\frac{F}{l} = \frac{2\,i_1\,i_2}{a} \times 10^{-2} \tag{10-20}$$

The direction of the force in equations (10-17) through (10-20) depends on the relative direction of current in the two conductors, as illustrated in Fig. 10-5.

If the two conductors are arranged as in Fig. 10-5*a* and are both carrying current "out of the page," the right hand rule shows that the lines of magnetic flux are counterclockwise. The directions of the lines between the conductors are opposed to each other. The path for the magnetic lines is, therefore, easier if the lines surround the two conductors as shown in Fig. 10-5*b* and the force is consequently in a direction to draw the conductors together (attraction).

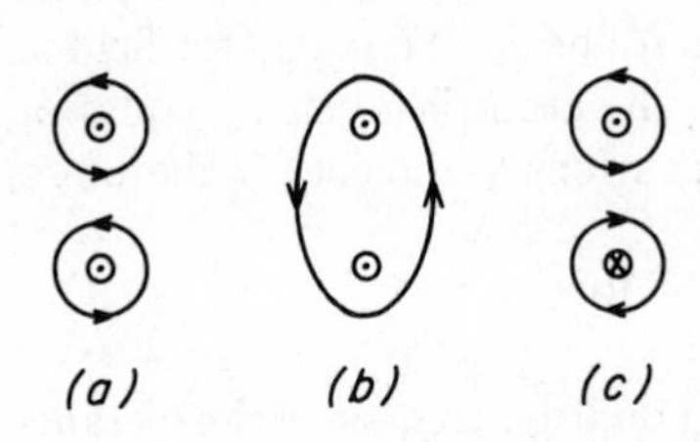

Fig. 10-5. Currents in parallel conductors.

When the conductors carry current in opposite directions, the direction of the field between them is indicated in Fig. 10-5*c*. This condition results in a crowding of the field between the conductors and the force is such as to push the conductors apart (repulsion).

The attraction or repulsion of the forces between parallel conductors can be checked by use of the left hand rule explained in connection with Fig. 10-1. In Fig. 10-5*a*, the field around the upper conductor resulting from current in the lower conductor is from right to left. The current is directed out from the page. By use of the left hand rule, we find the force on this conductor is downward. By the same rule, we find the force on the lower conductor is upward, and the resulting force is attraction. Use of the rule also demonstrates that when the currents are in opposite directions, the resulting force is repulsion.

Example 10-4. A long horizontal wire *C-D* is held in the position shown in Fig. 10-6*a*. A wire *A-B* 150 centimeters long is placed above wire *C-D* and arranged so that it can move up and down on frictionless slides, as indicated. Wire *C-D* weighs 0.06 gram-centimeters. If the wires are carrying 40 amperes of current, to what height will wire *A-B* rise (distance from *C-D*) in order for the force of gravity (weight of the wire) to just balance the force between the wires?

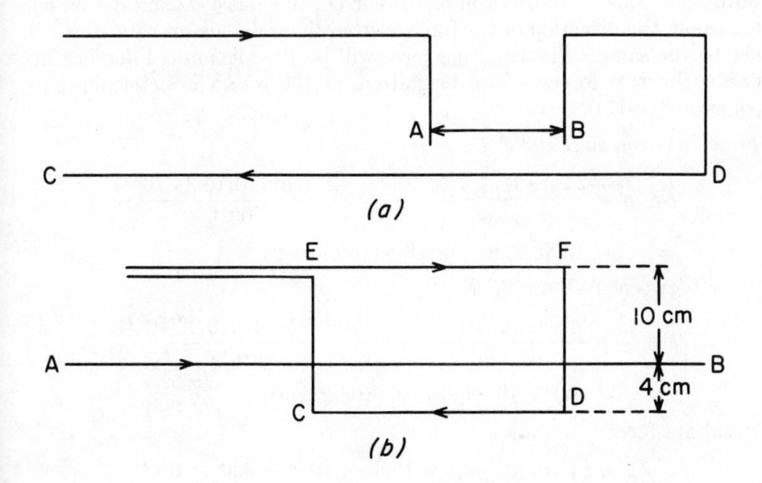

Fig. 10-6. Forces between parallel wires carrying current.

Solution. Tables of conversion constants show these relationships:

$$\text{newtons} \times 0.2248 = \text{pounds}$$

$$\text{kilograms} \times 2.205 = \text{pounds}$$

This problem can be solved by use of these relationships and equation (10-17). Since the magnetic force in pounds must equal the weight of the wire *A-B* in pounds, we may write the following relationship:

$$F = \frac{(2)\,(40)^2\,(1.5)}{a} \times 10^{-7} \times 0.2248$$

$$= \frac{(150)\,(0.06)}{1000} \times 2.205$$

$$\frac{(3)\,(1600)\,(0.2248)\,(10^{-7})}{a} = (0.009)\,(2.205)$$

$$1080 \times 10^{-7} = 0.01985a$$

$$a = \frac{1080 \times 10^{-7}}{1985 \times 10^{-5}} = 0.544 \times 10^{-2} \text{ meters}$$

$$= 0.544 \text{ cm}$$

Example 10-5. A long straight wire, as *A-B* in Fig. 10-6*b*, carries a current of 15 amperes. A rectangular loop is placed over this wire so that side *C-D* of the loop is 4 centimeters from *A-B*. Sides *C-D* and *E-F* are equal and are 20 centimeters in length, and a current of 10 amperes flows in the loop. The direction of current flow is shown in Fig. 10-6*b* and the effect of the lead-in wires for the loop is to be considered negligible. Find the resultant force on conductor *A-B*.

Solution. Since the direction of the current in sides *C-D* and *E-F* is not the same, the direction of the force exerted by each side on wire *A-B* will not be the same. The resulting force will be the algebraic difference between the two forces. The magnitude of the forces is determined by equation (10-17).

Force between *A-B* and *C-D*:

$$F_{C-D} = \frac{2\, i_{A-B}\, i_{C-D}\, l \times 10^{-7}}{a} = \frac{(2)\,(15)\,(10)\,(0.2)\,(10^{-7})}{0.04}$$

$$= 1500 \times 10^{-7} \text{ newtons (repulsion)}$$

Force between *A–B* and *E–F*:

$$F_{E-F} = \frac{2 i_{A-B}\, i_{E-F}\, l \times 10^{-7}}{a} = \frac{(2)\,(15)\,(10)\,(0.2)\,(10^{-7})}{(0.1)}$$

$$= 600 \times 10^{-7} \text{ newtons (attraction)}$$

Resultant force:

$$F_R = F_{C-D} - F_{E-F} = 1500 \times 10^{-7} - 600 \times 10^{-7}$$

$$= 900 \times 10^{-7} \text{ newtons (repulsion)}$$

The direction of the resultant is the same as the direction of the larger of the two forces, F_{C-D}.

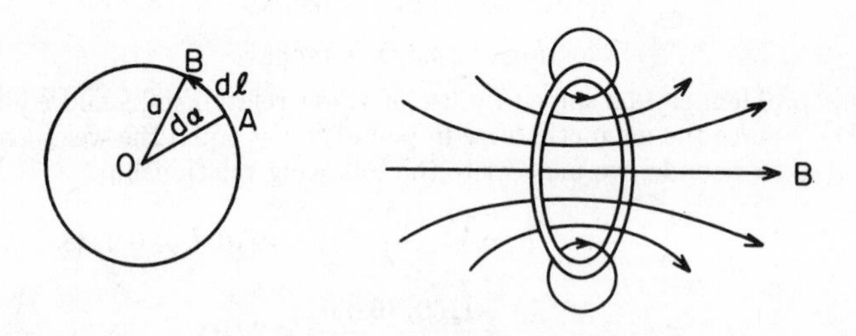

Fig. 10-7. Field around a single turn.

10-5. Magnetic Field of a Solenoid.

The magnetic field at the center *O* of a single circular turn of wire carrying a current *i* can be derived from Fig. 10-7. The magnetic flux *B* is proportional to the current and to the length of the curved path of the current. If the current is *i* in an element of length *dl*, the magnetic field *dB* at the center O in Fig. 10-7 may be written

$$dB = \frac{\mu_0 \, i \, dl}{4 \, \pi \, a^2} \tag{10-21}$$

where $\mu_0/4\pi$ is the constant of proportionality for the mks system of units. Since the angle AOB is very small, the angle in radians is equal to the tangent and to the sine of the angle. If the angle is designated as $d\alpha$, the element of length dl is equal to $a d\alpha$, where a is the radius, or distance from the length dl to the center O. Equation (10-21) may therefore be written

$$dB = \frac{\mu_0 \, i a d\alpha}{4 \, \pi \, a^2} = \frac{\mu_0 \, i d\alpha}{4 \, \pi \, a} \tag{10-22}$$

If every element dB is added for every length dl around the loop, we obtain the total field at the center of the turn,

$$B = \int dB = \frac{\mu_0 \, i}{4 \, \pi \, a} \int_0^{2\pi} d\alpha = \frac{\mu_0 \, i \, (2 \, \pi)}{4 \, \pi \, a}$$

or

$$B = \frac{\mu_0 \, i}{2a} \tag{10-23}$$

If, instead of a single turn of wire, we have a coil of N turns closely grouped together, equation (10-23) becomes

$$B = \frac{\mu_0 \, Ni}{2a} \tag{10-24}$$

The total flux is obtained by multiplying both sides of equation (10-24) by the area of the circular loop $(\pi \, a^2)$, in accordance with equation (10-6).

$$\Phi = \frac{\mu_0 \, Ni \, \pi \, a}{2} \tag{10-25}$$

Equations (10-24) and (10-25) show that although the flux density decreases when the radius a increases, the total flux actually increases. Since inductive reactance depends on the amount of change in flux, the inductive reactance of a transmission line increases when the distance between conductors increases. A transmission line is, in effect, a giant one-turn coil of wire.

A solenoid consists of several turns of wire on a cylindrical frame or spool and it has an air core. Since the coils are spread out over a length l of the frame, equations (10-24) and (10-25) do not apply.

Just as an electrical circuit requires an electromotive force to cause current flow, a magnetic circuit requires a magnetomotive force to produce a magnetic field. The magnetomotive force (mmf) per unit length of the magnetic field is given the symbol H and the unit *ampere-turns per meter* and is called *magnetic intensity.*

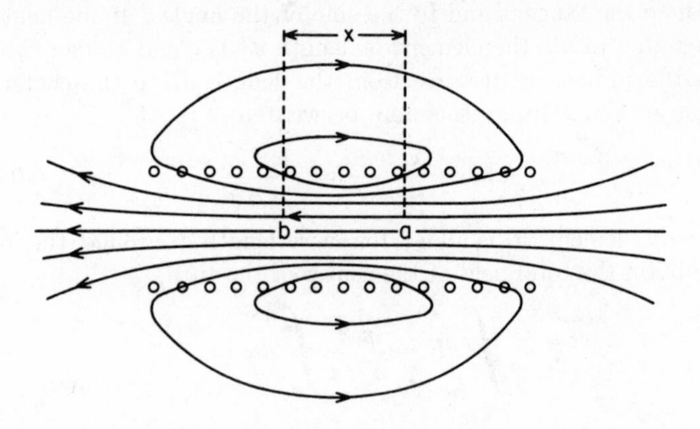

Fig. 10-8. Magnetic field around a solenoid.

Magnetic intensity is defined mathematically by the equation

$$B = \mu H \tag{10-26}$$

where μ is the *permeability* of the material in which the magnetic field exists. This quantity μ is the product of two other quantities, as indicated by the following equation:

$$\mu = K_m \mu_0 \tag{10-27}$$

K_m is the *relative permeability* of the material and μ_0 is the constant 12.57×10^{-7} webers per ampere-meter. The value of K_m for air is approximately 1.00 and K_m is generally given that value.

By definition,

$$H = \frac{Ni}{l} \tag{10-28}$$

where Ni is the number of turns multiplied by the current in amperes (ampere-turns) and l is the length of the coil in meters. Substituting this value for H in equation (10-26) gives the equation

$$B = \frac{\mu Ni}{l} \tag{10-29}$$

For air, equation (10–29) reduces to the following form:

$$B = \frac{\mu_0 Ni}{l} \qquad (10\text{-}30)^{\|}$$

Equation (10-30) applies only to a relatively small length at the center of the solenoid, as indicated in Fig. 10-8. Beyond this short length, some of the flux takes a short path and does not appear at the end of the coil. The flux taking this short path is called "leakage flux" because it reduces the efficiency of electromagnetic devices. By careful design, this leakage flux can be reduced but never eliminated.

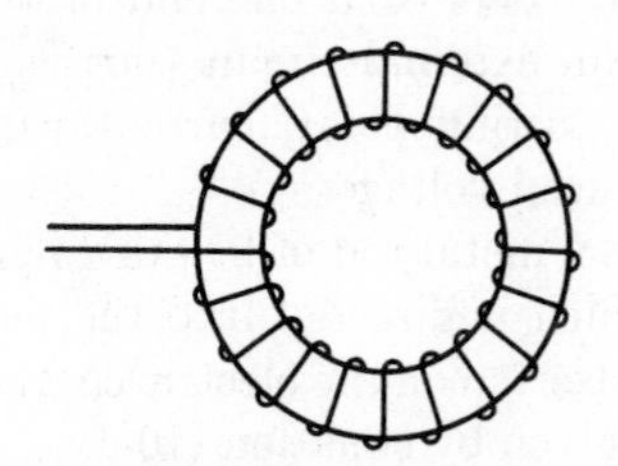

Fig. 10-9. A toroid.

If the solenoid is now bent into a ring or doughnut-shaped coil as shown in Fig. 10-9, it is called a *toroid*. A toroid with an air core is, in effect, a solenoid of infinite length, and equation (10-30) applies at all points in the winding. The flux density is not uniform because the magnetic path at the inner circumference is shorter than at the outer circumference. As toroids are made, however, the difference between the lengths of the outer and inner radii is small compared to the length of either radius, and the flux density varies only slightly.

Example 10-6. A solenoid 15 centimeters long is wound with two layers of wire. If the inner layer consists of 80 turns and the outer layer of 70 turns and the current is 5 amperes, find the magnetic induction at the center of the solenoid. If the two layers are wound in opposite directions, what is the magnetic induction?

‖ A rigorous proof of equation (10-30) involves Ampere's law which is beyond the scope of this book. The rigorous proof can be found in nearly any good text on physics, such as *University Physics* by Sears and Zemansky.

Solution. Both parts of this problem can be solved directly by using equation (10-30).

$$B = \frac{\mu_0 Ni}{l} = \frac{(12.57 \times 10^{-7})\,(70 + 80)\,(5)}{0.15} = 628.5 \times 10^{-5}$$

$$= 6.28 \times 10^{-3} \text{ webers/meter}^2$$

$$B = \frac{(12.57 \times 10^{-7})\,(80 - 70)\,(5)}{0.15} = 41.9 \times 10^{-5}$$

$$= 0.419 \times 10^{-5} \text{ w/m}^2$$

10-6. Induced Electromotive Force. When an electrical conductor is moved through a magnetic field, an electrical voltage is induced in the conductor. If the conductor is so arranged that a closed metallic path exists from one end of the conductor to the other and through an external circuit (not within the same magnetic field) to the starting point, current will flow in the same direction as the induced voltage.

Fig. 10-10*a* shows a metal rod of length l moving to the right in a magnetic field which is directed into the page (away from the viewer). The force exerted on the electric charges within this metal rod or conductor is given by equation (10-4a).

$$F = Bil$$

Since work is equal to force times distance, we may write

$$dW = F ds = Bil\,v dt \tag{10-31}$$

where dW is a small element of work, ds is a small element of distance, v is the velocity of the motion, and dt is the time in which dW and ds are measured. We have learned that current is given by the equation

$$i = \frac{dq}{dt} \tag{10-32}$$

so that

$$dq = i\,dt \tag{10-33}$$

Inserting this value in equation (10-31) gives the relationship

$$dW = B\,l\,v\,dq \tag{10-34}$$

The emf or voltage is, therefore,

$$E = \frac{dW}{dq} = Blv \tag{10-35}$$

where E is the emf in volts and the other quantities have the significance already given them.

Assuming that the electric current is caused by the motion of positive charges (in accordance with our previously discussed convention), the current and voltage will be upward in Fig. 10-10*a*.

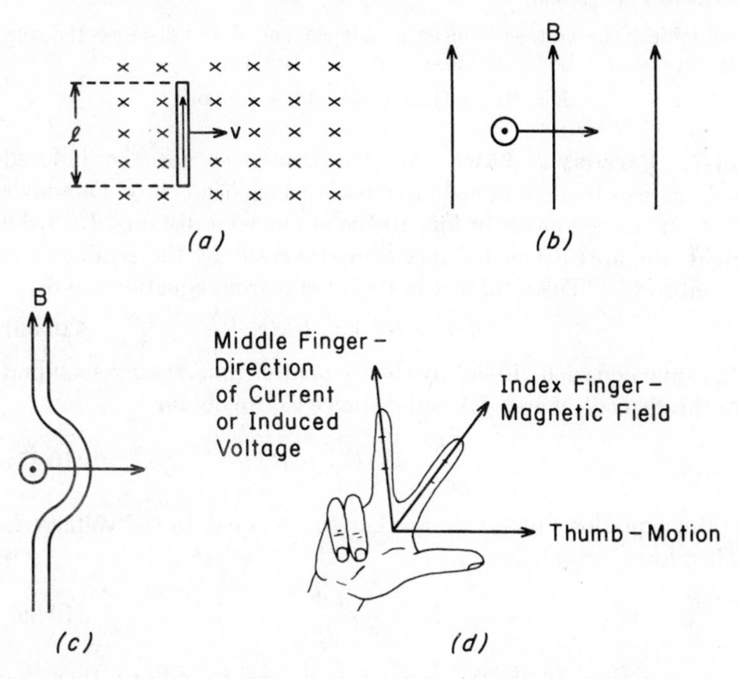

Fig. 10-10. Induced voltage.

Reversing either the magnetic field or the motion—but not both—will reverse the direction of the current and voltage. The determination of the direction can be understood by considering Fig. 10-10*b* and *c*. If the conductor is moved to the right in an upward-directed magnetic field (Fig. 10-10*b*), the flux tends to bend around the conductor as shown in Fig. 10-10*c*. If the right hand is placed so that the fingers indicate the direction of the field as it curves around the wire, the thumb will point outward from the page as indicated by the dot in the circle in Fig. 10-10*c*.

This same information can be obtained by another right hand rule as indicated in Fig. 10-10*d*. If the index finger of the right hand points in the direction of the flux and the thumb points in the direction in which the conductor is moving through the field, the middle finger will point in the direction of the induced voltage or current.

Example 10-7. A straight conductor 15 centimeters long is moved at right angles through a field whose density is 1.5 webers per square meter. Find the induced emf in the conductor if it is moving at a velocity of 20 meters per second.

Solution. The voltage induced is independent of the distance the conductor travels. Equation (10-35) gives the result:

$$E = Blv = (1.5)\,(0.15)\,(20) = 4.5 \text{ volts}$$

10-7. Faraday's Law. Another expression for the induced voltage can be determined on a basis which leads into Faraday's law. If the conductor in Fig. 10-10*a* is moved a distance ds to the right, the area dA of the flux field traversed by the conductor is equal to lds. The total flux in this area is from equation (10-6):

$$d\,\Phi = B\,dA = Blds \tag{10-36}$$

Dividing equation (10-36) by the element of time dt corresponding to the element of area dA and distance ds, we obtain

$$\frac{d\,\Phi}{dt} = B\,l\frac{ds}{dt} = B\,l\,v \tag{10-37}$$

But equation (10-35) shows that Blv is equal to the voltage E. Therefore,

$$E = -\frac{d\,\Phi}{dt} \tag{10-38}$$

In equation (10-38) the minus sign is used to indicate that the induced voltage is always in a direction which opposes the forces that cause the voltage to be induced. Equation (10-36)—which is called Faraday's law—is especially adaptable to use with transformers where the value of Φ changes but the conductors remain stationary.

If the coil in which the voltage is induced consists of N turns, equations (10-35) and (10-38) may be written

$$E = NBlv \tag{10-35a}$$

$$E = -N\frac{d\,\Phi}{dt} \tag{10-38a}$$

Equation (10-35a) assumes that only one side of the coil is moving in a magnetic field. If the coil is moving in such a way that both sides are moving in magnetic fields of opposite polarity—as in a motor or a generator—the length l must equal the total length of the coil in the two fields.

Example 10-8. A magnetic field varies at the rate of 200×10^{-4} webers in 0.1 second. If the flux links a coil of 100 turns, what is the voltage induced in the coil?

Solution. Equation (10-38a) is used for the solution.

$$E = -\frac{(100)(200 \times 10^{-4})}{(0.1)} = -20 \text{ volts}$$

Since the negative sign in equation (10-38a) is used to indicate only direction, it can be ignored when only the magnitude of the voltage is desired. The answer to this problem, then, is 20 volts, as the negative sign has no significance in the solution.

10-8. Lenz's Law. H. F. E. Lenz (1804-1865) is credited with the discovery of the law which bears his name. Lenz's law states that the direction of an induced current is such as to oppose the cause producing it. In other words, if a conductor which is a part of a closed electrical circuit is placed in a changing (varying) magnetic field, the current induced in the conductor will produce a magnetic flux opposed to that of the original field. Lenz's law accounts for the negative sign in equation (10-38a).

The conductor may be a part of the circuit which produces the flux or a part of another circuit which is linked by that flux. In Fig. 10-11*a* is shown a solenoid carrying current from a generator G. This generator delivers a varying voltage. As the current increases, the flux around the coil increases, so that the flux density B increases. According to equation (10-35), an increase in B results in an increase in the induced voltage. The direction of this voltage is such that it opposes the applied voltage from the generator, thereby retarding the buildup of current in the coil.

When the current from the voltage source G decreases, the flux in the coil decreases. As indicated by equation (10-38a), the change in flux causes an increase in voltage, but this voltage is now in the same direction as the applied voltage and tends to keep the current flowing in the same direction and at the same value. Thus, the voltage induced in the solenoid or coil opposes the change in flux but not the flux itself.

Bar magnets and electromagnets—including solenoids—have magnetic "poles" at each end where most of the magnetic field leaves and enters the magnet. The magnetic flux leaves the north pole of the magnet and enters the south pole, as indicated in Fig. 10-11*a*. When two opposite magnetic poles are brought together, some of the flux from the north pole of one magnet will enter the south pole of the other and exert an attractive force between the two magnets. When two like poles are brought together, however, the magnetic fields at the ends of the magnets will become crowded and will exert a repelling force.

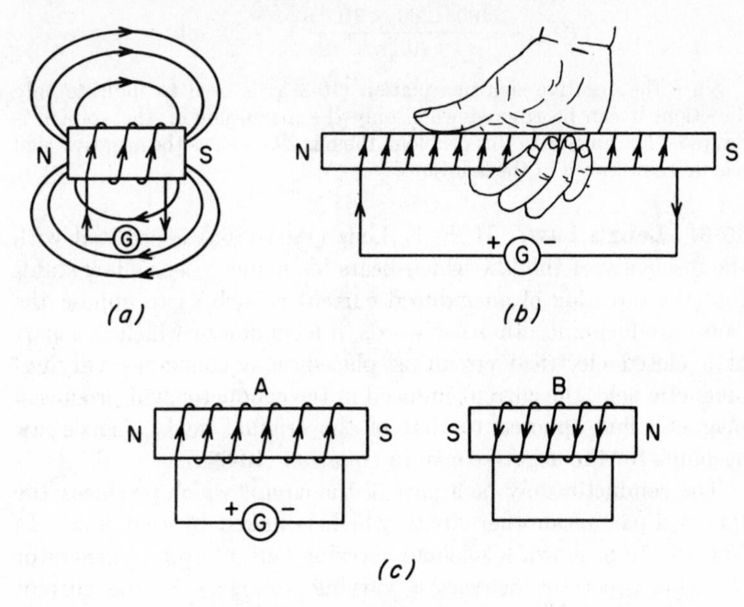

Fig. 10-11. Induced currents.

A right hand rule can be used to determine the north pole of an electromagnet or a solenoid, as shown in Fig. 10-11*b*. Grasp the electromagnet with the fingers of the right hand pointing in the direction of current flow and the thumb will point in the direction of the north pole.

If a solenoid is supplied by a varying voltage from voltage source G in Fig. 10-11*c*, the right hand rule will determine the location of the north and south magnetic poles as indicated. If a coil which is connected to a closed circuit is brought near the first coil, the varying magnetic field from the first coil links the second coil, causing current to flow.

In Fig. 10-11*c*, coil A is energized in such a way that a north pole N appears at the left and a south pole at the right. When coil B is brought near the south pole of coil A, a voltage is induced in coil B which causes a south pole at the left and a north pole at the right, with a resulting repulsion between the two coils. If coil A is energized by alternating current, the condition shown in Fig. 10-11c is reversed as the alternating current reverses, but always in such a way as to oppose a change in the inducing current, in accordance with Lenz's law.

The opposing voltage induced by a coil in its own windings is called the counter-emf (or back emf) of self-induction. When the voltage is induced in another coil, it is called an induced voltage. When coils are placed in the same magnetic field as shown in Fig. 10-11c, coil A and coil B each exert self-induction on their own turns. In addition, coil A exerts mutual induction in coil B and coil B exerts mutual induction in coil A.

This discussion regarding mutual induction and induced voltages is incomplete as given here. Further discussion is deferred until the study of transformers in Chapter 11.

10-9. Induced EMF in a Rotating Coil. Today most electrical power is obtained by use of a rotating machine, called a generator, which consists of coils of wire rotating in a magnetic field. If l is the length of the coil whose sides are placed perpendicular to the direction of the field, and w is the width of the coil (distance between the two sides), the velocity v of the coil is found by multiplying the width by its angular velocity. Thus,

$$v = \omega \frac{w}{2} \tag{10-39}$$

where ω is equal to 2π times the frequency at which the coil passes a pair of poles (one north and one south).

The coil is perpendicular to the field in only one place, when $\sin \alpha = 1$ and $\alpha = 90°$, α being measured with respect to a plane which is perpendicular to the magnetic field. When the edges of the coil are traveling parallel to the field, the flux within the coil is not changing, and no voltage can be induced in the coil at that time. Multiplying equation (10-39) by $\sin \alpha$ gives

$$v \sin \alpha = \omega \frac{w}{2} \sin \alpha \tag{10-40}$$

Inserting $v \sin \alpha$ in equation (10-35a) for v gives the equation for the voltage in a rotating coil:

$$E = NBlv \sin \alpha = \tfrac{1}{2} NBl\omega w \sin \alpha \tag{10-41}$$

There are two sides to a coil, and both sides are generating voltage in the same direction. Therefore, equation (10-41) can be written

$$E = NBlw\omega \sin \alpha \quad (10\text{-}42)$$

The product lw is equal to the area A of the coil. Therefore,

$$E = NBA\,\omega \sin \alpha \quad (10\text{-}43)$$

When $\sin \alpha = 1$, equation (10-43) gives the maximum voltage generated in the coil:

$$E_m = NBA\,\omega \quad (10\text{-}44)$$

Substituting equation (10-44) in equation (10-43) gives the expression for the voltage obtained in Section 8-4,

$$e = E_m \sin \alpha \quad (10\text{-}45)$$

where e is the instantaneous voltage and α is equal to ωt or $2\pi ft$.

10-10. Magnetic Properties of Matter. All substances must be considered to be conductors of magnetic flux. A magnetic field cannot be stopped or controlled by the use of insulators because there is no magnetic insulator or insulation. On the contrary, if we want to prevent the presence of large or small stray magnetic fields in instruments that might be damaged by them, we must use magnetic shields which are such good conductors of magnetism that the fields will use them instead of the instruments.

From the standpoint of magnetic conduction, matter can be classified under three types:

1. *Paramagnetic materials* which will conduct magnetic lines only very slightly better than a vacuum.

2. *Diamagnetic materials* which will conduct magnetic lines less readily than a vacuum.

3. *Ferromagnetic materials* which may conduct magnetic lines several hundred times as readily as a vacuum.

The ability of a material to conduct magnetism is referred to as *relative permeability* and is given the symbol K_m as indicated in equation (10-27). For the three types of materials, K_m has values as follows:

1. Paramagnetic materials have a relative permeability slightly greater than 1.

2. Diamagnetic materials have a relative permeability slightly less than 1.

3. Ferromagnetic materials usually have relative permeabilities many times greater than 1. When a coil of wire is wound around

annealed iron, and a current flows in the coil, the relative permeability of the iron may be 300 when the value of the magnetic intensity H (see equation 10-28) is 10 ampere-turns per meter. However, when the current is increased so that the magnetic intensity is 20 ampere-turns per meter, the relative permeability may change to 400. If the intensity is increased to 150, the relative permeability may reach 5300. A further increase in the magnetic intensity may be accompanied by a decrease in permeability, indicating that the material is becoming saturated. If the magnetic intensity is increased to a high enough value (say, more than 1,000,000 ampere-turns per meter) the relative permeability will approach the value 1, indicating complete saturation. The figures given here are merely approximate and will vary according to alloy, heat treatment, method of manufacture, etc. Even when all conditions of manufacture are held as constant as industrially possible, an annealed iron manufactured and tested today may show magnetic characteristics somewhat different from those of the same kind of iron manufactured yesterday. The difference will be slight but may be important.

For most electrical engineering purposes, all non-ferromagnetic materials, including air and vacuum, are considered to have a relative permeability of 1.

One method of checking permeability is to shape the iron into a circle and wind a coil around it, making it, effectively, a toroid with an iron or steel core. Such a coil is called a Rowland ring. The magnetic intensity of this ring is given by equation (10-28) which is repeated here:

$$H = \frac{Ni}{l}$$

The magnetic intensity is independent of the nature of the core. A second coil is wound over the main coil of the Rowland ring for a short distance and is connected to a meter. When a voltage is impressed on the coil, the meter registers a voltage that is higher than it would be if the ring had an air core. The difference in voltage with an air core and with a ferromagnetic core is a measure of the permeability of the material.

Example 10-9. A Rowland ring, made of iron, has a mean circumferential length of 40 centimeters and cross-section of 1 square centimeter. It is wound uniformly with 450 turns of wire. Measurements made with a search coil around the ring show that the current in the windings is 0.05

ampere and the flux in the ring is 6×10^{-6} weber. Compute the flux density, the magnetic intensity, the permeability, and the relative permeability.

Solution. The flux density is found by use of equation (10-6).

$$B = \frac{\Phi}{A} = \frac{6 \times 10^{-6} \text{ webers}}{10^{-4} \text{ meter}} = 6 \times 10^{-2} \text{ w/m}^2$$

The magnetic intensity is found from equation (10-28).

$$H = \frac{Ni}{l} = \frac{(450)\,(0.05) \text{ amp-turns}}{0.4 \text{ meter}} = 56.3 \text{ amp-turns/m}$$

The permeability μ is found by use of equation (10-26).

$$\mu = \frac{B}{H} = \frac{6 \times 10^{-2}}{56.3} = 1066 \times 10^{-6} \text{ w/amp-m}$$

The relative permeability is obtained by use of equation (10-27).

$$K_m = \frac{\mu}{\mu_0} = \frac{1066 \times 10^{-6}}{12.57 \times 10^{-7}} = 850$$

The relative permeability is just a number and has no unit of measurement.

10-11. Magnetization Curves. From equation (10-26), we see that the permeability of a material is

$$\mu = \frac{B}{H} \tag{10-46}$$

The density (B) and the intensity (H) of a magnetic field can be determined by various methods, including the Rowland ring method. Using the density (B) as the ordinate and the intensity (H) as the abscissa, curves showing the relation between these quantities can be drawn for any ferromagnetic material. Fig. 10-12 shows curves for four materials: cast iron, soft steel castings, annealed sheet steel, and wrought iron.

Of the materials shown in Fig. 10-12, only one—annealed sheet steel—has characteristics that are useful in the design of electrical machinery. The curve for this material is approximately straight until the flux density is 0.77 weber per square meter. At this point, the curve changes its slope gradually, forming what is called the "knee" of the curve, indicating that the material is becoming saturated. At complete saturation, the increase in flux density with an increase in magnetic intensity is approximately the same as for air.

The other three materials have no straight line portion or—

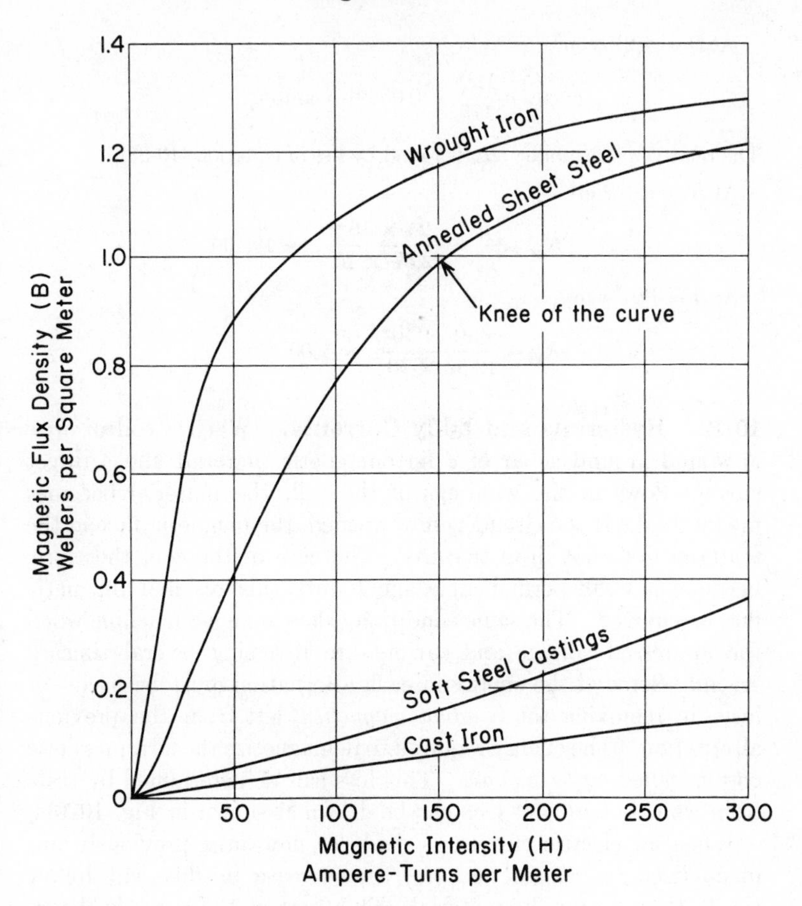

Fig. 10-12. Some *B-H* curves.

as in cast iron—have such a low flux density that they are generally unsuitable for use in electrical machinery.

The materials depicted by curves in Fig. 10-12 are merely representative, as there are many ferromagnetic materials available.

Example 10-10. Using Fig. 10-12, find the permeability and relative permeability for wrought iron when the flux density is 0.6 and 1.21 webers per square meter.

Solution. The permeability is found by use of equation (10-46).

At $B = 0.6 \text{ w/m}^2$,

$$\mu = \frac{B}{H} = \frac{0.6}{25} = 0.024 \text{ w/amp-m}$$

At $B = 1.21 \text{ w/m}^2$,

$$\mu = \frac{1.21}{175} = 0.00691 \text{ w/amp-m}$$

The relative permeability K_m is found by use of equation (10-27).

At $B = 0.6 \text{ w/m}^2$,

$$K_m = \frac{\mu}{\mu_0} = \frac{24 \times 10^{-3}}{12.57 \times 10^{-7}} = 19{,}100$$

At $B = 1.21 \text{ w/m}^2$,

$$K_m = \frac{6.91 \times 10^{-3}}{12.57 \times 10^{-7}} = 5500$$

10-12. Hysteresis and Eddy Currents. When a coil of wire is wound around a bar of a ferromagnetic material and a direct current flows in the windings of the coil, the material becomes magnetized. If the circuit is now opened, the magnetic flux in the material does not drop to zero. The core of the coil, therefore, becomes a weak permanent magnet until this residual magnetic flux is removed. The same condition exists in an a-c machine when the impressed voltage and current are reversing several times a second. Some of the energy in each alternation must be used—or lost—in removing the *residual magnetism* left from the previous alternation. The energy required to demagnetize the ferromagnetic core is called *hysteresis loss*. This loss can be determined by tests from which a *hysteresis loop* can be drawn as shown in Fig. 10-13*a*.

When an electric current is made to flow in a previously unmagnetized ferromagnetic core, the increase in flux will follow the B-H curve for the material. This part of the curve is shown from 0 to 1 in Fig. 10-13*a*. If the circuit is now opened, the flux will not return to zero but will drop to a value such as 2 in the figure. The flux from 0 to 2 is therefore called the *retentivity* of the material, since this is the flux retained when the coil current is zero. A current must now be put through the coil in the opposite direction. If this reverse current is equal to the original current, the flux will pass along the curve through point 3 to 4, which is equal in value to point 1 but with both B and H negative with respect to the previous values. At point 3, the magnetic flux is zero, and a magnetic intensity equal to the distance from 0 to 3 is required to demagnetize the core. This value of H from 0 to 3 is called *coercive force*.

The same conditions exist from point 4 back to 1 through 5 and 6.

The value of B from 0 to 5 is also called retentivity and is equal to the value from 0 to 2. The value of H from 0 to 6 is also called coercive force and is equal to the value from 0 to 3.

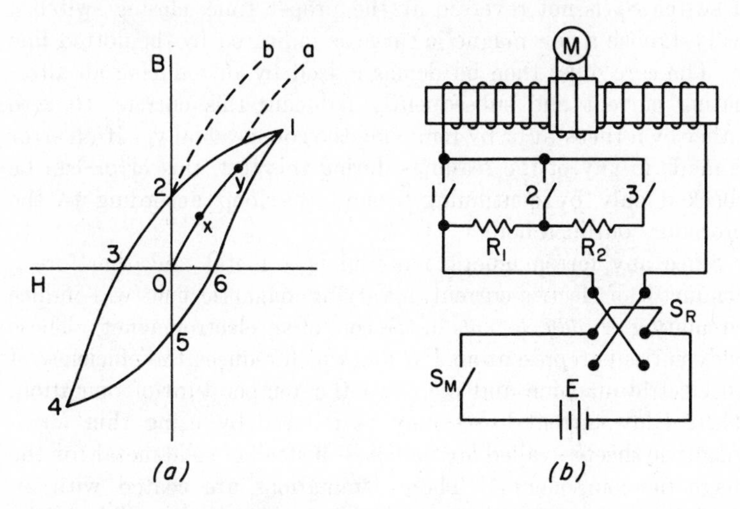

Fig. 10-13. Circuit for hysteresis check.

A circuit for determining points on the hysteresis loop is shown in Fig. 10-13*b*. Closing switch 3 will put part of the battery voltage E (minus the drop through R_1 and R_2) across the coil. The deflection of the meter M will indicate a flux along the B-H curve, as at X in Fig. 10-13*a*. Switches S_M and S_R are closed. Closing switch 2 will determine point Y on the curve, and closing switch 1 will establish point 1, the maximum condition for the voltage used in this test.

The switches are now opened in the reverse order, 1, 2, and 3. When switch 3 is opened, the magnetic condition is indicated by point 2 in Fig. 10-13*a*, with $H = 0$ and B equal to the retentivity. Reversing switch S_R must now be reversed in position to reverse the current through the coil. Closing switches in the order 3, 2, 1, will determine points on the line 2, 3, and 4. Opening the switches in the order 1, 2, 3 will determine point 5 of the hysteresis loop, and closing them in the order 3, 2, 1 will return the conditions to point 1.

In this test, the operator must be very careful to close and open the switches in the proper order and the reversing switch must be changed in position at the right time. If the test is at point 1 in Fig. 10-13*a* and switch 1 is opened, switch 2 must be opened next.

If switch 1 is closed instead, the condition will not return along the hysteresis curve to point 1 but will establish a new magnetic curve as indicated by the dotted line *a*. When point 2 is reached, if switch S_R is not reversed at the proper time, closing switch 3 will establish a new magnetic curve as indicated by the dotted line *b*. The core must then be demagnetized by introducing an alternating current and subsequently reducing this current to zero either by a rheostat or by removing the core gradually. If an error is made in any of the readings during this test, this error can be checked only by continuing around the loop according to the procedure outlined here.

Since any ferromagnetic material is a metal and therefore a conductor of electric current, a varying magnetic field will induce circulating or *eddy currents* in the core of an electromagnet. These eddy currents represent an I^2R loss which reduces the efficiency of an electric machine and increases the temperature of operation. These eddy current losses may be reduced by using thin ferromagnetic sheets—called *laminations*—instead of solid metal for the magnetic components. These laminations are coated with an insulating varnish to present as high a resistance as possible in the path of the eddy currents.

10-13. Reluctance and Magnetomotive Force. Magnetic flux bears some similarities to an electric current. For example, some force is required to move the flux. Since all materials do not have the same permeability, some materials offer a higher resistance to the flow of flux than do others. This resistance to magnetic flux is called *reluctance* and is given the symbol $\mathcal{R}$. The magnetic "voltage" is called *magnetomotive force* and is given the symbol $\mathfrak{F}$ or, simply, mmf.

If H is multiplied by the length of a part of the magnetic circuit, we have the relation

$$\mathfrak{F} = Hl = Ni \tag{10-47}$$

Equation (10-47) shows that the unit for magnetomotive force in the mks system is the ampere-turn. The length l is the length of the coil in meters and is not necessarily the length of the magnetic circuit.

Equation (10-6) shows the relation between total flux Φ and magnetic density B:

$$\Phi = BA$$

But $B = \mu H$, as shown by equation (10-26), and $H = Ni/l$ as shown by equation (10-28). Substituting these values in equation (10-6), we find that

$$\Phi = \frac{\mu NiA}{l} = Ni\left(\frac{A\mu}{l}\right) = \frac{Ni}{\dfrac{l}{\mu A}} \qquad (10\text{-}48)$$

The relation $l/\mu A$ is called the reluctance, and therefore the total flux Φ is found by the equation

$$\Phi = \frac{\mathfrak{F}}{\mathfrak{R}} \qquad (10\text{-}49)$$

Example 10-11. A core of annealed sheet steel is wound with 1500 turns of wire through which a current of 0.012 ampere is flowing. If the length of the coil (and the magnetic path) is 20 centimeters and the area of the core is 3 square centimeters, find the reluctance of the path, the magnetomotive force, and the total flux.

Solution. The magnetic intensity H is first determined from equation (10-28).

$$H = \frac{Ni}{l} = \frac{(1500)\,(0.012)}{0.2} = 90 \text{ amp-turns/m}$$

The flux density B is now determined from the proper curve of Fig. 10-12 to be 0.72 weber per square meter. The permeability, from equation (10-46), is

$$\mu = \frac{B}{H} = \frac{0.72}{90} = 0.008 \text{ w/amp-m}$$

The reluctance, as indicated by equation (10-48), is

$$\mathfrak{R} = \frac{l}{\mu A} = \frac{2 \times 10^{-1}}{(8 \times 10^{-3})\,(3 \times 10^{-4})} = 83{,}300 \text{ units}$$

The mmf is determined by equation (10-47).

$$\mathfrak{F} = Ni = (1500)\,(0.012) = 18 \text{ amp-turns}$$

The total flux can be determined by use of either equation (10-6) or equation (10-49).

$$\Phi = BA = (72 \times 10^{-2})\,(3 \times 10^{-4}) = 216 \times 10^{-6} \text{ webers}$$

$$\Phi = \frac{\mathfrak{F}}{\mathfrak{R}} = \frac{18}{83{,}300} = 216 \times 10^{-6} \text{ webers}$$

Example 10-12. If the magnetic circuit of Example 10-11 has an air gap of 0.2 centimeter in addition to the 20 centimeters of annealed sheet steel path, how many ampere-turns would be required to maintain a magnetic field density of 0.72 weber per square meter, assuming that the area of the air gap is the same as the area of the steel core?

Solution. The total reluctance of the circuit is the reluctance of the steel path plus the reluctance of the air gap. The permeability of air is 12.57×10^{-7} webers per ampere-meter. The reluctance of the steel, as determined in Example 10-11, is 83,300. The reluctance of the air gap is $l/\mu A$.

$$\mathcal{R}_A = \frac{2 \times 10^{-3}}{(12.57 \times 10^{-7})(3 \times 10^{-4})} = 5.3 \times 10^6 = 5{,}300{,}000$$

The total reluctance is the sum of the two.

$$\mathcal{R}_T = \mathcal{R}_A + \mathcal{R} = 5{,}300{,}000 + 83{,}300 = 5{,}383{,}300 \text{ or } 5.4 \times 10^6$$

The total flux, from Example 10-11, is to be 216×10^{-6} webers. The mmf in ampere-turns is found by use of equation (10-49).

$$\mathfrak{F} = \mathcal{R}_T \Phi = (5.4 \times 10^6)(216 \times 10^{-6}) = 1166 \text{ amp-turns}$$

Since only 18 ampere-turns were required when there was no air gap, this example shows the engineering penalty that must be paid when an air gap is required, as in a motor. In this example, the air gap is only 1 per cent as long as the steel, yet its reluctance is nearly 65 times as great.

Problems Based on Chapter 10

P10-1. A conductor shaped as shown in Fig. P10-1 carries a current of 50 amps and lies in a uniform magnetic field of 0.03 w/m². Find the magnitude and direction of the force on the conductor.

Ans. 1.5 newtons, into the page.

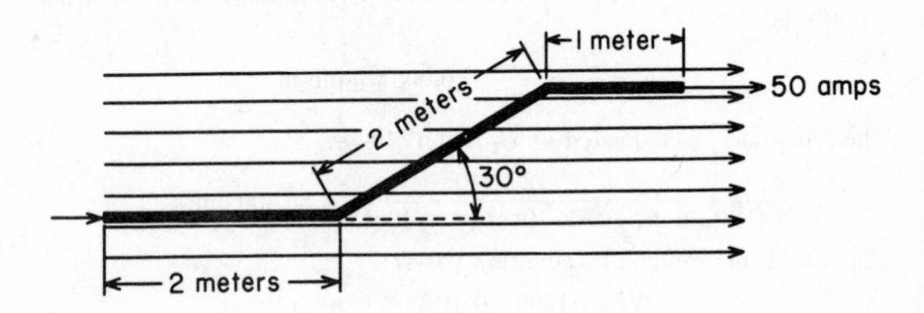

Fig. P10-1.

P10-2. An electron is moving in a direction perpendicular to a uniform magnetic field at a velocity of 5 m/sec. If the magnetic density of the field is 0.02 w/m², what is the force on the electron?

Ans. 1.602×10^{-20} newtons. (Note that the charge on an electron is -1.602×10^{-19} coulomb.)

P10-3. In Fig. P10-3, a uniform magnetic field of 0.4 w/m² is directed parallel to the x-axis. Using the values and direction of current given in the figure, find the amount and direction of the forces on (a) conductor a-b, (b) conductor b-c, and (c) conductor c-d.

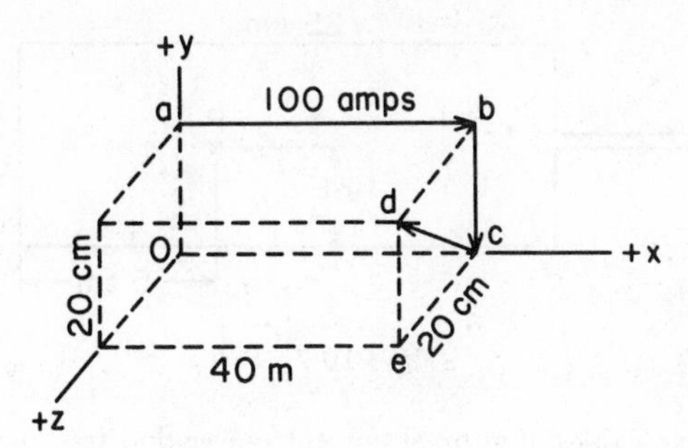

Fig. P10-3.

Ans. (a) Zero because the current is parallel to the field. (b) 8 newtons, toward side *d-e*. (c) 11.3 newtons, toward point *b*.

P10-4. The total flux threading a coil whose area is 5 cm^2 is 0.005 weber. If the coil consists of 10 turns and its axis (center line) is perpendicular to the magnetic field, what is the force exerted on one side of the coil when the current in the coil is 20 amps and each turn is 15 cm long?

Ans. ($B = 10$ w/m^2) $F = 300$ newtons.

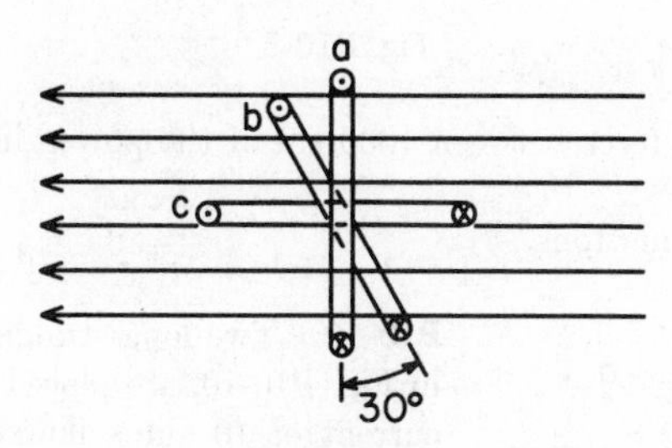

Fig. P10-5.

P10-5. In Fig. P10-5, a coil is shown in three positions in relation to a magnetic field. The coil is 10 cm long, 8 cm wide, and carries a current of 10 amps. The field has a total flux of 0.05 weber. What is the amount and direction of the torque exerted on the coil in the three positions shown if the coil consists of 5 turns?

Ans. (a) Zero. (b) 1.25 m-n, ccw. (c) 2.50 m-n, ccw.

P10-6. A long straight wire carries a current of 15 amps. What is the flux density at a distance of 3 cm from the wire?

Ans. $10^{-4} = 0.0001$ w/m^2.

P10-7. Find the flux density at point *P* in Fig. P10-7 if the current in the single turn of wire is 60 amps. Neglect the effect of the field around the lead-in wires.

Ans. 6.31×10^{-4} w/m^2.

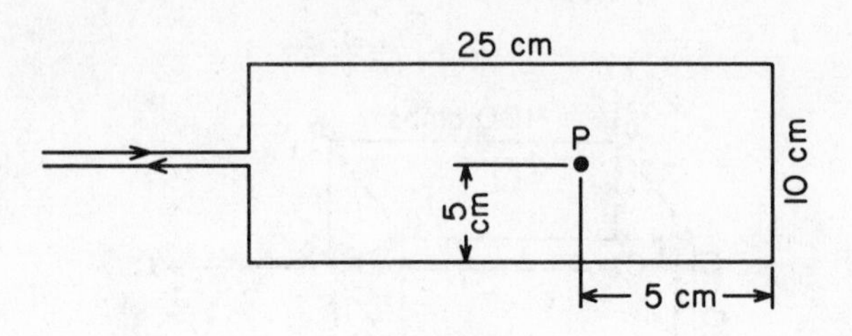

Fig. P10-7.

P10-8. The two cables of a direct current power line are 20 cm apart, as shown in Fig. P10-8. Find the flux density at a point midway between the conductors of the telephone line in the figure if the power line current is 75 amps.
Ans. 23×10^{-7} w/m^2.

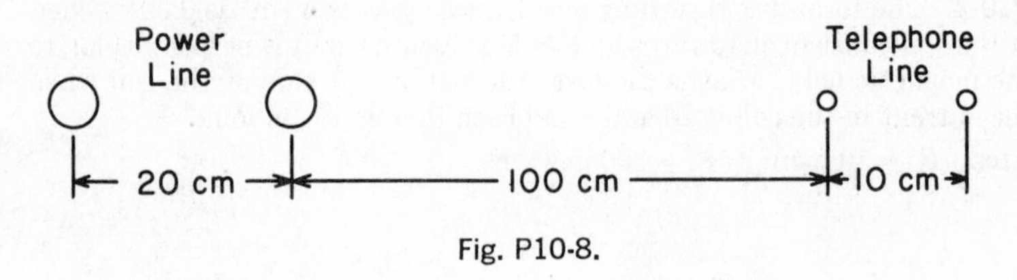

Fig. P10-8.

P10-9. Find the force between 1000 cm of the power line conductors of problem P10-8.
Ans. 56×10^{-3} newtons.

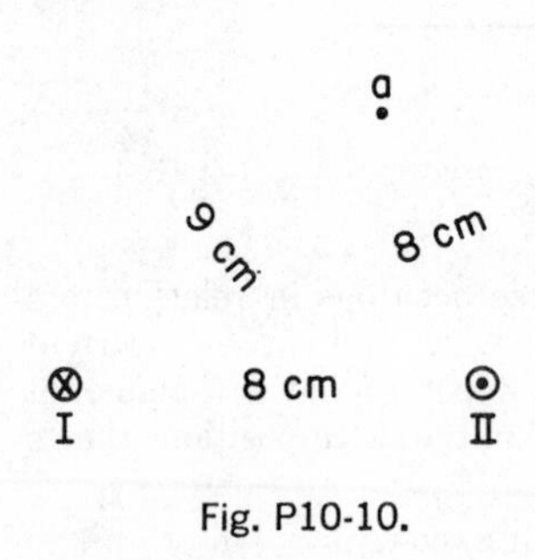

Fig. P10-10.

P10-10. Two long straight wires, I and II in Fig. P10-10, are placed 8 cm apart. If a current of 10 amps flows in wire I, what must be the current in wire II for the flux density at point a to be zero if point a is 8 cm from II and 9 cm from I? With this current in II, what is the force per meter between the two wires?
Ans. Current in II = 8.9 amps. $F = 22.3 \times 10^{-5}$ newtons meter.

P10-11. In Fig. P10-11, wires I and II represent the two sides of a one-turn coil, and III is the end view of a long straight conductor. The coil is 15 cm in length, parallel to the straight conductor, and carries 20 amps of current in the direction indicated. Wire III carries 25 amps. Find the amount and direction of the force exerted between the coil and the wire.
Ans. 1250×10^{-7} newtons at an angle of 27.3° upward to the left from line ab.

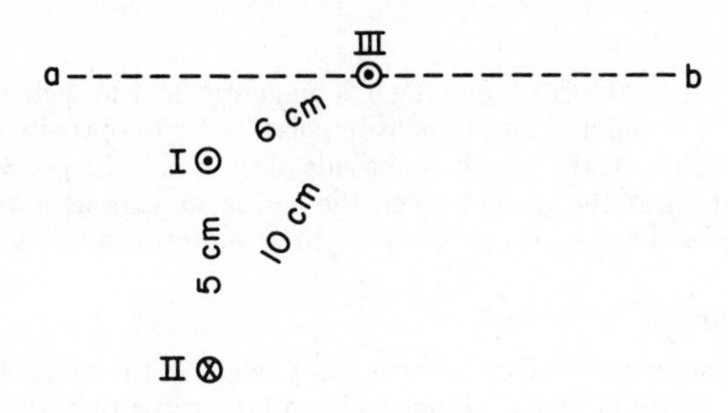

Fig. P10-11.

P10-12. A solenoid 15 cm in length is wound with 1000 turns of wire carrying a current of 2 amps. What is the flux density at the center of the coil? If the solenoid has a cross-sectional area of 2 cm², what is the total flux?

Ans. $B = 0.0167$ w/m². $\Phi = 333 \times 10^{-8}$ w.

P10-13. A toroid has an outer diameter of 8 cm and an inner diameter of 6 cm. If there are 3000 amp-turns on the coil, what is the flux density in the air core?

Ans. 0.01715 w/m². (Note that the mean length is 22 cm.)

P10-14. The induction B of a uniform magnetic field between the poles of an electromagnet is 0.8 w/m². Find the induced emf in a straight conductor 20 cm long moving at a velocity of 1.5 m/sec perpendicular to the magnetic field and its own length.

Ans. 0.24 volt.

P10-15. The dotted lines in Fig. P10-15 indicate distances, lengths, and directions. A uniform magnetic field of 0.5 w/m² is directed parallel to the x-axis as indicated by the arrow pointing from C toward x. AB, BC, and DE are separate conductors moving at a velocity of 1 m/sec in the following directions: AB toward D; BC toward AE; and DE in the direction of the magnetic field. Find the voltage induced in every one of the conductors.

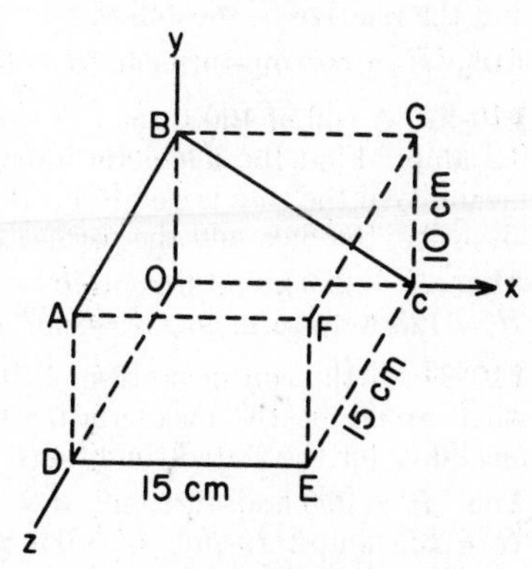

Fig. P10-15.

Ans. $E_{AB} = 0.075$ volt. $E_{BC} = 0.05$ volt. $E_{DE} = 0$ volt.

P10-16. If conductor AB moves toward EC, all other conditions as described in problem P10-15 remaining the same, what is the voltage induced in AB? What is the voltage if AB moves toward FG, parallel to the magnetic field?

Ans. 0.0416 volt. 0 volt.

P10-17. A coil of 20 turns is moving in a magnetic field in such a way that its two sides are under fields of opposite polarity (or in opposite directions in the same field). If the length of one side of the coil is 10 cm, what is the voltage induced at the instant when the coil is moving at a velocity of 15 m/sec in a direction perpendicular to a uniform magnetic field of 0.5 w/m^2?

Ans. 30 volts.

P10-18. A rectangular coil of 20 turns has a length in the magnetic field of 28 cm and a width of 18 cm. If the coil is rotating in a uniform magnetic field at the angular velocity of 377 radians/sec (f = 60 cycles/sec), find the maximum and the effective values of the voltages induced in the coil if the density of the magnetic field is 0.6 w/m.

Ans. E_m = 228 volts. E_{RMS} = 161 volts.

P10-19. A solenoid 10 cm long is made of a coil of 200 turns. What are the density and the intensity of the magnetic field when a current of 1 amp is flowing in the coil?

Ans. B = 25.14 $\times$ 10^{-4} w/m^2. H = 2000 amp-turns/m.

P10-20. When it has an annealed iron core, a coil has a flux of 1.44 w/m^2 at a magnetic intensity of 500 amp-turns/m. Find the permeability and the relative permeability.

Ans. μ = 28,800 $\times$ 10^{-7} w/amp-m. K_m = 2290.

P10-21. The permeability of an annealed iron core is 56,000 $\times$ 10^{-7} w/amp-m when the current is 0.08 amp and the coil consists of 200 turns on a core 20 cm in length. Find the magnetic intensity, the flux density, and the relative permeability.

Ans. H = 80 amp-turns/m. B = 0.45 w/m^2. K_m = 4460.

P10-22. A coil of 100 turns is 8 cm in length. The current in the coil is 0.2 amp. Find the magnetic intensity, the magnetic flux, and the permeability if the core is cast iron. If the current drops to 0.1 amp, find the intensity, the flux, and the permeability. (See Fig. 10-12, p. 249.)

Ans. H = 250 amp-turns/m. B = 0.13 w/m^2. μ = 52 $\times$ 10^{-5} w/amp-m. H = 125 amp-turns/m. B = 0.07 w/m^2. μ = 56 $\times$ 10^{-5} w/amp-m.

P10-23. If the coil in problem P10-22 had an annealed sheet steel core, what would be the magnetic intensity, the flux density, and the permeability for the stated conditions?

Ans. H = 250 amp-turns/m. B = 1.17 w/m^2. μ = 47 $\times$ 10^{-4} w/amp-m. H = 125 amp-turns/m. B = 0.9 w/m^2. μ = 72 $\times$ 10^{-4} w/amp-m.

P10-24. What are the reluctance and the magnetomotive force for the conditions stated in problem P10-22 if the core has a cross-sectional area of 2 cm^2?

Ans. $\mathfrak{F}$ = 20 amp-turns. $\mathcal{R}$ = 770,000. $\mathfrak{F}$ = 10 amp-turns. $\mathcal{R}$ = 715,000.

P10-25. What are the reluctance and the magnetomotive force for the conditions stated in problem P10-23 if the core has a cross-sectional area of 2 cm^2?

Ans. $\mathfrak{F}$ = 20 amp-turns. $\mathcal{R}$ = 8500. $\mathfrak{F}$ = 10 amp-turns. $\mathcal{R}$ = 5550.

11 ALTERNATING-CURRENT MACHINERY

11-1. The Transformer. The weber is defined as the magnetic flux which links an electric conductor in one second in order to induce an average emf of one volt. Since a coil of a transformer is made up of N turns (or conductors), the average voltage induced in the coil is given by the equation

$$E_{av} = \frac{N\,\Phi_m}{t} \tag{11-1}$$

where E_{av} is the average induced emf in volts, N is the number of turns in the coil, Φ_m is the maximum magnetic flux in webers, and t is the time in seconds required for the magnetic field to change from zero to Φ_m or from Φ_m to zero.

The flux is induced by the current and is, therefore, in step with the current and the voltage. Since the current is a sine wave, the ferromagnetic core is chosen so that the flux will also be a sine wave. Under these conditions, the time required for the flux to change from zero to Φ_m is one-fourth of a cycle, or $t = 1/4f$. Equation (11-1) can therefore be written

$$E_{av} = \frac{N\,\Phi_m}{1/4f} = 4fN\,\Phi_m \tag{11-2}$$

In Section 8-7, it was shown that the average value of a sine wave is 0.636 times the peak value and the effective value is 0.707 (or $1/\sqrt{2}$) times the peak value. The form factor is 1.11. Therefore, the effective value E of the induced voltage is given by the equations

$$E = 1.11\,E_{av} \tag{11-3}$$

$$E = 4.44fN\,\Phi_m \tag{11-4}$$

If E is the primary voltage E_p, then N_p is the number of turns in the primary coil. If E is the voltage in the secondary of the transformer E_s, then N_s is the number of turns in the secondary coil.

Since, in a transformer, both coils are wound around the same core, Φ_m is the same for both E_p and E_s. Therefore,

$$E_p = 4.44\,f\,N_p\,\Phi_m \qquad \text{(A)}$$

$$E_s = 4.44\,f\,N_s\,\Phi_m \qquad \text{(B)}$$

Dividing equation (A) by equation (B) gives the ratio

$$\frac{E_p}{E_s} = \frac{N_p}{N_s} = a \qquad \text{(11-5)}$$

Equations (11-4) and (11-5) are the fundamental equations for the transformer. Equation (11-5) gives the turns ratio and voltage of transformers. The turns ratio can also be represented by the letter a.

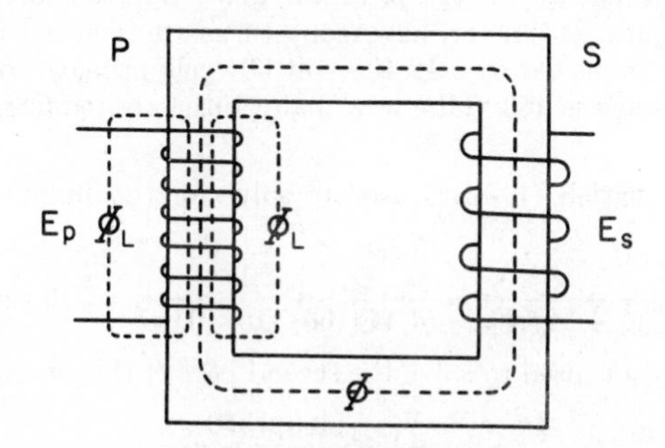

Fig. 11-1. Diagram of elementary transformer.

In an ideal transformer whose transfer of energy from one voltage to another is accompanied by no losses (100 per cent efficient), the power in the secondary equals the power in the primary.

$$P_p = P_s$$

Therefore,

$$E_p I_p = E_s I_s \qquad \text{(11-6)}$$

Equation (11-6) represents the relationship between the primary power P_p and the secondary power P_s. I_p is the primary current and I_s is the secondary current, both in amperes. The turns ratio in terms of voltage and current may be written

$$\frac{E_p}{E_s} = \frac{I_s}{I_p} = a \qquad \text{(11-7)}$$

Equation (11-7) shows that the turns ratio a of a transformer is directly proportional to the voltage and inversely proportional to the current.

If the volt-amperes on each side of the transformer are equal—as in an ideal transformer—we may write

$$I_p^2 Z_p = I_s^2 Z_s \tag{11-8}$$

Therefore,

$$\frac{I_s^2}{I_p^2} = \frac{Z_p}{Z_s} = a^2 \tag{11-9}$$

where Z_p and Z_s are the primary and secondary impedances in ohms. Equation (11-9) shows that the ratio of the impedances is directly proportional to the square of the turns ratio of the transformer. An elementary drawing of a transformer is shown in Fig. 11-1.

Example 11-1. The iron core of a transformer has a cross-sectional area of 15 square centimeters. If the peak flux density in the core is to be 0.01 weber per square centimeter, how many turns are required for a winding that is to be connected to a 12,400-volt 60-cycle primary source? If the secondary voltage is 480 volts, how many turns are required for the low voltage coil?

Solution. Equation (11-4) is used to solve for the number of primary turns.

$$N_p = \frac{E_p}{4.44 f \Phi_m} = \frac{12{,}400}{(4.44)(60)(15)(0.01)} = 310 \text{ turns}$$

Equation (11-5) is used to solve the second part of this problem.

$$N_s = \frac{E_s N_p}{E_p} = \frac{(480)(310)}{12{,}400} = 12$$

11-2. Vector Diagram of Transformer with Secondary Open-Circuited. Equations (11-1) through (11-9) were derived on the basis of an ideal transformer (a transformer without losses). In an actual transformer, E_p is the electromotive force of self-induction in the primary coil, and E_s is the voltage corresponding to E_p induced in the secondary. E_p, then, is the voltage of the primary after the primary losses are considered and E_s is the voltage of the secondary before the secondary losses are considered. Therefore, from equation (11-7) we may write

$$E_s = \frac{E_p}{a} \tag{11-10a}$$

or

$$E_p = aE_s \tag{11-10b}$$

Losses in voltage will cause V_p—the applied voltage on the primary—to be greater than E_p, and V_s—the terminal voltage for the secondary—to be less than E_s.

For convenience in our preliminary study of an actual transformer, we may assume a perfect transformer without losses. This assumption will require that the following conditions exist:*

1. The flux is proportional to the mmf that produces it. In other words, the core is unsaturated and has a constant permeability. The current producing the flux will therefore be a sine wave.

2. There are no iron losses (hysteresis and eddy currents) in the magnetic circuit.

3. All the flux induced by the current in the primary lies within the magnetic core and therefore links both windings of the transformer.

4. The primary winding has no resistance.

The reference vector for a transformer is the flux induced by the primary current. This flux induces E_p and E_s, which are in phase with each other and are 90 electrical degrees behind the flux. Since the transformer is assumed to have no losses, the current which induces the magnetic field is in phase with the flux. The voltage impressed across the primary winding is equal to E_p but is 180 electrical degrees out of phase with it and, consequently, 90 degrees ahead of the current.

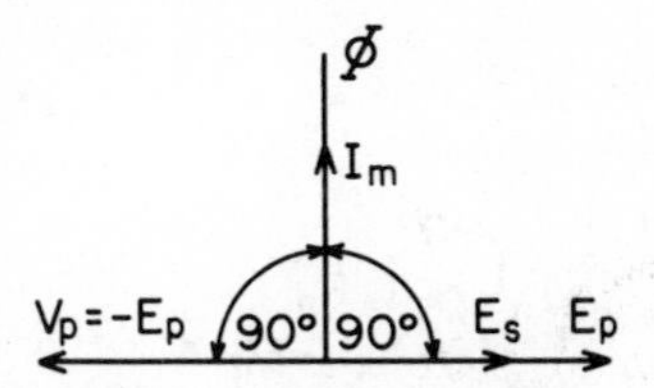

Fig. 11-2. Vector diagram of ideal transformer with secondary open-circuited.

The relationship between these vectors is shown in the vector diagram of Fig. 11-2. In this diagram, the following designations are used:

Φ—Effective value of the magnetic flux.

I_m—Effective value of the current producing the magnetic flux. This current is called the *magnetizing current.*

E_p—The voltage induced in the primary winding by the flux Φ. This voltage is the emf of self-induction, sometimes called *counter-emf* or *back emf.*

---

* Although these conditions are not actually found in any transformer, they are very closely approached in transformer design. In large size transformers, for example, the conditions are so nearly accomplished that the transformers' efficiencies are in the range of 99 per cent or higher, even when the transformers are operating at only one-fourth of their rated loads.

E_s—The voltage induced in the secondary winding by the flux Φ.

V_p—The voltage impressed on the primary, causing the flow of the magnetizing current.

In an actual transformer, the primary resistance is so low that it is often neglected. When the secondary circuit is open, the primary current is very small. The copper losses can therefore be neglected, and the only losses are those resulting from hysteresis and eddy currents, called *core losses* or *iron losses*. If a wattmeter were connected to measure the power into the transformer, it would read the hysteresis and eddy current losses directly.† The voltage can be applied to either the low-voltage or the high-voltage winding, as long as the voltage applied is the rated voltage of that winding and the other winding is open-circuited.

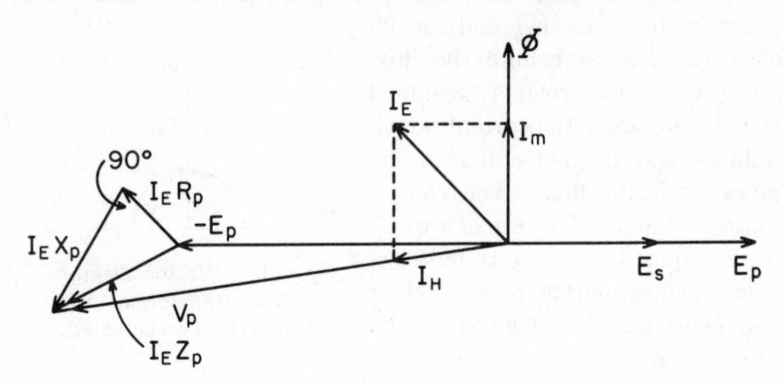

Fig. 11-3. Currents in a transformer with secondary circuit open.

The hysteresis loss has been determined to be expressed by the equation

$$P_h = K_h V f B_m^{1.6} \tag{11-11}$$

The eddy-current loss is given by the equation

$$P_e = K_e V f^2 t^2 B_m^2 \tag{11-12}$$

In equations (11-11) and (11-12), P_h is the hysteresis loss in watts, K_h is a constant depending on the magnetic qualities of the iron or steel core, V is the volume of iron or steel in the core, f is the fre-

† Strictly speaking, the wattmeter would not read the iron losses accurately, as the magnetizing current I_m is not sinusoidal. In an actual test, correction is made for the non-sinusoidal wave shape, but the test is based on the information given here.

quency, B_m is the maximum flux density, P_e is the eddy-current loss in watts, K_e is a constant depending on the electrical resistance of the core, and t is the thickness of the core laminations. In the mks system, V is in cubic meters, B_m is in webers per square meter, f is in cycles per second, and t is in meters.

Since the core losses represent an energy loss, the component of the primary current that supplies this loss is in phase with the impressed voltage V_p. When the secondary circuit of the transformer is open, there are, then, only two current components present—I_m, the magnetizing current, which is 90° behind V_p, and I_H, the core loss current. These components may be added vectorially, as in Fig. 11-3, to obtain the exciting current I_E. The magnetic flux Φ is still the reference vector and is 90° ahead of E_p and E_s. E_1 is reflected back into the primary as $-E_p$. The actual current flowing is the exciting current I_E. The product $I_E X_p$ is the voltage drop caused by the primary inductive reactance. These two voltage drops add vectorially to the actual voltage drop $I_E Z_p$, resulting from the primary impedance. The vector addition of $I_E Z_p$ and $-E_p$ gives the actual voltage V_p impressed across the primary of the transformer.

11-3. Vector Diagram of Transformer Under Load. When a load is connected to the secondary of a transformer, as indicated for the elementary transformer in Fig. 11-4, the total impedance of the circuit is given by the equation

$$Z_{sl} = (R_s + R_l) + j(X_s + X_l) \tag{11-13}$$

The total voltage across this impedance is the induced voltage E_2. The secondary current is

$$I_s = \frac{E_s}{(R_s + R_l) + j(X_s + X_l)} \tag{11-14}$$

In these equations, Z_{sl} is the total impedance in ohms of the transformer secondary winding plus the load, R_s and R_l are the resistances in ohms of the transformer secondary plus the load, X_s and X_l are the inductive reactance in ohms of the transformer secondary plus the load, E_s is the voltage induced in the secondary winding, and I_s is the current in the secondary circuit.

In accordance with Lenz's law, when current flows in the secondary, it will flow in a direction which will produce a magnetic flux which acts in opposition to that of the primary flux. Reduction of the flux will result in reduction of the primary impedance, allowing more primary current to flow. This increase in primary current is of such a magnitude as to restore the amount of flux in the winding to approximately the original value Φ that existed when there was no load on the secondary circuit.

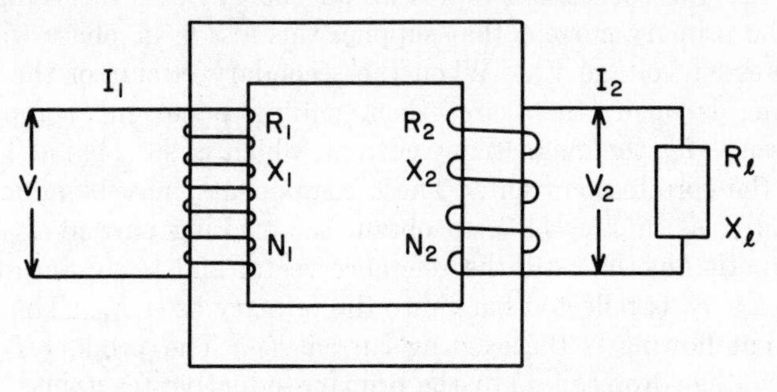

Fig. 11-4. Elementary transformer under load.

The number of demagnetizing ampere-turns (the mmf acting to reduce the flux induced by the primary) is equal to $N_s I_s$, or all of the secondary current multiplied by all of the turns in the secondary winding. The number of primary ampere-turns required to neutralize the demagnetizing effect of the secondary current is equal to the number of turns N_p in the primary multiplied by a current I'_p which is the secondary current I_s reflected into the primary in accordance with equation (11-7). Therefore,

$$N_p I'_p = N_s I_s \tag{11-15}$$

Since the primary flux remains approximately unchanged, the magnetizing current I_m remains approximately unchanged. Since hysteresis and eddy-current losses depend primarily on the amount of flux in the core, the value of the core loss current I_m remains approximately the same, and the exciting current I_E remains approximately the same. These statements are verified to some extent by equations (11-11) and (11-12), which indicate that hysteresis and eddy-current losses are independent of the load as long as B_m and f remain constant.

When an inductive load is connected across a transformer secondary winding, a current I_s flows, lagging the induced voltage E_s as shown in Fig. 11-5. This secondary current causes a resistance voltage drop $I_s R_s$ in phase with the current I_s. An inductive reactance voltage drop $I_s X_s$ results from the flow of the secondary current through the inductive reactance of the secondary. These two vectors are added vectorially to give the actual voltage drop $I_s Z_s$ across the impedance of the secondary. The impedance drop is added vectorially to the induced voltage E_s to give the terminal voltage V_s of the transformer secondary.

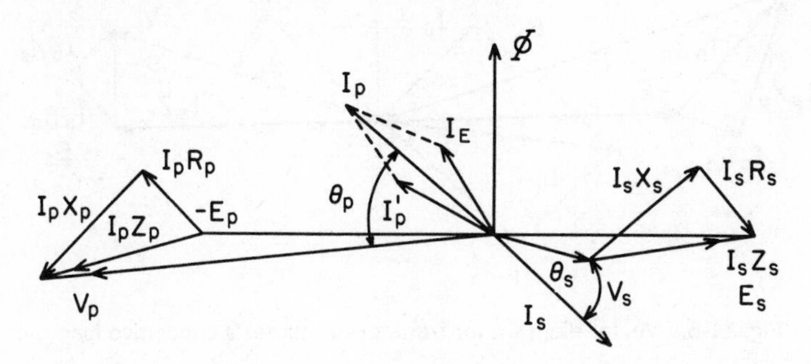

Fig. 11-5. Vector diagram for transformer under an inductive load.

The secondary current is reflected into the primary, 180° out of phase, by the relationship based on that of equation (11-15):

$$I_p' = \frac{N_s}{N_p} I_s = \frac{I_s}{a} \tag{11-16}$$

This reflected current I_p' is added vectorially to the exciting current I_E to obtain the actual primary current I_p. The primary current causes a resistance voltage drop $I_p R_p$ which is in phase with the current, and an inductive reactance voltage drop $I_p X_p$, which add vectorially to equal the actual primary voltage drop $I_p Z_p$. This voltage drop is now added to the primary emf of self-induction $-E_p$ to equal the actual voltage V_p impressed on the primary windings.

The vector diagram of a transformer under an inductive load is shown in Fig. 11-5. In this diagram, Φ is still the reference vector and the induced voltages, E_p and E_s, are still 90° behind the flux. The power factor angle of the load is θ_s, and θ_p is the power factor angle of the load and the transformer. These power factor angles are not equal, since the inductance of the transformer windings is included in the determination of θ_p. Both I_s and I_p lag their respective voltages, V_s and V_p, when the load is inductive.

When the load connected to the secondary windings is capacitive, I_s leads E_s as shown in Fig. 11-6. V_s is again the vector sum of

E_s and I_sZ_s, but with a capacitive load the terminal voltage may actually be larger than E_s.

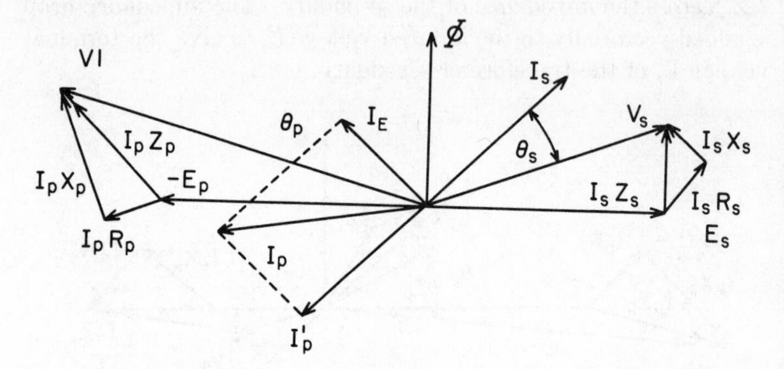

Fig. 11-6. Vector diagram for transformer under a capacitive load.

The vector diagram is completed in the same way as for the inductive load, but this time θ_p may be lagging, zero, or leading, depending on the relative conditions between the impedance of the load and the transformer.

When the resistance in ohms is known, a convenient method for determining copper losses is to use the relationship

$$P_c = \left(\frac{VA}{V}\right)^2 \times R \qquad (11\text{-}17)$$

The validity of equation (11-17) may not be apparent at first glance. However, current is equal to volt-amperes divided by volts, and equation (11-17) is just another way of finding $I^2 R$, which, by Ohm's law applied to the equation for power, is the power loss in the resistance.

Equation (11-17) enables the copper loss to be determined at any volt-ampere loading of the transformer. If VA is taken as the capacity of the transformer, the result is the loss at full load. V is the voltage of the winding involved in the computation, and R is the resistance of that winding. Thus, for the primary winding,

$$P_c = \left(\frac{VA}{V_p}\right)^2 \times R_p \qquad (11\text{-}17a)$$

and for the secondary winding,

$$P_c = \left(\frac{VA}{V_s}\right)^2 \times R_s \qquad (11\text{-}17b)$$

In these equations, VA is the volt-ampere loading at a given time, and is the same for primary and secondary at that time.

Example 11-2. A 10-kva 7200-120 volt transformer has a resistance in the high-voltage winding of 12 ohms and in the low-voltage winding of 0.0033 ohm. Find the copper loss at full load, at half load, and at a load of 1 kva.

Solution. The copper loss is the sum of the losses in both windings. The method of solution is to use equations (11-17a) and (11-17b).

At full load,

$$P_H = \left(\frac{10,000}{7200}\right)^2 \times 12 = 23.3 \text{ watts}$$

$$P_L = \left(\frac{10,000}{120}\right)^2 \times 0.0033 = 22.9 \text{ watts}$$

$$P_T = 23.3 + 22.9 = 46.2 \text{ watts}$$

At half load,

$$P_H = \left(\frac{5000}{7200}\right)^2 \times 12 = 5.8 \text{ watts}$$

$$P_L = \left(\frac{5000}{120}\right)^2 \times 0.0033 = 5.7 \text{ watts}$$

$$P_T = 5.8 + 5.7 = 11.5 \text{ watts}$$

At 1-kva load,

$$P_H = \left(\frac{1000}{7200}\right)^2 \times 12 = 0.23 \text{ watt}$$

$$P_L = \left(\frac{1000}{120}\right)^2 \times 0.0033 = 0.22 \text{ watt}$$

$$P_T = 0.23 + 0.22 = 0.45 \text{ watt}$$

Example 11-3. A 10-kva 2400-240 volt single-phase transformer has a loss of 182 watts at full load. The primary winding has a resistance of 3.6 ohms, and the secondary has a resistance of 0.036 ohm. Assuming that the only losses in the transformer at full load are the copper and core losses, find the core loss.

Solution. The primary copper loss at full load is

$$P_c = \left(\frac{10,000}{2400}\right)^2 \times 3.6 = 62.5 \text{ watts}$$

The secondary copper loss at full load is

$$P_c = \left(\frac{10,000}{240}\right)^2 \times 0.036 = 62.5 \text{ watts}$$

The total copper loss is the sum of these two, or 125 watts. The core loss is the difference between the total watts loss and the copper loss. Therefore,

$$P_{H+E} = 182 - 125 = 57 \text{ watts core loss}$$

Table 11-1. Transformer Full-Load Current in Amperes at Rated Line Voltages

SINGLE PHASE

Rating in Kva	RATED LINE VOLTAGE													Rating in Kva
	240	480	2400	4160	4800	6600	7200	7620	11500	12000	13200	16500	34500	
1½	6.25	3.13	0.63	0.36	0.31	0.23	0.21	0.20	0.13	0.12	0.11	0.09	0.04	1½
2½	10.42	5.20	1.04	0.60	0.52	0.38	0.35	0.33	0.22	0.21	0.19	0.15	0.07	2½
3	12.50	6.25	1.25	0.72	0.63	0.45	0.42	0.39	0.26	0.25	0.23	0.18	0.09	3
5	20.83	10.41	2.08	1.20	1.04	0.76	0.69	0.66	0.43	0.42	0.38	0.30	0.15	5
7½	31.24	15.62	3.12	1.80	1.56	1.14	1.04	0.98	0.65	0.62	0.57	0.45	0.20	7½
10	41.67	20.83	4.16	2.40	2.08	1.52	1.39	1.31	0.87	0.83	0.76	0.61	0.29	10
15	62.50	31.25	6.25	3.60	3.13	2.27	2.08	1.97	1.30	1.25	1.14	0.91	0.43	15
20	83.33	41.67	8.33	4.81	4.17	3.03	2.78	2.62	1.74	1.67	1.52	1.21	0.58	20
25	104.2	52.10	10.42	6.01	5.21	3.79	3.47	3.28	2.17	2.08	1.89	1.52	0.72	25
37½	156.2	78.10	15.62	9.01	7.81	5.68	5.21	4.92	3.26	3.12	2.84	2.27	1.09	37½
50	208.3	104.1	20.83	12.02	10.41	7.58	6.94	6.56	4.35	4.17	3.79	3.03	1.45	50
75	312.5	156.2	31.25	18.00	15.62	11.36	10.42	9.84	6.52	6.25	5.68	4.55	2.17	75
100	416.7	208.3	41.67	24.00	20.83	15.15	13.89	13.12	8.70	8.33	7.58	6.06	2.90	100
150	625.0	312.5	62.50	36.00	31.25	22.70	20.83	19.68	13.04	12.50	11.36	9.09	4.35	150
200	833.3	416.7	83.33	48.10	41.67	30.30	27.78	26.25	17.39	16.67	15.15	12.12	5.80	200

THREE PHASE

Rating in Kva	RATED LINE VOLTAGE													Rating in Kva
	208	240	480	2400	4160	4800	6600	7200	8320	11500	12000	16500	34500	
4½	12.48	10.83	5.41	1.08	0.62	0.54	0.39	0.36	0.31	0.23	0.22	0.16	0.07	4½
5	13.88	12.03	6.01	1.20	0.69	0.60	0.44	0.40	0.35	0.25	0.24	0.17	0.08	5
7½	20.82	18.04	9.02	1.80	1.04	0.90	0.66	0.60	0.52	0.38	0.36	0.26	0.13	7½
9	24.98	21.65	10.83	2.17	1.25	1.09	0.79	0.72	0.62	0.45	0.43	0.31	0.15	9
10	27.75	24.06	12.03	2.41	1.39	1.20	0.87	0.80	0.69	0.50	0.48	0.35	0.17	10
15	41.63	36.09	18.04	3.61	2.08	1.80	1.31	1.20	1.04	0.75	0.72	0.52	0.25	15
22½	62.5	54.13	27.06	5.41	3.12	2.71	1.97	1.80	1.56	1.13	1.08	0.79	0.38	22½
25	69.4	60.14	30.07	6.01	3.47	3.01	2.19	2.00	1.73	1.26	1.20	0.87	0.42	25
30	83.3	72.17	36.09	7.22	4.16	3.61	2.62	2.41	2.08	1.51	1.44	1.05	0.50	30
37½	104.1	90.21	45.11	9.02	5.20	4.51	3.28	3.01	2.60	1.88	1.80	1.31	0.63	37½
45	124.8	108.3	54.13	10.83	6.25	5.41	3.94	3.61	3.12	2.26	2.17	1.57	0.75	45
50	138.8	120.3	60.14	12.03	6.94	6.01	4.38	4.01	3.47	2.51	2.41	1.75	0.84	50
75	208.2	180.4	90.21	18.04	10.41	9.02	6.56	6.01	5.20	3.76	3.61	2.62	1.26	75
100	277.5	240.6	120.3	24.06	13.88	12.03	8.74	8.02	6.94	5.02	4.81	3.50	1.67	100
112½	312.2	270.6	135.3	27.06	15.61	13.53	9.84	9.02	7.81	5.65	5.41	3.94	1.88	112½
150	416.3	360.9	180.4	36.09	20.82	18.04	13.12	12.03	10.41	7.53	7.22	5.25	2.51	150
200	555.0	481.1	240.6	48.11	27.76	24.06	17.50	16.04	13.88	10.04	9.62	7.00	3.35	200
225	624.5	541.3	270.6	54.13	31.23	27.06	19.68	18.04	15.61	11.30	10.83	7.87	3.77	225
300	833.0	722.0	360.9	72.2	41.64	36.09	26.24	24.06	20.82	15.06	14.43	10.50	5.02	300
450	1248.0	1083.0	541.3	108.	62.46	54.13	39.37	36.09	31.22	22.59	21.65	15.75	7.53	450
600	1665.0	1443.0	721.7	144.	83.27	72.17	52.49	48.12	41.64	30.12	28.87	21.00	10.04	600

Table calculated and compiled by Harold M. Williams while employed by the California Electric Power Co. Used with permission.

11-4. Transformer Efficiency. Just as in any type of equipment, the power efficiency of a transformer is simply the output divided by the input.

The losses in a transformer are core loss and copper loss. The core loss is represented by the symbol P_{H+E}, but thus far we have not had a single term to represent the copper loss. As was shown in Section 11-3, the copper loss can be found by use of the current and resistance of the primary and secondary. Another way is to express the primary resistance in terms of the secondary, refer this resistance into the secondary, and assume that the secondary resistance is the sum of the two components. The total copper loss is found by considering that the secondary current flows through this equivalent resistance. If R_{es} is the total resistance of the two transformer windings expressed in terms of the secondary, then

$$R_{es} = R_s + \frac{R_p}{a^2} \tag{11-18}$$

Since a is the ratio of transformation (or the turns ratio) of the transformer, the term R_p/a^2 is the primary resistance referred to the secondary. The efficiency of the transformer may then be expressed by the equation

$$\text{Efficiency} = \frac{V_s I_s \cos \theta_s}{V_s I_s \cos \theta_s + P_{H+E} + I_s^2 R_{es}} \tag{11-19}$$

The copper loss can also be expressed as the product of the primary equivalent resistance R_{ep} and the primary current. The value of R_{ep} is found by the equation

$$R_{ep} = R_p + a^2 R_s \tag{11-20}$$

where $a^2 R_s$ is the secondary resistance referred to the primary.

Table 11-1 can be used for obtaining the full load currents of single-phase and three-phase transformers at standard voltages up to 34,500 volts. Single-phase transformer ratings are for transformers of 200 kva or less. Three-phase transformer ratings are for transformers of 600 kva or less.

Example 11-4. Find the efficiency of the transformer described in Example 11-3 if the power factor of the load is 67 per cent.

Solution. In Example 11-3, the copper losses and core losses were found from the given data. The efficiency can be found directly by use of equation (11-19). The transformer has a 10-kva capacity with a primary voltage of 2400 and a secondary voltage of 240. From Table 11-1 we find that the primary current is 4.16 amperes and the secondary current is 41.67 amperes.

Example 11-3 showed that the losses total 182 watts (copper and core losses combined). Equation (11-19) will give the efficiency directly:

$$\text{Efficiency} = \frac{(240)\,(41.67)\,(0.67)}{(240)\,(41.67)\,(0.67) + 182} = \frac{6700}{6700 + 182}$$

$$= \frac{6700}{6882} = 0.974 \text{ or } 97.4\%$$

The core loss cannot be calculated directly unless we know the value of the constants K_h and K_e in equations (11-11) and (11-12). When the copper losses are not known, they can be calculated by use of equation (11-18) and the secondary current (or equation (11-20) and the primary current). From equation (11-18) we obtain

$$R_{es} = R_s + \frac{R_p}{a^2} = 0.036 + \frac{3.6}{100} = 0.072 \text{ ohm}$$

The copper loss is, therefore,

$$P_c = (41.67)^2\,(0.072) = 125 \text{ watts}$$

This result agrees with that obtained in Example 11-3. This value can then be added to the core loss – which is usually determined by test – and the efficiency calculated from the results.

11-5. All-Day Efficiency. A distribution transformer feeding a single customer, or a group of customers, may be very lightly loaded during parts of the day and heavily loaded for only very short periods. Consequently, transformer efficiency at a particular load may be relatively unimportant, but the performance over a 24-hour period may be extremely important to a power company. The measurement of this performance is called *all-day efficiency.*

Equation (11-19) can be converted to a form to give the all-day efficiency by multiplying the quantities by the time. Thus,

All-day efficiency

$$= \frac{\Sigma \text{ power output} \times \text{time}}{\Sigma \text{ power output} \times \text{time} + P_{H+E} \times 24 + \Sigma\, I_s^2\, R_{es} \times \text{time}} \qquad (11\text{-}21)$$

The quantity Σ power output $\times$ time would be determined in practice by watt-hour (or kilowatt-hour) meters. It is the total output of the transformer for a given 24-hour period. The quantity $P_{H+E} \times 24$ is the core loss for 24 hours. Since the core loss is essentially constant at all loads, we need only determine this loss at no load and multiply this by 24 hours. The quantity $\Sigma\, I_s^2\, R_{es} \times$ time is the copper loss for the 24 hours. Since this loss is not constant, we must determine the loss for every load and multiply this quantity by the number of hours that the load is connected.

The importance of knowing the all-day efficiency is illustrated by Example 11-5.

Example 11-5. A load whose maximum demand is 10 kva single phase is to be connected to the secondary of a suitable transformer. Two 10-kva transformers are available. Transformer A has a core loss of 50 watts and a full load copper loss of 150 watts. Transformer B has a core loss of 100 watts and a full load copper loss of 50 watts. The load varies according to the following cycle: 10 kva at 0.8 PF for 1½ hours,[‡] 8 kva at 0.85 PF for 2 hours, 5 kva at 0.9 PF for 1 hour, 3 kva at unity power factor for 3 hours, and no load the remainder of the 24-hour period. Find the all-day efficiency of the two transformers. Which of the two transformers would be chosen for this load?

Solution. At full load, Transformer A has a total loss of 50 + 100 = 150 watts, and Transformer B has a total loss of 75 + 75 = 150 watts. Since the capacities and the losses of the two transformers at full load are identical, the full load efficiencies are the same.

The total load in watt-hours over the 24-hour period is as follows:

$$
\begin{aligned}
(10{,}000)\ (0.8)\ (1.5) &= 12{,}000 \text{ WH} \\
(8{,}000)\ (0.85)\ (2) &= 13{,}600 \text{ WH} \\
(5{,}000)\ (0.9)\ (1) &= 4{,}500 \text{ WH} \\
(3{,}000)\ (1.0)\ (3) &= 9{,}000 \text{ WH} \\
\hline
\text{Total} &= 39{,}100 \text{ WH}
\end{aligned}
$$

The losses must be calculated for each transformer:

Transformer A

Core loss: (50) (24) = 1200 WH

Copper loss (proportional to the square of the load):

$$
\begin{aligned}
\text{Full load} &= (150)\ (1.5) &&= 225.0 \text{ WH} \\
8 \text{ kva load} &= (150)\ (0.8)^2\ (2) &&= 192.0 \text{ WH} \\
5 \text{ kva load} &= (150)\ (0.5)^2\ (1) &&= 37.5 \text{ WH} \\
3 \text{ kva load} &= (150)\ (0.3)^2\ (3) &&= 40.5 \text{ WH} \\
\hline
\text{Total copper loss} & &&= 495.0 \text{ WH}
\end{aligned}
$$

Total loss in Transformer A: 1200 + 495 = 1695 WH

‡ Under some circumstances, operating a transformer at full rated load may be considered unwise. However, with a load such as a farm, dairy, residential area, small manufacturing plant, etc., where the load is light for a few hours, and heavy for only short periods, operation of a transformer at full load or even at an overload for short periods may be good practice from an economic standpoint. Transformers have a two-hour overload rating of about 20 per cent which can be used for these short periods, especially when the transformer operates at light loads or even no load for long periods of time.

Transformer B

Core loss: (100) (24) = 2400 WH

Copper loss:

Full load	= (50) (1.5)	=	75.0 WH
8 kva load	= $(50)(0.8)^2(2)$	=	64.0 WH
5 kva load	= $(50)(0.5)^2(1)$	=	12.5 WH
3 kva load	= $(50)(0.3)^2(3)$	=	13.5 WH
Total copper loss		=	165.0 WH

Total loss in Transformer B: 2400 + 165 = 2565 WH

The all-day efficiencies are now obtained by use of equation (11-21).

Transformer A

$$\text{All-day efficiency} = \frac{39{,}100}{39{,}100 + 1695} = \frac{39{,}100}{40{,}795} = 0.958 = 95.8\%$$

Transformer B

$$\text{All-day efficiency} = \frac{39{,}100}{39{,}100 + 2565} = \frac{39{,}100}{41{,}665} = 0.938 \text{ or } 93.8\%$$

Transformer A would be chosen for this load. Note that a transformer for this type of load requires a low core loss compared to its copper loss. When the load is constant over a long period of time, low copper loss may be more desirable. Reduction in iron loss can be accomplished by increasing the amount of iron in the core, thereby increasing the cost, physical size, and weight of the transformer. When the size and weight of the transformer are increased, the strength of the transformer supports —especially for a pole-top installation—may have to be increased. All of these requirements must be considered before a transformer can be chosen for a particular load.[§]

11-6. Per Cent and Per Unit Values. Transformers are rated in reference to the voltage drop below the theoretical secondary value determined by use of equation (11-5). For convenience, this drop is expressed in terms of per cent or per unit, based on corresponding values of *per cent impedance* or *per unit impedance* since the transformer impedance causes a per cent loss in the voltage when the transformer is supplying a load.

If the secondary impedance is referred to the primary, we obtain the equivalent impedance Z_T of the transformer:

$$Z_T = Z_p + a^2 Z_s \tag{11-22}$$

[§] The economic principles that an engineer must consider in choosing a transformer or any other piece of equipment are discussed in books such as *Principles of Engineering Economy* by Eugene L. Grant and W. G. Ireson (4th ed.; New York: Ronald Press, 1960).

This equation is similar in form to equation (11-20). Z_T is the impedance that would be measured from the primary side of the transformer.

The voltage drop in the transformer can be calculated by assuming that the primary current I_p flows through the total or effective transformer impedance Z_T. This drop is obtained by multiplying equation (11-22) by I_p:

$$V_d = I_p Z_T = I_p (Z_p + a^2 Z_s) \tag{11-23}$$

In equation (11-23), V_d is the total voltage drop of the transformer in terms of primary volts. The per unit value of this voltage drop is obtained by dividing equation (11-23) by the primary voltage V_p:

$$\frac{V_d}{V_p} = \frac{I_p Z_T}{V_p} \tag{11-24}$$

If equation (11-24) is now multiplied by V_p/V_p, we obtain

$$Z_{pu} = \left(\frac{V_p}{V_p}\right)\left(\frac{I_p Z_T}{V_p}\right) = \frac{Z_T V_p I_p}{V_p^2} \tag{11-25}$$

in which Z_{pu} is the per unit value of the transformer impedance and $V_p I_p$ is the volt-ampere capacity of the transformer. Equation (11-25) is more generally written in terms of kva and KV. The final and more generally approved form of this equation is

$$Z_{pu} = \frac{Z_T \times \text{kva}}{(\text{KV})^2 \times 1000} \tag{11-26}$$

Transformer characteristics as listed in catalogues include per cent impedance rather than per unit. Per cent impedance is obtained by multiplying equation (11-26) by 100.

$$\%Z = \frac{Z_T \times \text{kva}}{(\text{KV})^2 \times 10} \tag{11-27}$$

Equations similar to (11-26) and (11-27) can be derived for resistance and reactance, using the same method.

$$R_{pu} = \frac{R_T \times \text{kva}}{(\text{KV})^2 \times 1000} \tag{11-28}$$

$$\% R = \frac{R_T \times \text{kva}}{(\text{KV})^2 \times 10} \tag{11-29}$$

$$X_{pu} = \frac{X_T \times \text{kva}}{(\text{KV})^2 \times 1000} \tag{11-30}$$

$$\%X = \frac{X_T \times \text{kva}}{(\text{KV})^2 \times 10} \qquad (11\text{-}31)\|$$

Although equations (11-26) through (11-31) were obtained on the basis of single-phase transformers, they are equally well adaptable to three-phase. In three-phase calculations, kva is the three-phase rating of the transformer and KV is the line-to-line voltage in kilovolts, assuming a balanced system.

Example 11-6. A single-phase 50-kva 4160-240 volt transformer has an impedance of 1.6 per cent. Find the impedance in terms of the primary and in terms of the secondary. What are the approximate impedances of the primary and secondary windings?

Solution. The impedance in terms of the primary can be found by use of equation (11-27). Solving this equation for Z_T we obtain

$$Z_T = \frac{\%Z \times (\text{KV})^2 \times 10}{\text{kva}} \qquad (11\text{-}32)$$

Therefore, the transformer impedance in terms of the primary is

$$Z_{TP} = \frac{(1.6)\,(4.16)^2\,(10)}{50} = 5.54 \text{ ohms}$$

Equations (11-26) through (11-32) can also be used for the impedance in terms of the secondary KV.

$$Z_{TS} = \frac{(1.6)\,(0.24)^2\,(10)}{50} = 0.01846 \text{ ohm}$$

The approximate impedance of each winding can be found by use of equations (11-9) and (11-22). Assuming that these equations are exactly correct (or near enough for practical purposes) we may write, from equation (11-22),

$$Z_{TP} = Z_p + a^2 Z_s$$

But, from equation (11-9), $Z_p = a^2 Z_s$. Therefore, we find that

$$Z_{TP} = 2Z_p = 5.54 \text{ ohms}$$

$$Z_p = \frac{5.54}{2} = 2.77 \text{ ohms}$$

The ratio of transformation a is found from equation (11-5).

$$a = \frac{E_p}{E_s} = \frac{4160}{240} = 17.3 \text{ to } 1$$

‖ Equations (11-26) through (11-31) are of great importance in the calculation of short circuit current available at any given point in a system. In this kind of computation, the kva term becomes "Base KVA" and all impedances of the system are converted to this base. When only the transformer is considered, however, kva refers to the capacity of the transformer.

Therefore,

$$Z_s = \frac{Z_p}{a^2} = \frac{2.77}{(17.3)^2} = 0.00925 \text{ ohm}$$

These values can be checked by referring Z_T to the secondary by writing

$$Z_{Ts} = Z_s + \frac{Z_p}{a^2} \tag{11-33}$$

Inserting the values already obtained, we find that

$$Z_{Ts} = 0.00925 + \frac{2.77}{(17.3)^2} = 2(0.00925) = 0.01850 \text{ ohm}$$

Allowing for slide rule accuracy, this value compares favorably with the 0.01846 ohm found previously.

11-7. Regulation of a Transformer. The regulation of a transformer is defined by the equation

$$\%V \text{ Reg} = \frac{V_{NL} - V_{FL}}{V_{FL}} \times 100 \tag{11-34}$$

Equation (11-34) for a transformer is identical with equation (3-12) for a transmission line. The no-load voltage V_{NL} is determined from the following equation, which is also identical with the transmission line equation for the sending end of the line:

$$V_{NL} = \sqrt{(V_{FL} \cos \theta_L + IR)^2 + (V_{FL} \sin \theta_L + IX)^2} \tag{11-35}$$

where V_{NL} is the terminal voltage across the secondary when the load is removed, V_{FL} is the terminal voltage across the secondary at full load, I is the secondary or load current, R is the resistance in ohms of the secondary winding, and X is the inductive reactance in ohms of the secondary winding.

In equation (11-35), the term IR is sometimes ignored. The reactance of a transformer—especially in the larger sizes—is so high that it is often considered to be equal to the impedance. Reference to Table 11-2 (page 278) will indicate this point.

Table 11-2 divides distribution transformers into two groups: primary voltages below 5000 volts and primary voltages above 5000 volts. Since distribution transformers are designed to supply a load (or loads), the secondary voltages are usually 600 volts and below. The table gives per cent resistance, per cent reactance, and per cent impedance. This table shows that when a single-phase transformer has a capacity of 25 or more kva, the per cent reactance and per cent impedance are very nearly the same. Transformer catalogues almost never list per cent resistance or per cent reactance, all calculations being based on per cent impedance.

Table 11-2. Approximate Per Cent Impedances of Single-Phase Distribution Transformers

	Primary EMF 2400 to 4800 Volts			Primary EMF 7200 to 12,000 Volts		
KVA	%R	%X	%Z	%R	%X	%Z
3 5	2.1	2.0	2.9	2.2	2.1	3.0
10 15	1.9	2.1	2.8	2.0	2.0	2.8
25 37½ 50	1.4	2.5	2.9	1.5	2.3	2.7
75 100 167	1.2	3.3	3.5	1.1	3.7	3.9
250 333 500	1.0	4.7	4.8	1.0	5.1	5.2

In the foregoing discussion and in Table 11-2, only the per cent impedances of distribution transformers were considered. When a short-circuit calculation involves transformers larger than 500 kva capacity, Table 11-3 should be used. This table gives the per cent impedances of transformers up to 115,000 volts in rating. The per cent impedances to be used are given in the column headed "Standard Impedance, (%Z)."

The values given in Tables 11-2 and 11-3 are not accurate for all transformers within the voltage ratings listed. They are average values that can be used when the accurate values are not known for a particular transformer.

Transformer regulation can be obtained by using per cent or per unit impedance values. The derivation of the equation depends on reference to the simplified vector diagram shown in Fig. 11-7.

The horizontal component of the V_{NL} vector is determined from Fig. 11-7 to be

$$V_{NL} \text{ (horizontal)} = V_{FL} + I_s R \cos \theta_L + I_s X \sin \theta_L \qquad (11\text{-}36)$$

Table 11-3. Approximate Impedance of Three-Phase Power Transformers – Ratings Above 500 KVA (Secondary Voltage Ratings 2400 to 15,000 Volts)

Primary Voltage (KV)	Range of Impedance Values (%Z)	Standard Impedance (%Z)
11 - 23	5 to 8.5	5.5
24 - 34.5	5.4 to 9.0	6.0
46	5.7 to 10.2	6.5
67 - 69	6.3 to 10.5	7.0
115	7.1 to 12.7	7.5

The vertical component is

$$V_{NL}\ (\text{vertical}) = I_s R \sin\theta_L + I_s X \cos\theta_L \qquad (11\text{-}37)$$

In equations (11-36) and (11-37), V_{FL} is the full-load terminal voltage across the secondary, I_s is the rated current of the secondary at full load, R and X are the equivalent resistance and reactance of the transformer referred to the secondary, and θ_L is the load power factor angle. From these equations, we obtain the relationship

$$V_{NL} = \sqrt{(V_{FL} + I_s R \cos\theta_L + I_s X \sin\theta_L)^2 + (I_s X \cos\theta_L - I_s R \sin\theta_L)^2} \qquad (11\text{-}38)$$

The voltage regulation, expressed as a decimal, is, from equation (11-34),

$$\text{Reg} = \frac{V_{NL} - V_{FL}}{V_{FL}} \qquad (11\text{-}39)$$

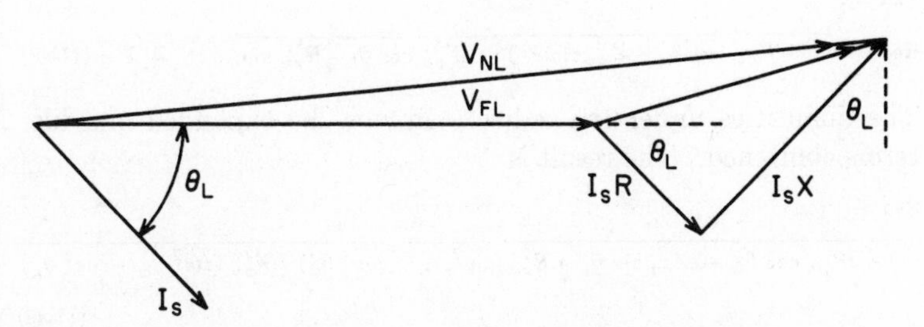

Fig. 11-7. Simplified vector diagram for a transformer.

Inserting equation (11-38) in equation (11-39) gives the relationship

$$\text{Reg} = \frac{\sqrt{(V_{FL} + I_s R \cos\theta_L + I_s X \sin\theta_L)^2 + (I_s X \cos\theta_L - I_s R \sin\theta_L)^2} - V_{FL}}{V_{FL}} \tag{11-40}$$

From equations (11-28) and (11-30) we can obtain simplified expressions for the per unit values of resistance and reactance.

$$R_{pu} = \frac{R \times V_{FL} I_s}{V_{FL}^2} = \frac{R I_s}{V_{FL}} \tag{11-41}$$

$$X_{pu} = \frac{X \times V_{FL} I_s}{V_{FL}^2} = \frac{X I_s}{V_{FL}} \tag{11-42}$$

Therefore, we find that

$$V_{FL} R_{pu} = R I_s \tag{11-43}$$

$$V_{FL} X_{pu} = X I_s \tag{11-44}$$

Inserting equations (11-43) and (11-44) in equation (11-40) gives equation (11-45).

$$\text{Reg} = \frac{\sqrt{(V_{FL} + V_{FL} R_{pu} \cos\theta_L + V_{FL} X_{pu} \sin\theta_L)^2 + (V_{FL} X_{pu} \cos\theta_L - V_{FL} R_{pu} \sin\theta_L)^2} - V_{FL}}{V_{FL}} \tag{11-45}$$

Taking V_{FL} out from under the radical, we obtain

$$\text{Reg} = \frac{V_{FL}\sqrt{(1 + R_{pu} \cos\theta_L + X_{pu} \sin\theta_L)^2 + (X_{pu} \cos\theta_L - R_{pu} \sin\theta_L)^2} - V_{FL}}{V_{FL}} \tag{11-46}$$

The full-load voltage V_{FL} can now be cancelled out of equation (11-46).

$$\text{Reg} = \sqrt{(1 + R_{pu} \cos\theta_L + X_{pu} \sin\theta_L)^2 + (X_{pu} \cos\theta_L - R_{pu} \sin\theta_L)^2} - 1 \tag{11-47}$$

The quantities under the radical can now be expanded and like terms combined. The result is

$$\text{Reg} = \sqrt{1 + 2R_{pu} \cos\theta_L + 2X_{pu} \sin\theta_L + R_{pu}^2 (\sin^2\theta_L + \cos^2\theta_L) + X_{pu}^2 (\sin^2\theta_L + \cos^2\theta_L)} \tag{11-48}$$

Since $\sin^2 \theta_L + \cos^2 \theta_L = 1$, we may write

$$\text{Reg} = \sqrt{R_{pu}^2 + 2R_{pu} \cos \theta_L + \cos^2 \theta_L + X_{pu}^2 + 2X_{pu} \sin \theta_L + \sin^2 \theta_L} - 1 \qquad (11\text{-}49)$$

Factoring the expressions under the radical sign puts equation (11-49) in the following form:

$$\text{Reg} = \sqrt{(R_{pu} + \cos \theta_L)^2 + (X_{pu} + \sin \theta_L)^2} - 1 \qquad (11\text{-}50)$$

If the resistance and reactance are expressed in per cent, equation (11-50) can be written in the form

$$\%\,\text{Reg} = \sqrt{(\%\,R + 100 \cos \theta_L)^2 + (\%\,X + 100 \sin \theta_L)^2} - 100 \qquad (11\text{-}51)$$

Thus we have an expression which will give the per cent regulation directly from the per cent values. When only the per cent impedance is available, the regulation can be approximated by omitting the $\%\,R$ term (or by letting $\%\,R = 1$) and substituting $\%Z$ for $\%\,X$. Therefore,

$$\%\,\text{Reg (approx.)} = \sqrt{(100 \cos \theta_L)^2 + (\%Z + 100 \sin \theta_L)^2} - 100 \qquad (11\text{-}52a)$$

or

$$\%\,\text{Reg (approx.)} = \sqrt{(1 + 100 \cos \theta_L)^2 + (\%\,Z + 100 \sin \theta_L)^2} - 100 \qquad (11\text{-}52b)$$

Another approximate formula can be derived by expanding equation (11-47) by the binomial theorem and omitting all powers of R and X above the second as being negligibly small. This derivation results in the following equation which is also approximately correct:

$$\%\,\text{Reg} = \%\,R \cos \theta_L + \%\,X \sin \theta_L + \frac{(\%\,X \cos \theta_L + \%\,R \sin \theta_L)^2}{200} \qquad (11\text{-}53)$$

The equations given in this section are for lagging power factor, which is the usual condition in a power or lighting load. For a leading power factor, the equations are written as follows:

$$V_{NL} = \sqrt{(V_{FL} \cos \theta_L + I\,R)^2 + (V_{FL} \sin \theta_L - I\,X)^2} \qquad (11\text{-}35a)$$

$$\text{Reg} = \sqrt{(R_{pu} + \cos\theta_L)^2 + (X_{pu} - \sin\theta_L)^2} - 1 \qquad (11\text{-}50a)$$

$$\%\text{Reg} = \sqrt{(\% R + 100\cos\theta_L)^2 + (\% X - 100\sin\theta_L)^2} - 100 \qquad (11\text{-}51a)$$

$$\%\text{Reg (approx.)} = \sqrt{(100\cos\theta_L)^2 + (\% Z - 100\sin\theta_L)^2} - 100 \qquad (11\text{-}52c)$$

$$\%\text{Reg (approx.)} = \sqrt{(1 + 100\cos\theta_L)^2 + (\% Z - 100\sin\theta_L)^2} - 100 \qquad (11\text{-}52d)$$

$$\%\text{Reg} = \% R\cos\theta_L - \% X\sin\theta_L + \frac{(\% X\cos\theta_L + \% R\sin\theta_L)^2}{200} \qquad (11\text{-}53a)$$

Example 11-7. A 167-kva 2400-240 volt distribution transformer has a 3.5 per cent impedance. Find the regulation at unity power factor and at 80 per cent power factor.

Solution. According to Table 11-2, this transformer has a per cent resistance of 1.2 and a per cent reactance of 3.3. The regulation can be found by use of any of the appropriate equations given in this section, but equation (11-51) may be the most convenient.

At 80 per cent power factor, the regulation is

$$\%\text{ Reg} = \sqrt{(1.2 + 80)^2 + (3.3 + 60)^2} - 100 = 3\%$$

At unity power factor, the regulation is

$$\%\text{ Reg} = \sqrt{(1.2 + 100)^2 + (3.3 + 0)^2} - 100 = 1.2\%$$

11-8. Transformer Polarities. When single-phase transformers are connected in parallel on a single-phase system or in wye or in delta on a three-phase system, care must be taken to see that the proper terminals are connected. If transformer terminals are incorrectly connected, voltages on the secondary may be incorrect or the transformer may be destroyed by what amounts to a short circuit. These difficulties are avoided by checking the *polarity* of the transformer windings.

Polarity refers to the direction of induced voltages between the high-voltage and the low-voltage terminals. When only the two end turns of the windings are brought out, the terminals are marked $H1$ and $H2$ on the high-voltage side and $X1$ and $X2$ on the low voltage side. The voltage from $H1$ to $H2$ is in phase with the voltage from $X1$ to $X2$. When the low-voltage winding is center-tapped, this tap is labeled $X2$ and the two end terminals are marked

$X1$ and $X3$. When the low-voltage winding consists of two electrically isolated coils, coil 1 is labeled $X1$ to $X2$ and coil 2 is labeled $X3$ to $X4$.

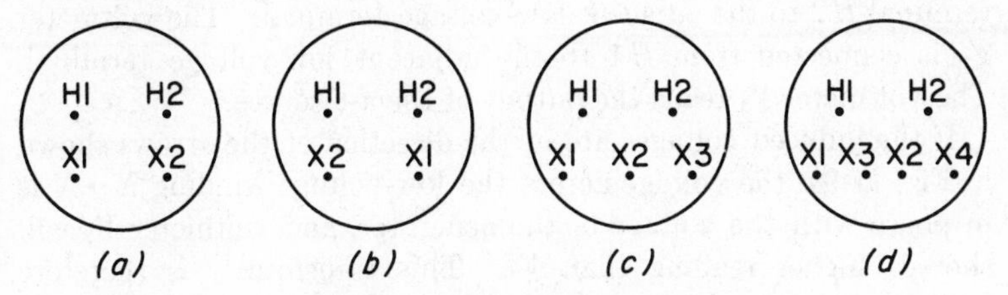

Fig. 11-8. Transformer polarities.

When the terminals are arranged as shown in Fig. 11-8*a*, the transformer is said to have *subtractive polarity*. When the terminals are arranged as shown in Fig. 11-8*b*, the transformer is said to have *additive polarity*. Fig. 11-8*c* and *d* show the arrangement of terminals for a center-tapped or a two-coil low-voltage winding.

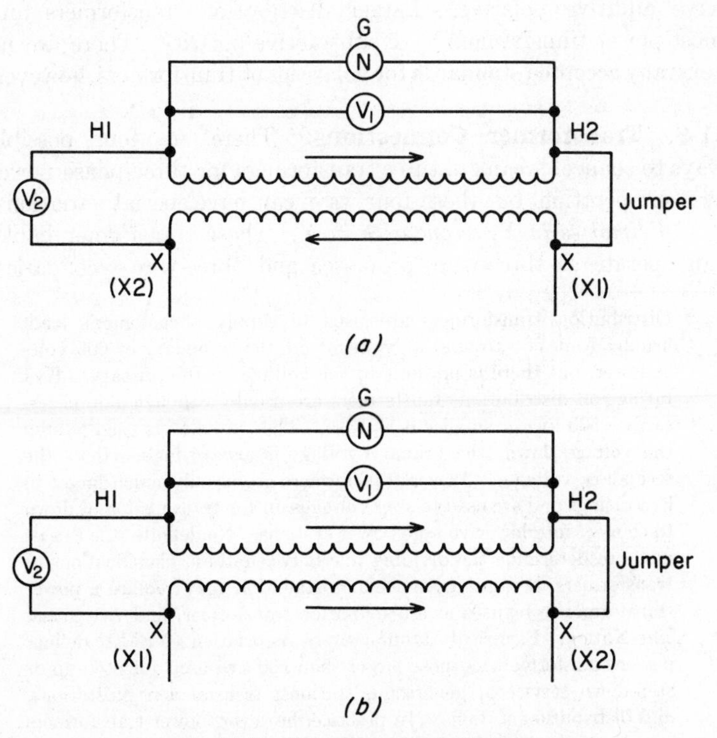

Fig. 11-9. Transformer polarity test.

Fig. 11-9 shows the test which is used for determining the polarity of a transformer. An a-c voltage is applied across the high voltage winding by voltage source G, and a jumper is connected from terminal $H2$ to the adjacent low-voltage terminal. The voltmeter V_2 is connected from $H1$ to the adjacent low-voltage terminal. The voltmeter V_1 reads the output of the a-c source.

If the induced voltages are in the direction of the arrows shown in Fig. 11-9*a*, the voltage across the low-voltage winding $X-X$ is in phase with the voltage of the generator, and voltmeter V_2 will show a higher reading than V_1. This transformer is therefore additive because the voltages across the windings add. On the other hand, voltmeter V_2 in Fig. 11-9*b* will read a lower voltage than V_1 because the two voltages are in opposition. This transformer has subtractive polarity because the voltages across the windings subtract. The correct terminal markings are shown in parentheses in Fig. 11-9.

Most distribution transformers[#] rated at 200 kva and smaller have additive polarity. Larger distribution transformers and most power transformers have subtractive polarity. There are no generally accepted standards for polarities of transformers, however.

11-9. Transformer Connections. There are four possible ways to connect a bank of three transformers for three-phase power system operation, but these four ways can have special variations.

1. *Primaries in Y, secondaries in Y.* These transformer banks can operate as three-wire primaries and three-wire secondaries,

[#] Distribution transformers are used to supply a customer's load, usually (but not always) at voltages on the secondary of 600 volts or lower, but there is no limit to the voltage on the primary. Kva ratings on distribution transformers are usually—though not necessarily—500 kva or smaller per phase. They are always used to step the voltage down (the primary voltage is always higher than the secondary voltage). Power transformers are usually much larger in kva ratings and are used to step voltages up for transmission or down to connect into lower voltage power systems. No definite rule can be made to determine the dividing line between these classifications of transformers, because a particular installation may require a power transformer to be used as a distribution transformer, and vice versa. The National Electrical Manufacturers Association (NEMA) defines power transformers as those larger than 500 kva used for step-up or step-down service at generating stations, transmission substations, and distribution stations. In practice, however, power transformers may be as small as 25 or 50 kva with voltages 22,000 volts and higher.

four-wire primaries and four-wire secondaries, three-wire primaries and four-wire secondaries, or four-wire primaries and three-wire secondaries. Either the primaries or the secondaries (or both) may have the neutral point grounded or ungrounded.

2. *Primaries in Y, secondaries in Δ.* The primaries may be three- or four-wire, and may be either grounded or ungrounded. The secondaries should be three-wire and should not be grounded.

3. *Primaries in Δ, secondaries in Δ.* Both primaries and secondaries should be three-wire and should not be grounded.

4. *Primaries in Δ, secondaries in Y.* The primaries should be three-wire and not grounded. The secondaries may be three-wire or four-wire and the neutral can be either grounded or ungrounded.

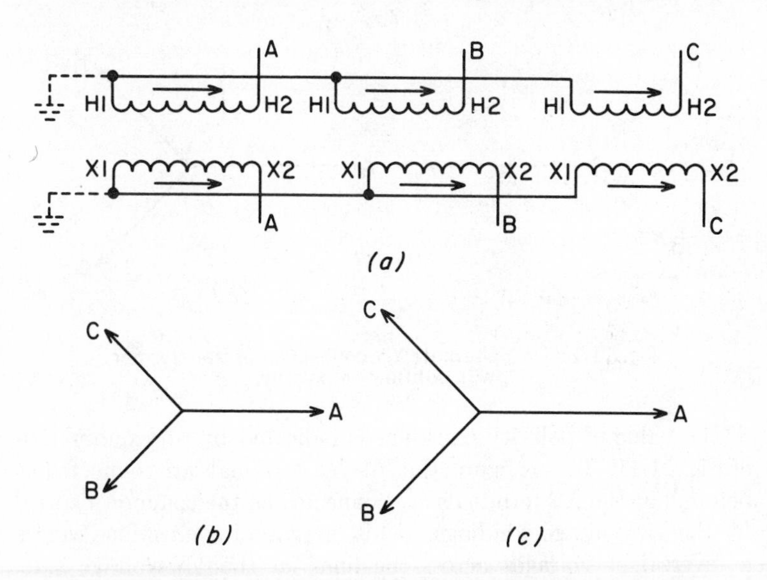

Fig. 11-10. Y-Y connection of transformer with subtractive polarity.

11-10. The Y-Y Connection. The Y-Y (wye-wye) connection is illustrated schematically in Fig. 11-10*a*. The diagram is of three single-phase transformers with subtractive polarity. The *H*1 terminals are connected together as the common neutral of the high-voltage side, and the *X*1 terminals are connected as the common neutral of the low-voltage side. The *H*2 and *X*2 terminals are connected to the incoming and outgoing lines, respectively. Dotted lines indicate where the ground connections are made when the two systems are grounded.

The vector diagrams for this connection are indicated in Fig. 11-10*b* (for the high-voltage) and in Fig. 11-10*c* (for the low-voltage). These vector diagrams show that the voltages on both sides of the transformer are in phase.

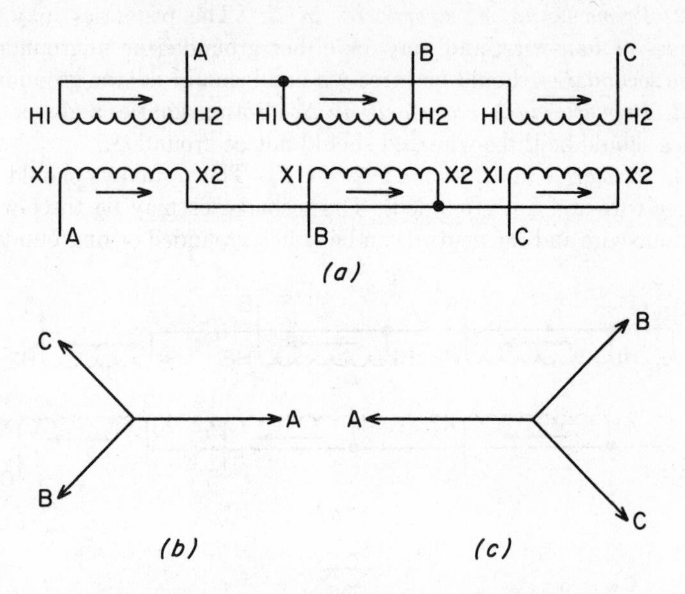

Fig. 11-11. An alternate Y-Y connection of transformer with subtractive polarity.

The value of polarity markings is indicated by an examination of Fig. 11-11. In this figure, the $H1$-$H2$ terminals are connected as before, but the $X2$ terminals are connected as the common neutral for the low-voltage windings. This reversal of connections causes a reversal of voltages across the lines on the low-voltage side. Because of this reversal of voltage direction, the transformers in Fig. 11-11 cannot be connected in parallel with those in Fig. 11-10.

If V_{AB} is the voltage between lines A and B of the primary side, the voltage between A and neutral is given by the equation

$$V_{H\phi} = \frac{V_{AB}}{\sqrt{3}} \tag{11-54}$$

Equation (11-54) gives the voltage between $H1$ and $H2$ of a single transformer, where $V_{H\phi}$ is the voltage between these two terminals and V_{AB} is the line-to-line voltage. Equation (11-5) gives the ratio of voltages across the two windings of one phase.

If $V_{L\phi}$ is the voltage between terminals $X1$ and $X2$,

$$\frac{V_{H\phi}}{V_{L\phi}} = \frac{N_H}{N_L} = a \tag{11-55}$$

If equation (11-55) is solved for $V_{H\phi}$ and for $V_{L\phi}$, we obtain the values

$$V_{H\phi} = a V_{L\phi} \tag{11-56}$$

$$V_{L\phi} = \frac{V_{H\phi}}{a} \tag{11-57}$$

The voltage between $X2$ of one winding and $X2$ of another (A to B on the low-voltage side, for example) may be designated by the symbol V_{ab}. The relationship between low-side phase and line voltages is

$$V_{ab} = \sqrt{3}\, V_{L\phi} \tag{11-58}$$

We now want to know the relationship between V_{AB} and V_{ab}. Substituting appropriate values from equations (11-54) and (11-58) in equation (11-55) we obtain

$$\frac{V_{H\phi}}{V_{L\phi}} = \frac{V_{AB}/\sqrt{3}}{V_{ab}/\sqrt{3}} = \frac{V_{AB}}{V_{ab}} = a \tag{11-59}$$

In a Y-Y connected bank of transformers, the ratio of line-to-line voltages is equal to the turns ratio of the transformer, as shown by equation (11-59) and the equations used to derive it.

11-11. The Y-Δ Connection. The Y-Δ (wye-delta) connection is illustrated schematically in Fig. 11-12*a*. Assuming the high-voltage line to have the same polarity as before, we see that Fig. 11-12*b* is the same vector diagram that appeared in Figs. 11-10*b* and 11-11*b*. Since A to neutral is the voltage between $H2$ and $H1$ of the high side in Fig. 11-12*a*, this is also the voltage which induces the phase voltage from $X1$ to $X2$ in the low-voltage winding. The vector diagram in Fig. 11-12*c*—arranged in the delta form—shows that the delta voltages in the low-voltage windings are in phase with the Y voltages in the high-voltage windings. Also, as for the Y-Y,

$$\frac{V_{H\phi}}{V_{L\phi}} = a \tag{11-60}$$

The relationship of equation (11-54) still applies. Since $V_{L\phi} =$

V_{ab}, the relation between the magnitudes of the high and low voltages is

$$\frac{V_{AB}}{\sqrt{3}} = a\,V_{ab} \tag{11-61}$$

Solving for the ratio of the voltages, we may write equation (11-61) as

$$\frac{V_{AB}}{V_{ab}} = a\sqrt{3} \tag{11-62}$$

In the discussion of the Y-Y connection, no mention was made of the phase relationship between the line voltages on either the high or the low side of the transformers, since these voltages were in phase with each other. The line voltage relationships are now given in Fig. 11-13, with the corresponding phase voltage relationships.

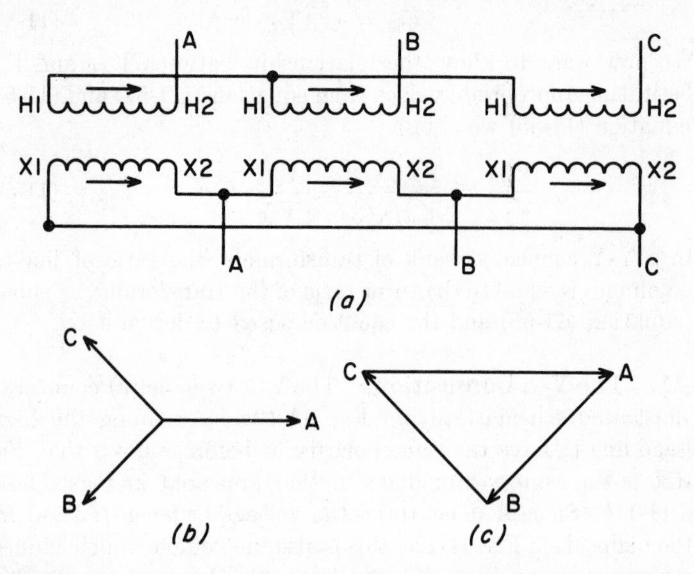

Fig. 11-12. Y-Δ connection of transformers with subtractive polarity.

Fig. 11-13aH shows the high-voltage relationships for the Y-Y connection, and Fig. 11-13aL shows the low-voltage relationships for the same connection. The three high-voltage line potentials are V_{CA}, V_{AB}, and V_{BC}, the input voltages to the high-voltage windings, and V_{ca}, V_{ab}, and V_{bc} are the line voltage outputs on the low-voltage side. The vectors for the line voltages are seen to be rotated 30° with respect to the corresponding transformer voltages.

V_{AN}-V_A, according to the phase designation, is 30° ahead of V_{CA}, which is usually designated as V_A of the incoming transmission line.

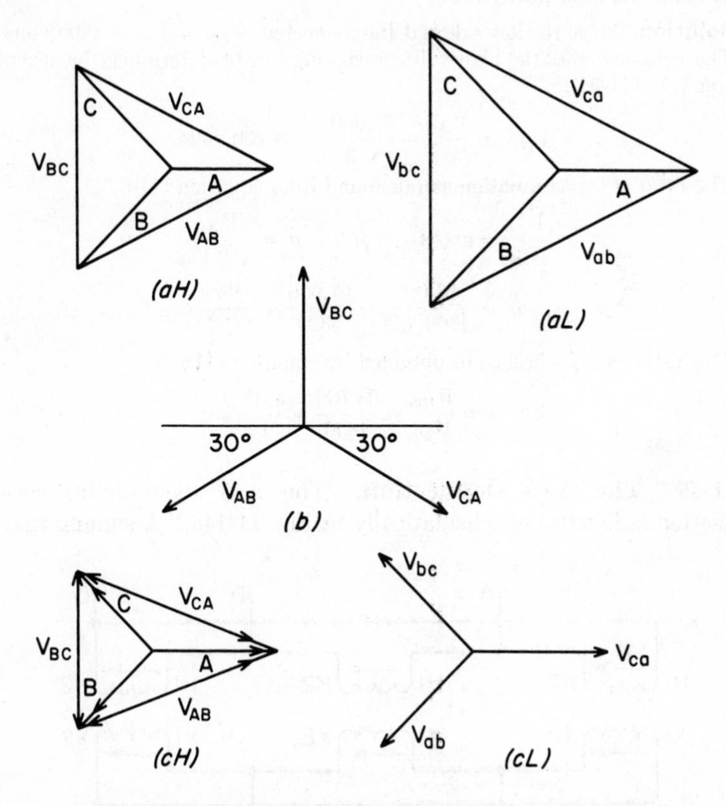

Fig. 11-13. Vector diagrams for Y-Y and Y-Δ connections.

The vector diagram for these high side line voltages is shown in Fig. 11-13*b*. These are the voltages across the Y side of the Y-Δ transformer. Fig. 11-13*aH* is repeated as Fig. 11-13*cH* to show the vector relationships for the Y-Δ. Fig. 11-13*cL* shows the vector relationships across the low-voltage side of this transformer. A comparison of Fig. 11-13*cH* and 11-13*cL* shows that the Y-Δ transformer rotates the line-to-line voltage by 30° in a clockwise direction. Therefore, transformers connected Y-Y cannot be connected in parallel with transformers connected Y-Δ, even if the voltage ratios of the transformers are chosen so that the low side voltages for both connections are equal in magnitude.

Example 11-8. Three single-phase transformers are to be connected Y-Δ as shown in Fig. 11-12*a*. The line-to-line voltages are to be 67,000 and 4800. Find the voltages across the transformer windings and the ratio of transformation (turns ratio).

Solution. Since the low side is delta-connected, $V_{L\phi} = V_{ab} = 4800$ volts. The voltage across the high-voltage winding can be determined by use of equation (11-54).

$$V_{H\phi} = \frac{V_{AB}}{\sqrt{3}} = \frac{67{,}000}{\sqrt{3}} = 38{,}700 \text{ volts}$$

The ratio of transformation can be found from equation (11-62).

$$\frac{V_{AB}}{V_{ab}} = a\sqrt{3} \qquad \text{or} \qquad a = \frac{V_{AB}}{\sqrt{3}\,V_{ab}}$$

$$a = \frac{67{,}000}{4800\sqrt{3}} = \frac{67{,}000}{8320} = \frac{8.05}{1}$$

This ratio can be checked or obtained by equation (11-60).

$$a = \frac{V_{H\phi}}{V_{L\phi}} = \frac{38{,}700}{4800} = \frac{8.05}{1}$$

11-12. The Δ-Δ Connection. The Δ-Δ (delta-delta) connection is illustrated schematically in Fig. 11-14*a*. Assuming that

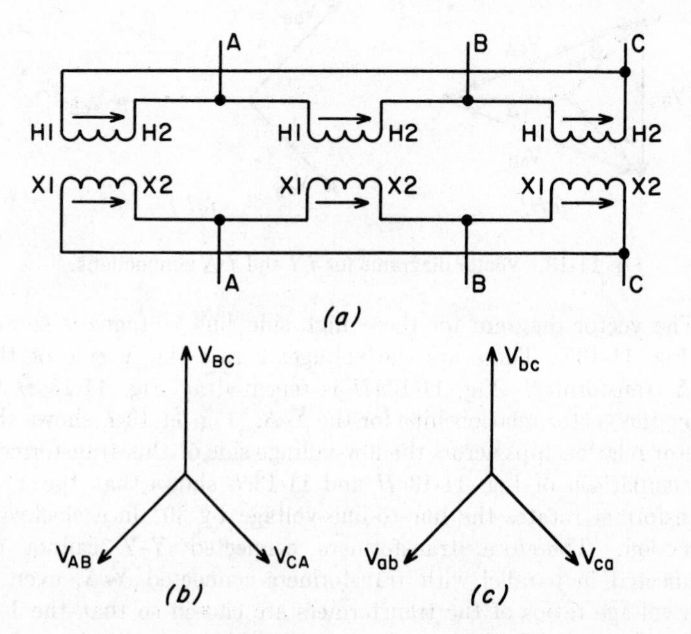

Fig. 11-14. Δ-Δ connection of transformers with subtractive polarity.

the high-voltage line potentials have the phase relationship assumed for the previous two connections and as shown vectorially in Fig. 11-13*b*, a check of the diagrams in Fig. 11-14*b* and *c* shows that there is no phase rotation in the Δ-Δ connection.

Since the coil between lines *A* and *B* of the high-voltage side links only the coil between *A* and *B* of the low-voltage side, the ratio of line-to-line voltages is identical with the turns ratio of the transformer.

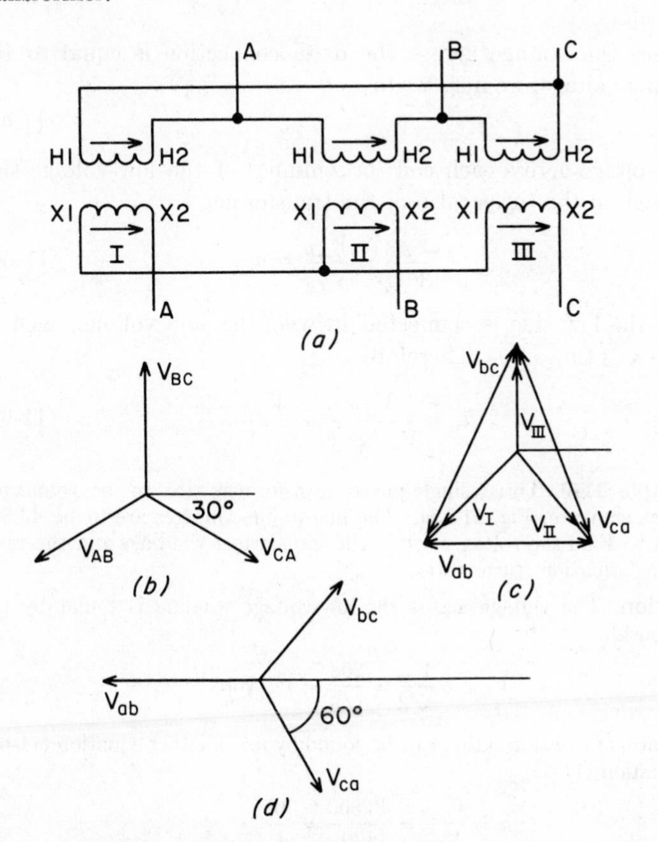

Fig. 11-15. Δ-Y connection of transformers with subtractive polarity.

11-13. The Δ-Y Connection. The Δ-Y (delta-wye) connection is illustrated schematically in Fig. 11-15*a*. Assuming the same phase relationship for the high side line voltages as before, we may draw the vector diagrams of Fig. 11-15*b* and *c*. Fig. 11-15*b* is the same as Fig. 11-13*b* since it is drawn for the same line voltages.

In Fig. 11-15*c*, V_{I} is the voltage across coil I in Fig. 11-15*a*, V_{II} is the voltage across coil II, and V_{III} is the voltage across coil III. Since the low side is connected in wye, V_{ca} is the vector sum of $V_{\text{III}} + V_{\text{I}}$ and V_{ab} and V_{bc} have similar relationships, as indicated by comparing Fig. 11-15*a* and *c*. Fig. 11-15*d* is the vector diagram of the low-voltage line potentials found in Fig. 11-15*c*. Since V_{ca} is 60° clockwise from the horizontal (reference) vector and V_{CA} was only 30°, the Δ-Y connection rotates the line voltage 30° clockwise.

Since the voltage across the delta connection is equal to the full line voltage, we may write

$$V_{H\phi} = V_{AB} \tag{11-63}$$

The voltage across each coil (or winding) of the low-voltage side is based on the turns ratio of the transformer.

$$\frac{V_{H\phi}}{V_{L\phi}} = \frac{V_{AB}}{V_{L\phi}} = a \tag{11-64}$$

Since the low side is connected in wye, the line voltage, such as V_{ab}, is $\sqrt{3}$ times $V_{L\phi}$. Therefore,

$$a = \frac{V_{AB}}{V_{ab}/\sqrt{3}} = \frac{V_{AB}\sqrt{3}}{V_{ab}} \tag{11-65}$$

Example 11-9. Three single-phase transformers are to be connected Δ-Y as shown in Fig. 11-15*a*. The line-to-line voltages are to be 43,800 and 208. Find the voltages across the transformer windings and the ratio of transformation (turns ratio).

Solution. The voltage across the low-voltage winding is found by the relationship

$$V_{L\phi} = \frac{V_{ab}}{\sqrt{3}} = \frac{208}{\sqrt{3}} = 120 \text{ volts}$$

The ratio of transformation can be found by use of either equation (11-64) or equation (11-65).

$$a = \frac{V_{AB}}{V_{L\phi}} = \frac{43{,}800}{120} = \frac{365}{1}$$

$$a = \frac{V_{AB}\sqrt{3}}{V_{ab}} = \frac{43{,}800\sqrt{3}}{120\sqrt{3}} = \frac{365}{1}$$

11-14. Three-Phase Current Values. Table 11-1 can be used for determining currents on both the low and the high sides of single-phase or three-phase transformers when the line-to-line voltages and the kva ratings of the transformers are known. In addition, Table 5-6 (p. 94) gives some constants for single-phase and direct-current voltages from 110 to 600 volts. Table 11-4 gives constants for three-phase voltages from 110 to 480 volts.

When Table 11-4 is used, the known kva of the transformer or of the load is multiplied by the constant in column C to obtain the current in amperes. Of course, Tables 11-1 and 11-4 assume reasonably balanced loads.

Table 11-4. Constants for Determining Currents on Three-Phase Systems

Volts	C
110	5.25
120	4.82
208	2.77
220	2.63
240	2.41
440	1.31
480	1.2

Example 11-10. A distribution transformer bank of three single-phase transformers is connected Δ-Y. The secondaries of the bank supply energy to a 208-volt, three-phase, four-wire system. The load on the system consists of a 72-kw three-phase unity power factor load, three 12-kw single-phase lighting circuits connected between one of the secondary lines and the common neutral, and four 5-hp 208-volt motors which operate at 80 per cent power factor and 85 per cent efficiency. Find the secondary line current. If the transformer turns ratio is 100 to 1, find the primary line voltage, the line current, and the kva rating of the transformer bank and of the individual transformers.

Solution. The voltage across the low-voltage secondary winding is found by the relationship

$$V_{L\phi} = \frac{208}{\sqrt{3}} = 120 \text{ volts}$$

Since the turns ratio is 100 to 1, the primary voltage (Δ) is

$$V_{H\phi} = V_{\text{LINE}} = (100)\,(120) = 12{,}000 \text{ volts}$$

The motor load in kva is found from the formula

$$\text{Motor load} = \frac{\text{hp} \times 746}{\text{PF} \times \text{eff}} \tag{11-66}$$

$$\text{Motor load} = \frac{(4)\,(5)\,(746)}{(0.8)\,(0.85)} = 22 \text{ kva}$$

The motor load must be expressed in kw and in kvars.

$$\text{Motor kw} = (22)\,(0.8) = 17.6 \text{ kw}$$

$$\text{Motor kvars} = (22)\,(0.6) = 13.2 \text{ kvars}$$

The other loads are balanced and are expressed directly in kw. The lighting load is 3 times 12 kw or 36 kw. The total kw load is, therefore,

$$\text{Total kw} = 17.6 + 36 + 72 = 125.6 \text{ kw}$$

The total reactive load is

$$\text{Total kvars} = 13.2 \text{ kvars}$$

The total kva is

$$\text{Total kva} = \sqrt{(125.6)^2 + (13.2)^2} = 126.3 \text{ kva}$$

The three-phase portion of Table 11-1 shows that a 150-kva transformer bank is needed, since this is the next size larger than 126.3 kva. This bank, therefore, requires three 50-kva single-phase transformers, and the single-phase portion of the table shows that this size is available.

The full load current on the transformer can be found from Table 11-1. A 150-kva three-phase transformer will draw 7.22 amperes on the high side (12,000 volts) and 416.3 amperes on the low side (208 volts). The cables connected to the high- and low-voltage windings of the transformer would be sized according to this current.

The actual current drawn at 208 volts can be found by reference to Table 11-4. The constant for 208 volts is 2.77. The secondary line current is, therefore,

$$(2.77)\ (126.3) = 350 \text{ amps}$$

The current in the primary winding is found by use of equation (11-7).

$$I_p = \frac{I_s}{a} = \frac{350}{100} = 3.5 \text{ amps}$$

The primary line current is, therefore,

$$I_{pL} = 3.5\sqrt{3} = 6.07 \text{ amps}$$

The currents can also be obtained by the equations developed in Chapter 9 for three-phase power.

$$I = \frac{\text{kva} \times 1000}{\sqrt{3} \times \text{volts}} \tag{11-67}$$

$$I_{sL} = \frac{126{,}300}{\sqrt{3} \times 208} = 350 \text{ amps}$$

$$I_{pL} = \frac{126{,}300}{\sqrt{3} \times 12{,}000} = 6.07 \text{ amps}$$

11-15. The Autotransformer. The autotransformer consists of a single winding with a secondary tap, as shown schematically in Fig. 11-16. If the currents in the primary and secondary are I_p and I_s, the current in the winding across the load is $I_s - I_p$. The primary voltage is V_p and the secondary voltage is V_s. Then the power P actually transformed in the windings of the transformer is given by the equation

$$P = V_s(I_s - I_p) = V_sI_s - V_sI_p \tag{11-68}$$

From equation (11-7) we may write

$$I_p = \frac{I_sV_s}{V_p}$$

Substituting this value in equation (11-68) gives the equation

$$P = V_sI_s - \frac{I_sV_s^2}{V_p} = \frac{V_pV_sI_s - I_sV_s^2}{V_p}$$

Factoring out I_sV_s, we obtain

$$P = V_sI_s\left(\frac{V_p - V_s}{V_p}\right) \tag{11-69}$$

V_sI_s is the volt-amperes supplied to the load. Therefore,

$$P = va\left(\frac{V_p - V_s}{V_p}\right) \tag{11-70}$$

Since transformers and loads are usually rated in kva rather than in va, equation (11-70) is usually written in the form

$$P = \text{kva}\left(\frac{V_H - V_L}{V_H}\right) \tag{11-71}$$

Autotransformers are used almost exclusively for step-down installations. Therefore, V_H and V_L are used in the formula instead of V_p and V_s to indicate the high and low voltages. Equation (11-71) indicates that not all of the load power undergoes transformation in an autotransformer.

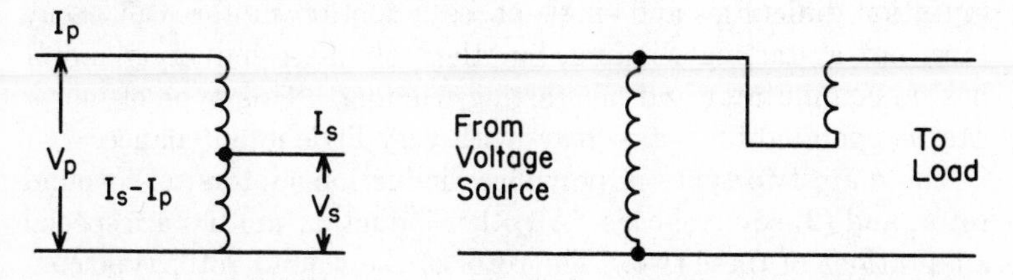

Fig. 11-16. Schematic diagram of an autotransformer.

Fig. 11-17. Schematic diagram of an autotransformer used as a voltage booster.

Although autotransformers are occasionally used in power work, their principal use is in motor starters where they apply half the supply voltage to the motor to reduce the current surge on starting. Occasionally, they are used as step-up transformers in the form of voltage boosters in transmission or feeder lines as shown in Fig. 11-17.

Application of equation (11-71) will show that autotransformers are usually not economically desirable when the ratio of transformation is greater than 2 to 1. Another disadvantage in using autotransformers is that the high-voltage and the low-voltage systems are electrically connected and could become hazardous to personnel and equipment.

Example 11-11. A load of 10 kilowatts is to be supplied at 480 volts and unity power factor is to be supplied by an autotransformer whose high voltage winding is connected to a 1200-volt system. What are the currents in the transformer windings and in the load? What is the actual power transformed?

Solution.

$$I_s = \frac{P}{V_s} = \frac{10{,}000}{480} = 20.8 \text{ amps}$$

$$I_p = \frac{I_s V_s}{V_p} = \frac{(20.8)\ (480)}{1200} = 8.3 \text{ amps}$$

$$I_s - I_p = 20.8 - 8.3 = 12.5 \text{ amps}$$

The power transformed is found from equation (11-70) or equation (11-71).

$$P = 10\left(\frac{1200 - 480}{1200}\right) = 10\left(\frac{720}{1200}\right) = 6 \text{ kva}$$

11-16. Polyphase Induction Motors. The polyphase induction motor is the simplest and most ruggedly constructed type of electrical motor available. Direct-current motors have commutation difficulties and single-phase induction motors can easily burn out a starting winding, but the polyphase induction motor has no commutator and no starting winding. This type of motor can be operated for many years with very little maintenance.

There are two types of polyphase induction motors: (1) wound rotor, and (2) squirrel-cage. All other induction motors are special adaptations of these two. The rotor of the wound rotor type contains wire coils that look very much like the coils of a direct-current armature except that there is no commutator. The leads from the wound rotor are usually brought out to what is called a "Y-box," which consists of resistors connected in wye. Some speed control is possible with this motor by means of a movable arm which varies the resistance in the Y-box. If all of the resistance is shorted out so that there is no resistance in series with the rotor winding, the motor will rotate at its highest speed. When resistance is added, the motor will slow down. A variation in speed of perhaps 5 per cent is possible with this type of motor and control.

The squirrel-cage motor uses bars of heavy copper, aluminum, or brass in place of wire coils. The ends of these bars are connected by short-circuiting rings of low-resistance metal. The speed and torque of these motors depend on the resistance of the bars. If the bars are of low resistance, the motor will operate at a faster speed but at a lower torque than if the bars have a high resistance. A special type of squirrel-cage motor uses two sets of bars. Such a motor will have a high starting torque because of the action of the motor magnetic flux on the high resistance bars. As the motor increases speed, it operates as an ordinary squirrel-cage motor with low resistance bars.

The "armature" winding of the motor is in the stationary part of the frame. Since this winding acts as a stationary armature winding, it is called the *stator* winding. This winding is connected to the a-c supply.

The operation of an induction motor is based on the principles of the transformer. The voltage in the stator causes a current which, in turn, induces a magnetic field which links the rotor winding, setting up a voltage and current in the rotor. A north pole in the stator induces a south pole in the rotor. Since the stator pole rotates as the voltage varies in amount and direction, the south pole in the rotor attempts to follow. However, if the rotor exactly followed the rotating stator pole, the flux linking a given area of the rotor would not change, and the rotor pole would collapse. Consequently, the rotor will always lag behind the stator field rotation. The stator field rotates at what is called the *synchronous speed*, and the rotor travels at a somewhat slower speed. The difference between the two is called the *slip*. The slip depends on the resistance of the rotor circuit, the strength of the field induced by the stator flux, and the load being driven by the motor.

Since a magnet must have both a north and a south pole, the synchronous speed depends on the number of pairs of poles in the stator. If P is the number of poles, then $P/2$ is the number of pairs of poles. The more poles a motor has, the slower the speed at which it can rotate. On the other hand, the higher the frequency of the a-c source, the faster the stator field can rotate and the faster the rotor can move. Since the frequency f is in cycles per second, we can obtain the frequency per minute by multiplying by 60. The synchronous speed of an a-c motor of any kind is, therefore,

$$\text{Synchronous speed} = \frac{60f}{P/2} = \frac{120f}{P} \qquad (11\text{-}72)$$

The actual speed of a motor can be determined by test, and is always less than the synchronous speed. When the actual speed is determined, the percentage slip can be calculated.

$$\%\ \text{slip} = \frac{\text{synchronous speed} - \text{actual speed}}{\text{synchronous speed}} \times 100 \qquad (11\text{-}73)$$

The slip of a squirrel-cage motor with low resistance in the rotor is usually less than 5 per cent. If the rotor has high resistance in the bars and in the short-circuiting rings, the slip may be much greater.

When a-c voltage is applied to the stator of an induction motor, the rotor is stationary and the voltage induced in the rotor has the same frequency as the supply. As the rotor starts to rotate, the frequency of the voltage induced in the rotor is diminished until at synchronous speed it would be zero. The frequency of the rotor voltage is therefore dependent on the slip and may be expressed by the equation

$$f_r = sf \qquad (11\text{-}74)$$

where f_r is the frequency of the voltage induced in the rotor, s is the slip expressed as a decimal, and f is the frequency of the voltage applied to the stator.

The voltage induced in the rotor when the rotor is standing still is equal to that induced in a transformer, and is given by equation (11-4):

$$E = 4.44 f N \Phi_m$$

The voltage induced in the rotor at any rotational speed depends on the slip:

$$E_r = 4.44\, s f N \Phi_m = sE \qquad (11\text{-}75)$$

The number of turns N in the rotor is determined by the number of bars or conductors under one stator pole. In a squirrel-cage motor, N can be very small.

Example 11-12. A frequency changer consists of two a-c generators on the same shaft. These generators are specially designed so that they can act as motors. For example, if a changer is connected between a 60-cycle system and a 50-cycle system, the 60-cycle generator will act as a motor when the 50-cycle system requires additional power not supplied by other sources, or it can act in reverse if necessary. How many poles must be on each generator and what is the synchronous speed at which they will rotate?

Solution. Since the machines are on the same shaft, they must operate at the same speed. From equation (11-72) we may write

For the 60-cycle machine:

$$\text{Synchronous speed} = \frac{(120)\ (60)}{P_{60}}$$

For the 50-cycle machine:

$$\text{Synchronous speed} = \frac{(120)\ (50)}{P_{50}}$$

Since the speeds are equal,

$$\frac{(120)\ (60)}{P_{60}} = \frac{(120)\ (50)}{P_{50}}$$

$$\frac{P_{50}}{P_{60}} = \frac{5}{6}$$

The number of poles must have the ratio of 5 to 6. Since we cannot have an odd number of poles, as 5, we may write

$$\frac{P_{50}}{P_{60}} = \frac{(5)\ (2)}{(6)\ (2)} = \frac{10}{12}$$

The 60-cycle machine will therefore have 12 poles and the 50-cycle machine will have 10 poles. The synchronous speed will be

$$\text{Synchronous speed} = \frac{(120)\ (60)}{12} = 600 \text{ rpm}$$

or

$$\text{Synchronous speed} = \frac{(120)\ (50)}{10} = 600 \text{ rpm}$$

Example 11-13. The actual speed of a 60-cycle 4-pole induction motor under load is determined to be 1750 rpm. What is the frequency induced in the rotor?

Solution. The synchronous speed is determined from equation (11-72).

$$\text{Synchronous speed} = \frac{(120)\ (60)}{4} = 1800 \text{ rpm}$$

The slip is found from equation (11-73).

$$\%\ \text{slip} = \frac{1800 - 1750}{1800} \times 100 = 2.78\%$$

The frequency induced in the rotor is found from equation (11-74).

$$f_r = sf = (0.0278)\ (60) = 1.67 \text{ cycles per sec}$$

Table 11-5. Approximate, Average Data On Normal-Torque, Normal Starting KVA Squirrel-Cage Induction Motors

440 Volts – 60 Cycles – 3 Phase

Motor HP	Synchronous RPM	EFFICIENCY Full-Load	EFFICIENCY 1/2 Load	POWER FACTOR Full-Load	POWER FACTOR 1/2 Load	Full-Load KILOWATTS	Full-Load AMPERES	Locked-Rotor AMPERES
2	3600	80.0	77.0	0.84	0.67	1.9	2.9	23
	1800	80.0	77.0	0.84	0.70	1.9	2.9	20
	1200	79.0	75.0	0.77	0.56	1.9	3.2	20
3	3600	81.0	78.0	0.85	0.69	2.8	4.3	25
	1800	81.0	78.0	0.85	0.71	2.8	4.3	25
	1200	80.0	77.0	0.80	0.61	2.8	4.6	25
5	3600	83.5	81.0	0.86	0.71	4.5	6.8	43
	1800	83.5	81.0	0.86	0.73	4.5	6.8	43
	1200	82.5	80.0	0.82	0.66	4.5	7.2	43
	900	82.0	79.0	0.76	0.58	4.5	7.9	42
10	3600	85.0	82.5	0.88	0.75	8.8	13.0	93
	1800	85.0	82.5	0.88	0.77	8.8	13.0	77
	1200	84.5	82.0	0.84	0.72	8.8	13.8	77
	900	84.0	81.0	0.80	0.65	8.8	14.6	77
20	1800	86.5	84.0	0.89	0.78	17.2	25.4	150
	1200	86.5	84.0	0.86	0.75	17.2	26.2	150
	900	85.0	82.5	0.84	0.70	17.5	27.3	150
	600	84.5	82.0	0.74	0.60	17.6	31.2	140
30	1800	87.5	85.0	0.90	0.80	25.5	37.2	215
	1200	87.5	85.0	0.88	0.77	25.5	38.0	215
	900	86.5	84.0	0.86	0.72	25.9	39.6	215
	600	86.0	83.5	0.78	0.64	26.0	43.8	200
50	1800	88.5	86.0	0.91	0.79	42.2	60.8	400
	1200	88.5	86.0	0.88	0.76	42.2	62.8	400
	900	88.0	85.5	0.85	0.69	42.4	65.5	400
	600	87.5	85.0	0.80	0.67	42.6	70.0	360
75	1800	90.0	87.5	0.91	0.79	62.1	89.9	600
	1200	89.5	87.0	0.88	0.76	62.5	93.3	600
	900	89.0	86.5	0.87	0.71	62.8	94.7	600
	600	88.5	86.0	0.82	0.69	63.2	101	550
100	1800	90.5	88.0	0.91	0.79	82.4	119	800
	1200	90.0	87.5	0.89	0.77	82.8	122	800
	900	89.5	87.0	0.87	0.71	83.2	126	800
	600	89.0	86.5	0.83	0.69	83.8	132	700
150	1800	91.0	88.5	0.91	0.79	123.0	177	1200
	1200	91.0	88.5	0.89	0.77	123.0	181	1200
	900	90.5	88.0	0.88	0.72	123.5	185	1200
	600	90.0	87.5	0.85	0.69	124.5	193	1000
200	1800	91.5	89.0	0.91	0.79	163.0	235	1600
	1200	91.5	89.0	0.89	0.77	163.0	240	1600
	900	91.0	88.5	0.88	0.72	164.0	245	1500
	600	91.0	88.0	0.86	0.69	164.0	250	1500
	450	90.5	87.0	0.82	0.65	165.0	264	1300

Note: For 220 volts the full-load amperes, and starting amperes will be twice those given above; for 2200 volts approximately one-fifth those given above.

Courtesy of Electric Machinery Manufacturing Company.

11-17. Motor Currents. The electrical power in watts drawn by an a-c motor is directly proportional to the horsepower and inversely proportional to the efficiency. This statement is expressed mathematically in the form

$$P = K\,\frac{\text{hp}}{\text{eff}}$$

where K is a constant. Since P is the power in watts and eff (efficiency) has no dimension, K must be in watts per horsepower and is equal to 746. Therefore, the equation becomes

$$P = \frac{746 \times \text{hp}}{\text{eff}} \qquad (11\text{-}76)$$

When P is in kilowatts (kw), equation (11-76) becomes

$$\text{kw} = \frac{0.746 \times \text{hp}}{\text{eff}} \qquad (11\text{-}77)$$

Since kw is equal to the kva multiplied by the power factor ($\cos\theta$), the kva equation for the motor can be written, from equation (11-66),

$$\text{kva} = \frac{0.746 \times \text{hp}}{\text{eff} \times \text{PF}}$$

The value for the current can be substituted from equation (11-67) in equation (11-66).

$$I = \frac{746 \times \text{hp}}{\text{eff} \times \text{PF} \times \sqrt{3} \times \text{volts}} \qquad (11\text{-}78)$$

Equation (11-78) gives the current in a three-phase motor of any horsepower at any stated efficiency, power factor, and line-to-line voltage.

Few motor catalogues give the efficiency and power factor of motors, and reference tables such as appear in the National Electrical Code** give only currents at specified voltages and horsepower ratings. However, Table 11-5 gives some information that can be used as a guide.

Table 11-5 gives some of the characteristics of 440-volt motors from 2 to 200 horsepower, including efficiency, power factor, kilo-

** This code is published by the National Fire Protection Association, 60 Battery March Street, Boston, Mass. 02110, as a guide for electrical light and power wiring. It is revised every three years.

watts, amperes, and locked rotor amperes. The locked rotor current corresponds to the starting current of the motor if the full line voltage is applied to the terminals when the motor is at a standstill. Table 11-5 can be partly adapted for use with 220 and 2200 volts by applying a multiplying factor. Full load amperes and locked rotor (starting) amperes for a 220-volt motor will be approximately twice those given in the table and for a 2200-volt motor will be about one-fifth of the values in the table. These estimates are only approximate, as a 220-volt motor will usually be less efficient and have a lower power factor than the corresponding 440-volt motor. A 2200-volt motor will usually be more efficient and have a higher power factor than motors rated at 480 volts or 440-volt motors operating on 480 volts. A 220-volt motor operating on 208 volts will draw approximately 6 per cent higher running current than it will on 220 volts but the locked rotor current will be slightly lower.

Table 11-6. Standard Ratings of Overload Protective Devices from 15 to 1000 Amperes

Amperes	Amperes
15	225
20	250
30	300
40	350
50	400
70	500
100	600
125	700
150	800
175	1000
200	

Example 11-14. A 100-hp, 60-cycle, 2200-volt, three-phase, 4-pole motor is to be installed to drive a mechanical load. What are its approximate starting and full-load running currents?

Solution. Table 11-5 shows speeds of 1800, 1200, 900, and 600 rpm for a 100-hp motor and all four speeds have different values for efficiency, power factor, load current, and starting current. The proper values can be determined by checking the speed by use of equation (11-72).

$$\text{rpm} = \frac{120f}{P} = \frac{(120)\ (60)}{4} = 1800\ \text{rpm}$$

According to Table 11-5, a 100-hp 4-pole motor on 440 volts will have an efficiency of 90.5 per cent and a power factor of 91 per cent. Equation (11-78) will give the full-load current.

$$I = \frac{(746)\ (100)}{(0.905)\ (0.91)\ (\sqrt{3})\ (2200)} = 23.8\ \text{amps}$$

This value can be checked by using the full-load current given in Table

11-5 and dividing by 5.

$$I = \frac{119}{5} = 23.8 \text{ amps}$$

The starting or locked-rotor current can be determined accurately only by test. In the absence of such test data, this current can be approximated for this motor by dividing 800 by 5.

$$I_{LR} = \frac{800}{5} = 160 \text{ amps}$$

11-18. Motor Protection. Alternating-current motors are subject to two general types of troubles: (1) overload (or overcurrent) and (2) undervoltage. Either type of fault can cause serious damage to the motor unless some type of device is used to disconnect the motor automatically from the supply voltage. The motor can be restarted almost immediately if the trouble is temporary, or if the cause of the trouble can be detected and removed. However, if the trouble persists, the motor will be disconnected every time an effort is made to restore it to service.

An *overload* can be caused by either a mechanical or an electrical condition which will cause a high current to flow. From the standpoint of the motor, an overload is a current which is greater than the motor's rated full-load current.

A few of the causes of overloads are:

1. Sudden application of a load. An example of this might be a motor driving a saw which is cutting a board. If the board becomes jammed, the saw will slow down, putting a temporary overload on the motor.
2. Worn bearings.
3. Driving belts or couplings out of alignment.
4. Loose mounting bolts.
5. Low oil or grease in the bearings.
6. Damp motor insulation which may cause rather large currents to flow (leak) through the insulation. Sufficient moisture (or even grease) can damage the insulation and cause large short-circuit currents to flow.

An *overload current* is any current that exceeds the full-load current of the motor as indicated on the nameplate (a metal label fastened to the motor). Approximate values of full-load current are given in Table 11-5, and these values can be used when the nameplate value of the motor is not available. Since the overload current is usually less than the locked-rotor current or starting current of the motor, choosing the proper protection for the motor is very important. The motor must not be disconnected from the voltage source while the starting current is flowing, yet must be disconnected quickly if a large current flows during motor operation.[††]

Low voltage is, technically, any condition where the voltage supplied to the terminals of the motor is less than 90 per cent of the nameplate voltage of the motor. Motors can and do operate very satisfactorily under this voltage condition. For example, 220-volt motors are used on 208-volt supply where the voltage is 95 per cent of that for which the motor is designed, and they can continue satisfactory operation even though the voltage may drop to only 200 volts. However, low voltage can be serious if the supply voltage drops to around 70 per cent or below. Of course, complete blackout (when source voltage is zero, as in a power failure) is a special case of a low voltage condition.

Low voltage may occur as the result of a power failure in the supply system, a short circuit, or some other serious electrical condition in the industrial plant in which the motor is located. Reduced voltage—including complete blackout—may last from a few seconds to several hours. At low voltage, the motor slows down, causing a reduction in the counter-emf of self-induction and allowing large currents to flow. These currents may be large enough to damage the motor, yet overload protection may be inoperative because of the low voltage condition.

Another serious consequence of low voltage is the effect on illumination. As explained in Chapter 5, the illumination output of a lighting unit drops off rapidly and is essentially zero when the voltage is 70 per cent of the rated lamp voltage (80 per cent for fluorescent lamps). Because of poor visibility and erratic motor operation, personnel in the area might be injured seriously if they tried to walk near moving machinery. Low voltage protection in this instance also acts as safety protection to men in the vicinity of the motors.

[††] The design and use of protective devices is one of the most interesting problems in electrical engineering. Some protective systems are required to remove either a motor or a part of a power system when trouble occurs, even when the current is small compared to the full-load current. This type of protection is required to detect the trouble by the speed at which the current increases and not by the value of the current flowing.

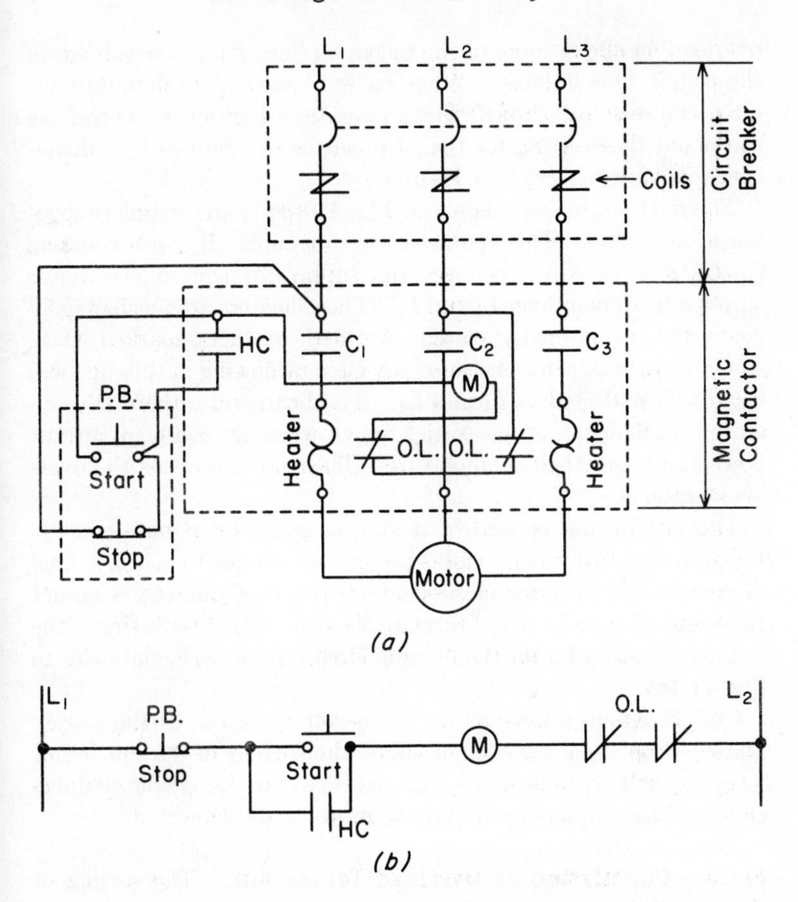

Fig. 11-18. A control and protection circuit for a three-phase induction motor.

Fig. 11-18*a* shows a diagram of a motor control circuit which includes protection against both overloads and low voltage conditions. In this figure, L_1, L_2, and L_3 are the three lines feeding the motor (corresponding to A, B, and C phase lines in the discussion of transformers). These three lines connect to the terminals of a circuit breaker as shown. The circuit breaker consists of three contacting elements, represented by the curved lines. The dotted lines connecting these contacting elements indicate that all three either close or open the circuit at one time. The zig-zag lines represent coils which are the overload coils in the breaker. The connections for these coils are not shown in the diagram, but an overload on one or more of the incoming lines induces a voltage in the coils. This induced voltage causes a current to flow into another coil (also not shown) which operates a trip lever to open the contacts. The setting for this trip can be determined by calculations explained in Section 11-19.

The next equipment shown in Fig. 11-18*a* is the magnetic contactor or starter. This contactor contains normally open contacts C_1, C_2, and C_3 which connect the supply voltage to the motor through heaters in lines L_1 and L_3. These heaters are mechanically connected to normally closed overload contacts marked O. L. There is no heater in L_2 because any current flowing in this line will usually be reflected in L_1 and L_3. The heaters are thermally operated mechanical devices which move when an overload current flows and raises their temperature. Their motion opens the overload contacts.

The pushbutton is used to start the motor by remote control. Pushing the start button closes the electric circuit to coil *M*. Coil *M* operates the arm that closes contacts *HC*, C_1, C_2, and C_3. Contact *HC* keeps the circuit closed through the coil. Fig. 11-18*b* shows the elementary diagram for the holding circuit shown schematically in Fig. 11-18*a*.

Coil *M* acts as a low-voltage or no-voltage relay. If the supply voltage drops to a low enough value, the current in the coil is not large enough to induce the flux necessary to keep the contacts closed. The contacts open and the motor is disconnected.

11-19. Calculation of Overload Protection. The setting of the circuit breaker trip coil in a motor circuit requires a consideration of both theoretical and practical principles of motor control and operation. For example, the full-load current of a 10-hp 3600-rpm 440-volt motor is about 13 amperes, according to Table 11-5, and any current above 13 amperes is an overload. However, the starting current of this motor is 93 amperes. The ideal protective device will operate to trip the motor when the current reaches 13.1, but will be unaffected by the 93 amperes at starting. Of course, it is impossible to produce a device that will fulfill both of these requirements.

However, there are ways to solve this problem. The overload protective device can be connected across a shunt circuit so that the protection is out of the circuit until the current to the motor falls below the trip setting. This method is somewhat expensive and risky. With the overload protection out of the circuit, there is no protection if a short circuit should occur either in the motor or in the wires connected to the magnetic contactor and the motor. Short circuit currents can range up to 40,000 amperes and, under some circumstances, up to 80,000 amperes or more. For this reason, keeping the overload protective device inoperative for even a few seconds is at least unwise.

One solution to the problem is to introduce a fairly long time delay into the overload device. If the time delay can be set long enough, the trip setting can be just high enough to allow the motor to operate at full load plus a margin of safety to prevent operation on currents too near full load current. The value approved by the National Electrical Code is 125 per cent of full load current. For the motor in this discussion, the setting would be 13 + 3.25, or 16.25 amperes. The heaters require a few seconds for the current in them to reach operating temperature, and therefore they would not trip on the starting current.

On the other hand, the heaters might not operate quickly enough on a short circuit or other sudden large change in current. For this reason, another tripping device is provided in the circuit breaker as "back up" protection.

The National Electrical Code includes a table giving the approved settings for overload devices for motors drawing full-load currents of from 1 to 500 amperes. The approximate setting can be obtained from Table 11-5 by using a multiplying factor of 2.5 with the full-load ampere value given in that table. For the 10-hp motor drawing 13 amperes load current, the overload protection in the circuit breaker should have a setting of 13 × 2.5, or 32.5 amperes.

A check of ratings of protective devices reveals that 32.5 amperes is not a standard size or setting. Table 11-6 shows the standard settings in amperes. Since there is no rating between 30 and 40 amperes, the correct setting for the circuit breaker trip coil for this 10-hp motor is 40 amperes.

11-20. Current Interrupting Capacities. The circuit breaker trip setting and the system voltage will not adequately identify the breaker required for particular motor installation. If a short circuit occurs on the motor side of a circuit breaker, current flowing through the breaker may reach many thousands of amperes instantaneously. The breaker must be able to open the circuit while this current is flowing. Failure to open the circuit while this short circuit current is flowing may cause considerable damage to surrounding equipment and even the destruction of a large part of the plant in which the breaker is located. The magnitude of the current which a circuit breaker is designed to interrupt is called the *interrupting capacity* of the breaker.

Interrupting capacities must be calculated for the particular installation in which the circuit breaker is to be installed. A small isolated industrial plant at the end of a 10-mile transmission line will have smaller short circuit currents than the same size plant located in a large industrial area in a city like Los Angeles, California, or Chicago, Illinois. On the other hand, if the isolated plant is serviced by a 2500-kva transformer, it will draw more short circuit current than it would from a 500-kva transformer.

Short circuit currents are usually called *fault*[‡‡] *currents.* To determine their magnitudes, a short circuit study must be made. This study requires the use of per cent and per unit values, including equations (11-26) through (11-31) and other equations that will be given in this section.

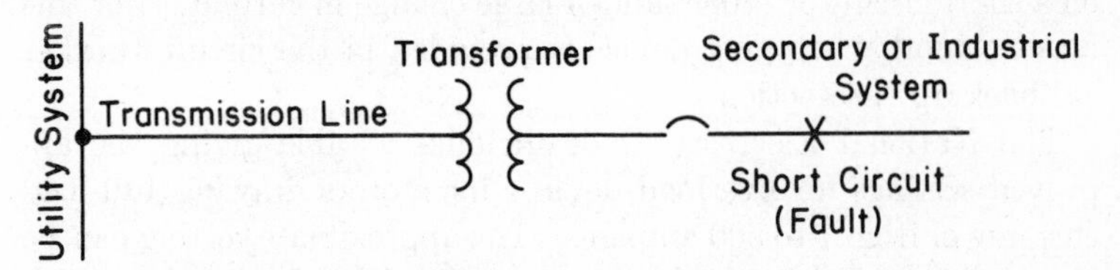

Fig. 11-19. One-line diagram of a system with a fault assumed on the secondary or industrial system.

The student is warned that the method of analysis given here is very much simplified but is acceptable for nearly every type of plant which is fed (or serviced) by one or more three-phase distribution transformers connected to the lines of a power utility system. Calculation of fault currents for a network or other type

---

‡‡ According to the definition approved by the American Institute of Electrical Engineers: "A wire or cable fault is a partial or total failure in the insulation or continuity of conductor." (American Standard Definitions of Electrical Terms, 35.40.213, American Institute of Electrical Engineers, New York, 1942) For the purposes of Section 11-20 of this book, a fault is considered to be specifically a *three-phase bolted short circuit.* It is called "bolted" because the fault currents calculated by this method are the same as if all three-phase conductors were tied together tightly by a bolt.

of system operated by the utility requires a calculating board or a digital computer and cannot be included here.[§§]

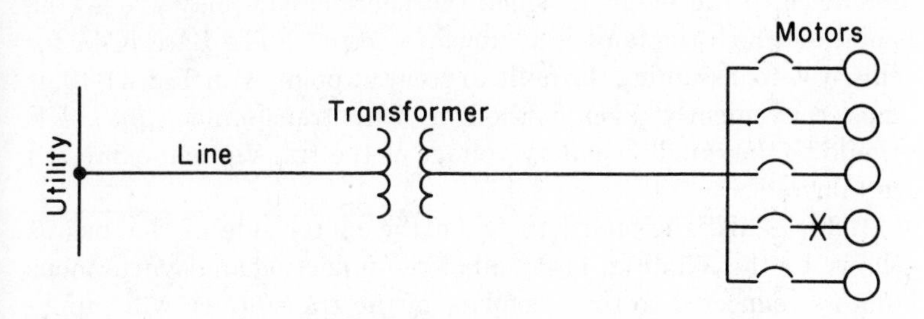

Fig. 11-20. One-line diagram of a system with a fault assumed on the motor side of the distribution bus.

In any short circuit study, the three-phase wiring diagram should always be reduced to a single-line diagram similar to those shown in Figs. 11-19 and 11-20. A single-line diagram is merely the representation of a three-phase system, using one line to represent three. It is much simpler than the complete wiring diagram and often accomplishes the same purpose.

After the single-line diagram is drawn, the second step in the study is to ask the power utility company what is the available short circuit capacity at the point where the industrial plant is to be built. This available short circuit capacity is then converted to per cent impedance by the formula

$$\%Z \text{ of utility} = \frac{\text{Base KVA} \times 100}{\text{available short circuit kva}} \tag{11-79}$$

If a transmission line is installed between the utility line and the transformer which is to feed the industrial load, its impedance must be determined by the method explained in Section 9-9 and be converted to per cent impedance by use of an equation similar to equation (11-27). The equation needed is

$$\%Z = \frac{Z_T \times \text{Base KVA}}{(\text{Base KV})^2 \times 10} \tag{11-80}$$

[§§] For a more complete analysis of short circuit calculations, see such books as *Industrial Power Systems Handbook* edited by Donald L. Beeman (New York: McGraw-Hill, Inc., 1955), and *Elements of Power System Analysis* by William D. Stevenson (2nd ed.; New York: McGraw-Hill, Inc., 1962).

The term *Base KVA* in equations (11-79) and (11-80), as well as in the equations that follow, refers to a capacity that is taken with reference to the point at which the short circuit may occur (the point at which the fault is assumed to occur). The Base KVA for this system, assuming the fault to occur at point X in Fig. 11-19, is most conveniently taken as the kva of the transformer. *Base KV* would be the rated secondary voltage of the transformer, expressed in kilovolts.

If the fault is assumed to be on the motor side of the bus as shown by the X in Fig. 11-20, all of the induction and synchronous motors connected to the secondary of the transformer will supply short circuit currents in addition to those supplied by the power utility system. Tests have shown that the contribution of induction motors amounts to about 25 per cent, as indicated in the equation

$$\%Z \text{ for motors} = \frac{\text{Base KVA} \times 25}{\text{kva of motors in operation}} \qquad (11\text{-}81)$$

Occasionally, it is necessary to convert quantities from one kva base to another. This conversion is necessary when a transformer is connected to the utility lines for transmission to a second transformer that feeds the motor bus. Conversion of Base KVA is also necessary when transformers connected in parallel do not have the same kva ratings. Kilovolt-amperes can be converted from one base to another by the formula

$$\%Z_{\text{new}} = \%Z_{\text{old}} \times \frac{\text{New Base KVA}}{\text{Old Base KVA}} \qquad (11\text{-}82)$$

where $\%Z_{\text{new}}$ is the per cent impedance on the chosen Base KVA, $\%Z_{\text{old}}$ is the per cent impedance on its own or some other Base KVA, and the New and Old Base KVA are the ratings corresponding to the impedance values.

Equation (11-80) indicates that per cent impedance is always in reference to a base voltage. If the impedance is required with reference to a different ("new") base voltage, the conversion is made by the equation

$$\%Z_{\text{new}} = \%Z_{\text{old}} \times \frac{(\text{Old Base KV})^2}{(\text{New Base KV})^2} \qquad (11\text{-}83)$$

When the short circuit contribution of the utility is given in amperes instead of kva, equation (11-79) cannot be used. The utility contribution can be determined by the equation

$$\%Z \text{ of utility} = \frac{\text{Base KVA} \times 100}{I_{usc} \times \sqrt{3} \times \text{KV of utility}} \qquad (11\text{-}84)$$

where I_{usc} is the symmetrical short circuit contribution of the utility system.

After all the per cent impedances are determined, they are added to give the total per cent impedance, $\%Z_T$. The symmetrical short circuit current is found from the Base KVA and the total per cent impedance by the formula

$$I_{ssc} = \frac{\text{Base KVA} \times 100}{\%Z \times \sqrt{3} \times \text{KV at short circuit location}} \qquad (11\text{-}85)$$

where I_{ssc} is the symmetrical short circuit current in amperes.

Short circuit currents are not symmetrical, however, except in very rare instances. If the fault occurs when the system voltage is zero, the fault current will start at zero, as shown in Fig. 11-21.

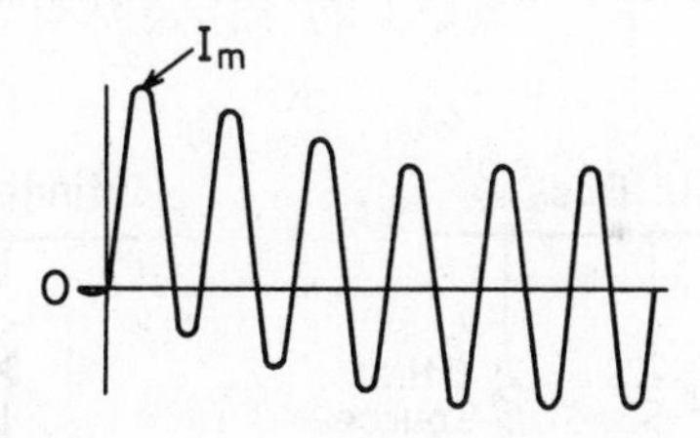

Fig. 11-21. Short circuit current wave.

The maximum value I_m of the short circuit will therefore be nearly twice the maximum value of the symmetrical short circuit current, or, at the point indicated, about 1.6 times the effective value I_{ssc} of the short circuit current. By the time the tripping coil can operate and the circuit breaker contacts open, the value will drop to about 1.25 times the effective value. If I_{asc} is the asymmetrical short circuit current, then

$$I_{asc} = 1.25\, I_{ssc} \qquad (11\text{-}86)$$

The asymmetrical short circuit current is the required interrupting capacity of the circuit breaker.

A word must be said about the way impedances should be added. In a power or distribution system, the per cent reactances and the per cent impedances are usually considered to be the same because the per cent resistance is usually very small. Therefore, series per cent impedances are added in the same manner as series resistances and series reactances. Therefore,

$$\%Z_s = \%Z_1 + \%Z_2 + \cdots + \%Z_n \qquad (11\text{-}87)$$

If the impedances are in parallel, their reciprocals are added:

$$\frac{1}{\%Z_p} = \frac{1}{\%Z_1} + \frac{1}{\%Z_2} + \cdots + \frac{1}{\%Z_n} \qquad (11\text{-}88)$$

In equations (11-87) and (11-88), $\%Z_s$ is the total series per cent impedance, $\%Z_p$ is the total parallel per cent impedance for a single set of parallel impedances, and $\%Z_1$, $\%Z_2$, $\cdots$ $\%Z_n$ are the series or parallel impedances.

After the individual per cent impedances are determined with the same Base KVA, the impedance diagram can be drawn with all sources of short circuit current tied to the same bus, called an *infinite bus*. The sources of this current include the utility, the induction motors, and any other source, such as synchronous generators or another utility system. A sample diagram is shown in Fig. 11-22.

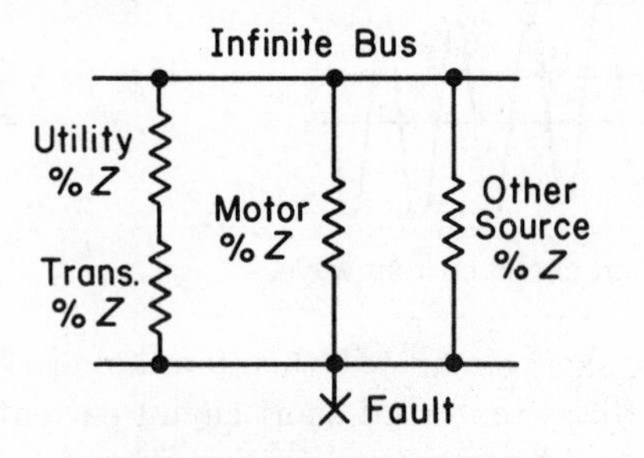

Fig. 11-22. An impedance diagram.

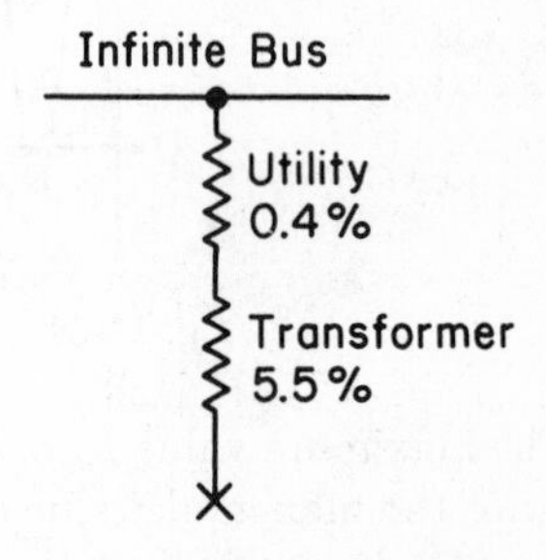

Fig. 11-23. Impedance diagram for a simple system.

Example 11-15. Fig. 11-19 represents a feeder to a system composed entirely of a lighting load. The maximum short circuit kva available from the utility system is 250,000 kva. The transformer has a rating of 1000 kva and has an impedance of 5.5 per cent. The voltage on the secondary is 208 volts. What is the required interrupting capacity of a circuit breaker on the secondary side of the transformer?

Solution. Since the utility contribution is given in kva, equation (11-79) is used. The Base KVA is the capacity of the transformer, or 1000 kva.

$$\%Z \text{ of utility} = \frac{\text{Base KVA} \times 100}{\text{Available SC KVA}} = \frac{(1000)\,(100)}{250{,}000} = 0.4\%$$

The impedance diagram for the system is shown in Fig. 11-23. Since only two impedances are shown and they are connected in series, the total impedance is determined from equation (11-87).

$$\%Z_s = 0.4 + 5.5 = 5.9\%$$

The symmetrical short circuit current available at X in Fig. 11-19 is found by use of equation (11-85).

$$I_{ssc} = \frac{(1000)\ (100)}{(5.9)\ (\sqrt{3})\ (0.208)} = 47{,}200 \text{ amps}$$

The interrupting capacity of the breaker is found by use of equation (11-86).

$$I_{asc} = \text{I.C.} = (1.25)\ (47{,}200) = 59{,}000 \text{ amps}$$

Example 11-16. A 2000-kva transformer is used to supply a load consisting of power and lighting at a voltage of 480 volts at the transformer secondary. The transformer impedance on its own base is 5.75 per cent. The available short circuit kva of the utility system is 250,000 kva. What is the required interrupting capacity of the breakers to be installed on a bus on the secondary side of the transformer?

Solution. The Base KVA is again taken as the rating of the transformer, or 2000 kva. The single-line diagram for the system is shown in Fig. 11-20 if the line between the utility and the transformer is short enough to be considered negligible.

The per cent impedance of the utility is again found from equation (11-79).

$$\%Z \text{ of utility} = \frac{(2000)\ (100)}{250{,}000} = 0.8\%$$

The transformer impedance is 5.75 per cent, which is added to the 0.8 per cent of the utility.

$$Z_s = 5.75 + 0.8 = 6.55\%$$

We can assume that the kva of induction motors which would be in operation at any given time is about 60 per cent of the transformer capacity, or about 1200 kva. The per cent impedance of the motors is found from equation (11-81).

$$\%Z \text{ for motors} = \frac{\text{Base KVA} \times 25}{\text{kva of motors}} = \frac{(2000)\ (25)}{1200} = 40\%$$

As shown in the impedance diagram (Fig. 11-22), the motor impedance is in parallel with the utility and the transformer. Since there is no "other source," the total impedance obtained from equation (11-88) is

$$\frac{1}{\%Z_p} = \frac{1}{6.55} + \frac{1}{40} = 0.153 + 0.025 = 0.178$$

$$\%Z_p = \frac{1}{0.178} = 5.62\%$$

The symmetrical short circuit current is found by use of equation (11-85).

$$I_{ssc} = \frac{(2000)\ (100)}{(5.62)\ (\sqrt{3})\ (0.48)} = 42{,}700 \text{ amps}$$

The interrupting capacity is found from equation (11-86).

$$\text{I.C.} = I_{asc} = (42{,}700)\ (1.25) = 53{,}400 \text{ amps}$$

Example 11-17. A 2500-kva transformer is connected in parallel with a 3000-kva transformer. The impedances of both transformers on their own respective bases are 6 per cent. Their voltage ratings are 34.5 KV to 12 KV. Their secondaries are connected to a line whose impedance is $0.05 + j0.17$ ohm. The line feeds several loads, including an industrial transformer whose voltage rating is 12,000 to 480 volts. If the available short circuit contribution of the utility is 150,000 kva, find the interrupting capacity of the breakers connected to the secondary of the 2000-kva transformer for a bolted fault at point X. The system is shown in Fig. 11-24.

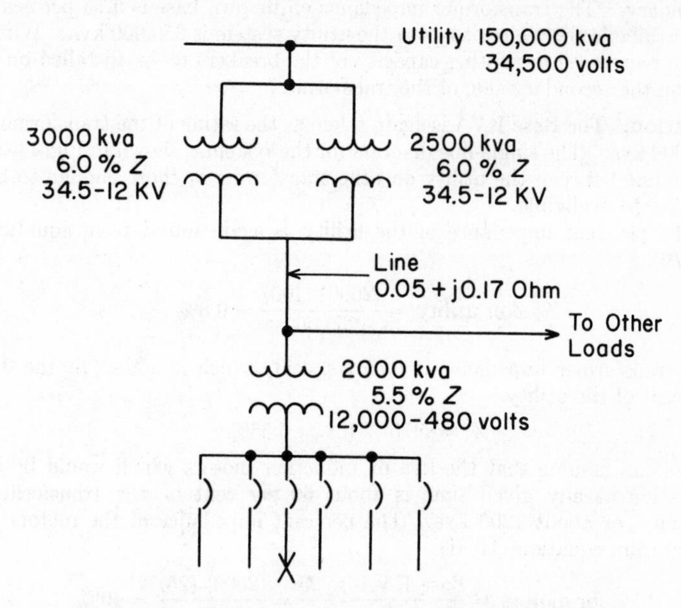

Fig. 11-24. Single-line diagram of a distribution system.

Solution. The "other loads" do not enter into the short circuit calculation unless generators or other sources of voltage are connected to them. The contribution of their induction motors can be neglected because of the line and transformer impedances through which their short circuit currents would have to flow.

Equation (11-79) gives the utility impedance on the 2000-kva base.

$$\%Z \text{ of utility} = \frac{(2000)\ (100)}{150{,}000} = 1.33\%$$

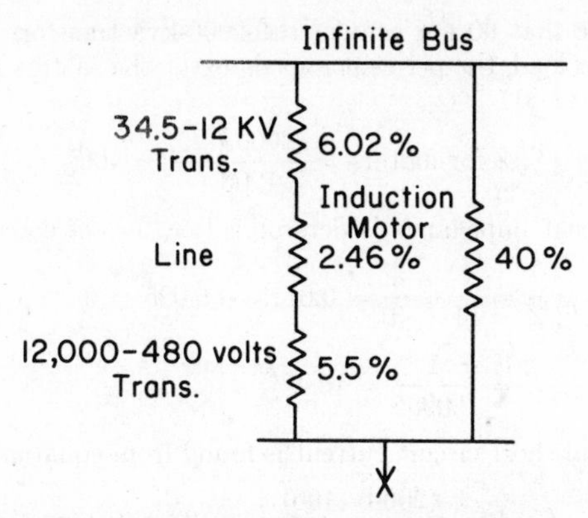

Fig. 11-25. Impedance diagram for distribution system shown in Fig. 11-24.

The impedances of the 3000- and the 2500-kva transformers must be converted to the 2000-kva base by equation (11-82).

$$\% Z_{3000} = \frac{(6)\ (2000)}{3000} = 4\%$$

$$\% Z_{2500} = \frac{(6)\ (2000)}{2500} = 4.8\%$$

Since these impedances are in parallel, their resultant is obtained from equation (11-88).

$$\frac{1}{\% Z_p} = \frac{1}{4} + \frac{1}{4.8} = 0.25 + 0.21 = 0.46$$

$$\% Z_p = \frac{1}{0.46} = 2.18\%$$

The impedance of the line is computed by the complex quantity method:

$$Z = 0.05 + j0.17 = 0.177 \text{ ohm}$$

Since the short circuit is to be computed for the 480-volt bus, the line impedance must be converted to the Base KV. As the impedance of 0.177 ohm is for 12 KV, we may use equation (11-9) for the conversion.

$$Z_{480} = \frac{Z_{12,000}}{a^2} = \frac{(0.177)\ (0.48)^2}{(12)^2} = 0.000282 \text{ ohm}$$

The per cent impedance is calculated by use of equation (11-80).

$$\% Z_{\text{LINE}} = \frac{Z_{480} \times \text{Base KVA}}{(\text{Base KV})^2 \times 10} = \frac{(0.000282)\ (2000)}{(0.48)^2\ (10)} = 2.45\%$$

The impedance of the 2000-kva transformer is already on the correct base. The total impedance of these components in series is

$$Z_T = 6.02 + 2.45 + 5.5 = 13.97\% \text{ or } 14\%$$

If we assume that 60 per cent of the 2000-kva transformer is for the induction motor load, the per cent impedance of the motors is determined from equation (11-81).

$$\%Z \text{ for motors} = \frac{(2000)\ (25)}{1200} = 40\%$$

The total per cent impedance is determined by use of equation (11-88).

$$\frac{1}{\%Z} = \frac{1}{14} + \frac{1}{40} = 0.0715 + 0.025 = 0.0965$$

$$\%Z = \frac{1}{0.0965} = 10.4\%$$

The symmetrical short circuit current is found from equation (11-85).

$$I_{ssc} = \frac{(2000)\ (100)}{(10.4)\ (\sqrt{3})\ (0.48)} = 23{,}200 \text{ amps}$$

The interrupting capacity required is, therefore,

$$\text{I.C.} = I_{asc} = (23{,}200)\ (1.25) = 29{,}000 \text{ amps}$$

11-21. Synchronous Machines. A *synchronous machine* is an a-c rotating device that operates at synchronous speed. Synchronous speed is defined by equation (11-72). There are three general types of synchronous machines:

1. *Synchronous generators*, also called alternators, or a-c dynamos.

2. *Synchronous motors*, which are, fundamentally, generators with electrical features which enable them to drive mechanical loads. (A generator is not designed to drive a mechanical load or even to start rotation without being driven by an engine—or prime mover—of some sort.)

3. *Synchronous condensers*, which are synchronous motors intended for power factor correction. A synchronous condenser does not drive a mechanical load.

The windings in the stator of a synchronous machine are very much like those of an induction motor and carry the a-c armature—or load—current. The rotor windings carry direct current and are wound so that the polarity of the electromagnetic poles does not change or "slip" as it does in an induction motor. The electromagnetic poles of the rotor are steady in strength and polarity and will stay with the stator field as it rotates. If anything should happen to cause the rotating field to slip its position so that a north pole of the rotor is opposite a north pole of the stator, the magnetic opposition between the two poles causes the motor to fall out of synchronous speed and stop.

A synchronous motor can be started as an induction motor and brought up to nearly synchronous speed. At full speed, the direct current supply is closed to the field before the mechanical load is applied. A few such motors have such poor starting torque that they require the aid of an induction motor to bring them up to speed. When the d-c field is connected, a voltage is induced in the stator windings by the flux from the rotor poles. If we assume that all losses in the synchronous motor are supplied by the starting motor, the voltage conditions in the synchronous motor can be represented by the vector diagram shown in Fig. 11-26*a*. In this figure, V_t is the supply voltage across the terminals of the motor and E_{ind} is the voltage induced in the motor windings by the rotating field. Under the assumed conditions, E_{ind} is equal in magnitude to V_t but in exact opposition to it. Consequently, no current can flow in the stator windings.

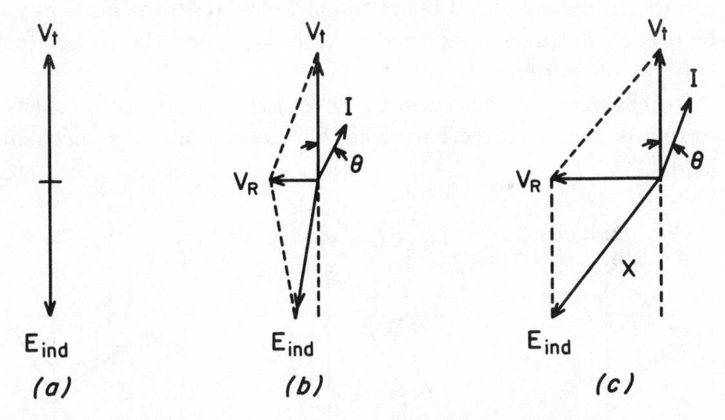

Fig. 11-26. Vector diagram for a synchronous motor.

If we now remove the starting motor, the synchronous motor will have to supply its own losses. This puts a small load on the synchronous motor, causing the rotor to shift its relative position very slightly so that the center of the rotor field poles will lag the rotating stator field by a small angle α. This shift in angle causes a slight shift in phase of the induced voltage E_{ind}. This condition is shown vectorially in Fig. 11-26*b*. The voltages V_t and E_{ind} are added vectorially to give the resultant voltage V_R, which causes a current I to flow in the stator winding.

If the mechanical load is now connected, the rotor shifts its position again so that the center of its magnetic field lags the center of the rotating magnetic field by a large angle α, as indicated in Fig. 11-26*c*. The position of E_{ind} shifts accordingly, so that the resultant voltage V_R is larger, causing a larger current I to flow in the stator windings. An increase in the mechanical load will cause a further shift in the relative position of the magnetic fields, a greater shift in E_{ind}, and a larger V_R, causing the motor to draw a larger current I from the line.

A synchronous motor driving a mechanical load could be used for the additional purpose of correcting power factor. Increasing the strength of the d-c field in the rotor causes an increase in E_{ind} and a shift in phase of both V_R and I. If the field is made strong enough, I will lead V_t and the motor operates at a leading power factor. One difficulty in using a motor to operate a mechanical load and to improve the power factor at the same time is that a variation in mechanical load could cause a considerable change in power factor. Another problem is that operation of the mechanical load may not be needed during some periods of the day when the power factor may be low without it.

Synchronous condensers are synchronous motors used exclusively for power factor correction. They do not operate any mechanical load.

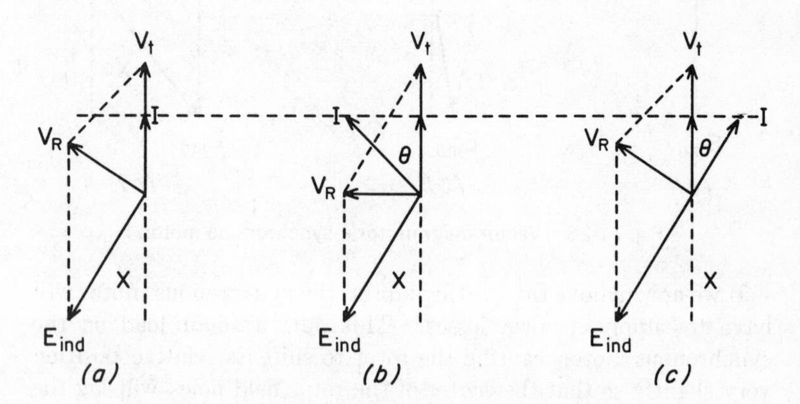

Fig. 11-27. Effect of field strength on power factor of a synchronous condenser.

When the field is at a strength such that the power factor of the condenser is unity ($\theta = 0°$), V_t and I are in phase as shown in Fig. 11-27*a*. If the field is strengthened (more current flows in the rotor winding), E_{ind} increases and V_R increases, causing the motor current I to increase. The component of I that is in phase with the supply voltage V_t does not change, but the magnitude of this current does increase. The current, therefore, shifts in phase in such a way that the motor operates at a leading power factor as shown in Fig. 11-27*b*.

If the field strength is weakened, the in-phase component of the motor current remains the same but the phase of the current shifts so that the motor operates at a lagging power factor as shown in Fig. 11-27*c*. The vector diagrams shown in Fig. 11-27 are for synchronous condensers. Consequently, the in-phase component of the current I is actually very small (only large enough to supply the losses in the motor). Even when the current I is very low, therefore, it is usually enough larger than the in-phase component for the power factor of the condenser to be zero or so close to zero that the difference is difficult to detect. Synchronous condensers and static capacitors are both considered to operate at zero power factor, leading.

Although synchronous condensers have greater losses than static capacitors and require the attention of trained electricians, they are sometimes preferred over the capacitors because their output can be controlled. Capacitors are either on or off, and changes in load require that some capacitors be removed or added as the load changes occur. The output of a synchronous condenser can be adjusted so that the plant power factor can remain approximately constant even with large changes in plant load.

Example 11-18. The load on an industrial plant consists of 1500 hp of 480-volt motors operating at an average efficiency of 80 per cent and a power factor of 70 per cent, lagging, plus 100 kva of lighting – including fluorescent – operating at 90 per cent power factor. Determine the kva rating of the synchronous condenser required to bring the over-all power factor up to 90 per cent.

Solution. The motor load in kva is found by use of equation (11-66).

$$\text{kva} = \frac{0.746 \times \text{hp}}{\text{eff} \times \text{PF}} = \frac{(0.746)\,(1500)}{(0.8)\,(0.7)} = 2000 \text{ kva}$$

Since this load is at 70 per cent power factor, the total kvars will be

$$\text{kvars} = 2000 \sin\theta = (2000)\,(0.714) = 1428 \text{ kvars}$$

The kw load of the motors is

$$\text{kw} = 2000 \cos\theta = (2000)\,(0.7) = 1400 \text{ kvars}$$

The kvar load of the lighting is

$$\text{kvar} = 100 \sin\theta = (100)\,(0.439) = 43.9 \text{ kvars}$$

The kw lighting load is

$$\text{kw} = 100 \cos \theta = (100)(0.9) = 90 \text{ kw}$$

The total load of the plant is

$$\text{kvars} = 1428 + 44 = 1472 \text{ kvars}$$

$$\text{kw} = 1400 + 90 = 1490 \text{ kw}$$

$$\text{kva} = 2100 \text{ kva at } 71\% \text{ power factor}$$

With a loading of 1490 kw, the kva for 90 per cent power factor is, from trigonometry,

$$\text{kva} = \frac{\text{kw}}{\cos \theta} = \frac{1490}{0.90} = 1660 \text{ kva}$$

The kvars for this condition are

$$\text{kvars} = \text{kva} \sin \theta = 725 \text{ kvars}$$

The synchronous condenser required will then be

$$\text{Rating} = 1472 - 725 = 747 \text{ kvars}$$

Problems Based on Chapter 11

P11-1. What voltage is induced in a transformer winding of 900 turns at a frequency of 60 cycles if the maximum flux is 10^{-2} webers? How many turns are required in the second winding if the voltage is to be 13,200 volts? What is the ratio of transformation?

Ans. 2400 volts. 4950 turns. 5.5 to 1.

P11-2. A transformer has 800 turns in its primary winding and 160 turns in its secondary winding. It is rated 10 kva at 480 volts. Determine (a) the ratio of transformation, (b) the approximate primary voltage, (c) the rated full-load secondary current, and (d) the rated full-load primary current, neglecting the no-load current.

Ans. (a) 5 to 1. (b) 2400 volts. (c) 20.8 amps. (d) 4.16 amps.

P11-3. Determine the equivalent resistances, reactances, and impedances of the following transformer when the values are referred to the primary winding and to the secondary winding: 2400-120 volts, $r_p = 11$ ohms, $r_s = 0.12$ ohm, $x_p = 21$ ohms, and $x_s = 0.25$ ohm.

Ans. Referred to primary: $r = 23$ ohms, $x = 46$ ohms, $z = 51.4$ ohms. Referred to secondary: $r = 0.23$ ohm, $x = 0.46$ ohm, $z = 0.514$ ohm.

P11-4. A transformer with a rating of 2400-240 volts has 2000 turns in the primary winding. Assuming a 3% voltage drop in the transformer when it is fully loaded, how many turns should be placed on the secondary to maintain its rated voltage at full load? With this number of turns on the secondary and the primary voltage held constant, what is the secondary no-load voltage?

Ans. 207 turns. 248 volts.

P11-5. A 13,200-240 volt transformer has a primary resistance of 38 ohms and a primary reactance of 68 ohms. What should be the approximate values of secondary resistance and reactance?

Ans. $r_s = 0.0126$ ohm, $x_s = 0.0225$ ohm.

P11-6. A 250-kva 2400-480 volt transformer has no-load losses of 1060 watts and full-load losses of 3760 watts. What is the efficiency when the transformer is fully loaded at 0.8 power factor? At three-fourths load? At half-load? At one-fourth load? What is the efficiency when the copper losses equal the core loss?

Ans. 98%. 98.4%. 98.4%. 97.5%. 98.5% at 0.628 full-load. (Note that *the point of most efficient operation of a transformer is that at which the core loss equals the copper loss.*)

P11-7. The resistances of a transformer whose secondary voltage rating is 240 volts are 4.5 and 0.015 ohms. What is the voltage for which the high voltage winding is designed?

Ans. 4160 volts.

P11-8. The windings of a 10-kva 2400-240 volt 60-cycle transformer have resistances of 6 and 0.06 ohms. The core loss is 60 watts. What is the full-load copper loss?

Ans. 208 watts.

P11-9. The transformer of problem P11-8 is loaded at 0.9 power factor as follows: 2 hours full load, 4 hours half load, and 5 hours quarter load. The transformer is continuously energized. What is the all-day efficiency?

Ans. 95.6%.

P11-10. If the transformer of problem P11-9 had operated at 0.6 power factor with the same kva loading, what would be its all-day efficiency?

Ans. 93.6%.

P11-11. A transformer is to deliver a maximum load of 9000 watts for a period of 6 hours every day. If the power factor of the load is 0.7, what is the required capacity of the transformer?

Ans. The load is 12.8 kva. Since the load is to be delivered for such a long time, the transformer capacity must be 15 kva, the next standard size. (A transformer can carry an overload for a short period if its operating temperature does not exceed the maximum recommended by the manufacturer. An overload lasting more than 2 hours can usually be expected to overheat the transformer.)

P11-12. A 2400-240 volt transformer has a high-voltage winding resistance and reactance of 0.25 and 2 ohms, respectively. What are the corresponding values for the low-voltage winding? What are per cent resistance, per cent reactance, and per cent impedance if the transformer capacity is 100 kva?

Ans. $R_s = 0.0025$ ohm. $X_s = 0.02$ ohm. $\%R = 0.866\%$. $\%X = 6.94\%$. $\%Z = 7\%$.

P11-13. Table 11-2 shows that a 50-kva 4800-240 volt transformer has approximately 1.4% resistance, 2.5% reactance, and 2.9% impedance.

What are the values of resistance, reactance, and impedance viewed from the 4800-volt and from the 240-volt windings?

Ans. From the 4800-volt winding, $R = 6.45$ ohms, $X = 11.45$ ohms, $Z = 13.35$ ohms. From the 240-volt winding, $R = 0.0161$ ohm, $X = 0.0288$ ohm, $Z = 0.0334$ ohm.

P11-14. What are the approximate values of R_p, X_p, Z_p, R_s, X_s, and Z_s of the transformer described in problem P11-13?

Ans. $R_p = 3.23$ ohms, $X_p = 5.73$ ohms, $Z_p = 6.68$ ohms, $R_s = 0.00805$ ohm, $X_s = 0.0144$ ohm, $Z_s = 0.0167$ ohm.

P11-15. What is the regulation of the transformer described in problem P11-2 if the load is unity power factor? 80% power factor? 50% power factor?

Ans. 1.4% at unity PF. 2.7% at 80% PF. 3% at 50% PF.

P11-16. A transformer is checked for polarity. It is rated at 4800-480 volts. If 50 volts are impressed across the primary (high-voltage) winding, what would be the voltage across both windings if the polarity is additive? If it is subtractive?

Ans. 55 volts additive. 45 volts subtractive.

P11-17. Three single-phase transformers are to be connected in a bank to supply a three-phase, 3-wire, 240-volt industrial distribution system to which are connected the following balanced three-phase loads: 50 kw at 80% power factor, 40 kw at 85% power factor, an incandescent lighting load of 15 kw at unity power factor, and a fluorescent lighting load of 10 kw at 90% power factor. What is the rating of each single-phase transformer, allowing for a maximum overload of 25%?

Ans. Actual load is 158 kva. Three 50-kva transformers meet the requirements (actual overload is 5.4%).

P11-18. Three single-phase transformers are each rated 2400 volts on the primary and 120 volts on the secondary. If the line voltage is 4000 volts, how would the transformers be connected?

Ans. Wye-wye.

P11-19. Of the four possible ways to connect transformers in three-phase systems, which will give the highest secondary voltage for a given primary voltage?

Ans. Delta-wye.

P11-20. A three-phase transformer bank is connected delta-wye. If the high-voltage side is 2400 volts and the turns ratio of each transformer is 20 to 1, what is the line-to-line voltage on the low-voltage side?

Ans. 208 volts.

P11-21. A 20,000-kva 25-cycle 4500-volt generator is to be connected to a three-phase 9000-volt system by means of three autotransformers. What is the capacity of each of the three autotransformers?

Ans. 3333 kva per transformer, or 10,000 kva for the entire bank. (This is the description of an installation used in a power system in the Middle West section of the United States.)

P11-22. An autotransformer is to supply power to a 2400-kva load. If the high-side voltage is 4800 volts and the low-side voltage is 480 volts, what is the capacity of the autotransformer?

Ans. 2160 kva.

P11-23. A 25-cycle motor has 4 poles. What is its synchronous speed?
Ans. 750 rpm.

P11-24. What is the maximum speed of a 25-cycle motor? Of a 60-cycle motor?

Ans. 1500 rpm. 3600 rpm.

P11-25. A frequency changer is connected between a 60-cycle and a 25-cycle system. How many poles will be in the two generators and at what speed will they rotate?

Ans. 10 and 24 poles. 300 rpm.

P11-26. A 60-cycle 2-pole motor operates at 3450 rpm. What is the slip?

Ans. 4.2%.

P11-27. Two three-phase 220-volt 25-hp motors have an efficiency of 90% and a power factor of 80%. What total current would they draw and what is the kva of the combination?

Ans. 136 amps. 51.8 kva.

P11-28. What protection should a 50-hp 1800-rpm 220-volt motor have?

Ans. 76 amps running protection (rating of the heaters). 175 amps breaker setting for starting current (actual calculation shows 152 amps).

P11-29. A 2500-kva transformer feeds a 600-volt load. If the available short circuit capacity on the high side is 150,000 kva and the transformer impedance is 5.75%, what is the required interrupting capacity of the breakers connected to a bus on the 600-volt system if 2200 kva of induction motors are in operation at the time a short circuit is assumed to occur?

Ans. 51,500 amps.

P11-30. The available short circuit capacity of the utility company at a certain point is 83,500 kva. A privately owned transmission line that connects the utility lines to an industrial plant has an impedance of 0.206 ohm and connects to the primary of a 12,000-480 volt 500-kva transformer whose impedance is 3.5%. If it is assumed that 400 kva of induction motors are connected to the 480-volt bus, find the symmetrical and asymmetrical short circuit currents (interrupting capacity) for the rating of breakers connected to the 480-volt bus.

Ans. I_{ssc} = 16,300 amps. I_{asc} = I.C. = 20,400 amps.

A APPENDIX

ABBREVIATIONS

a-c	alternating-current (adjective).
a.c. or AC	alternating current (noun).
amp	ampere.
amps	amperes.
amp-hr	ampere-hour.
AWG	American Wire Gage. This is the standard for the measurement of electrical conductor sizes in the United States.
BES	British Engineering System (of units).
B & S	Brown and Sharpe Wire Gage. This is the original name for what is now more generally called the American Wire Gage.
Btu	British thermal unit.
°C	degrees Celsius. The Celsius temperature scale was formerly called the Centigrade scale.
cc	cubic centimeter(s). Sometimes written cm^3.
ccw	counterclockwise.
cgs	centimeter-gram-second system of units.
CM	circular mil area (of electrical conductors).
cm	centimeter(s).
cm^2	square centimeter(s). Sometimes written sq cm.
coul	coulomb(s).
cps	cycles per second.
cu in.	cubic inch(es). Sometimes written $in.^3$.
cw	clockwise.
db	decibel(s).
d-c	direct-current (adjective).
d.c. or DC	direct current (noun).
deg	degree(s).
eff	efficiency.
emf or EMF	electromotive force.

°F — degrees Fahrenheit. Temperature scale named after its inventor, Gabriel Daniel Fahrenheit, German physicist (1686–1736).
fpm — feet per minute.
fps — feet per second.
f or freq — frequency.
ft — foot (feet).
ft-lb — foot-pound.
gen — generator.
h — henry(s).
hp — horsepower.
hr — hour.
hrs — hours.
I.C. — interrupting capacity.
in. — inch(es). The period is used with this abbreviation to avoid confusion.
kc — kilocycle(s). One thousand cycles per second.
kg — kilogram(s). One thousand grams.
KV — kilovolt(s). One thousand volts.
kva or KVA — kilovolt-ampere(s). One thousand amperes.
kvar — kilovar. One thousand vars.
kvars — kilovars.
kw — kilowatt(s). One thousand watts.
kwh — kilowatt-hour(s). One thousand watt-hours.
lb — pound.
lbs — pounds.
log — logarithm to the base 10. If a logarithm is to any other base, the base is indicated, as $\log_3$ (for base 3).
m — meter(s).
ma — milliampere(s). One thousandth of an ampere.
mc — megacycle(s). One million cycles per second.
MCM — thousand circular mils.
mg — milligram(s). One thousandth of a gram.
mh — millihenry(s). One thousandth of a henry.
min — minute(s).
mks — meter-kilogram-second system of units.
mmf — magnetomotive force.
m-n — meter-newtons.
mph — miles per hour.

MV	megavolt(s). One million volts.
mv	millivolt(s). One thousandth of a volt.
MW	megawatt(s). One million watts.
mw	milliwatt(s). One thousandth of a watt.
NBFU	National Board of Fire Underwriters.
NEC	National Electrical Code.
NEMA	National Electrical Manufacturers' Association.
NFPA	National Fire Protection Association.
No.	number.
PF	power factor.
reg	regulation.
rms	root mean square.
rpm	revolutions per minute.
rps	revolutions per second.
sec	second(s).
sq cm	square centimeter(s). Sometimes written cm^2.
sq in.	square inch(es). Sometimes written $in.^2$.
V	volt(s).
w	weber(s).
w/m^2	webers per meter squared.
WH	watt hours.

SIGNS AND SYMBOLS

a	transformer turns ratio.
A	area, except in problems involving the Murray or Varley Loop where A refers to a known resistance. See also Norton's theorem.
B	susceptance, or magnetic flux per unit area.
C	capacitance.
E	voltage, usually across a source, as a generator or a battery.
$\mathcal{E}$	electric field intensity.
F	force (in general).
$\mathfrak{F}$	magnetomotive force.
G	generator, or conductance.
H	magnetic intensity.
I	electric current.
I_{asc}	asymmetrical short circuit current.
I_{ssc}	symmetrical short circuit current.
I_{usc}	short circuit current available at serving utility.

k	constant for use with the mks system of units, equal to 9×10^9 newton-meters squared per coulomb squared ($n\text{-}m^2/coul^2$).
K_m	relative permeability in the mks system, equal to μ/μ_0.
l	length.
L	inductance.
M or m	mass.
N	number of turns of wire in a coil.
Ni	ampere-turns.
P	power.
P_c	copper loss.
P_e	eddy-current loss.
P_h	hysteresis loss.
q	electrical charge in coulombs.
$\mathcal{R}$	reluctance.
R	resistance.
$\%R$	per cent resistance.
R_{pu}	per unit resistance.
T	absolute temperature or time constant.
v	velocity.
V	voltage across a load.
W	watt(s) or energy. Sometimes used as a symbol for work.
X	reactance, in general.
X_C	capacitive reactance.
X_L	inductive reactance.
$\%X$	per cent reactance.
X_{pu}	per unit reactance.
Y	admittance.
Z	impedance.
$\%Z$	per cent impedance.
Z_{pu}	per unit impedance.

GREEK LETTER SYMBOLS

ϵ_0	constant for use with the mks system of units, equal to 8.85×10^{-12} coulombs squared per newton-meter squared ($coul^2/n\text{-}m^2$).
μ	permeability in the mks system, equal to B/H.

μ_0	constant for use with the mks system of units, equal to $4\pi \times 10^{-7}$ or 12.57×10^{-7} webers per ampere-meter (w/amp-m).
μf	microfarad. One-millionth of a farad.
$\mu\mu$f	micro-microfarad. One-millionth of a microfarad.
ρ	resistivity.
ϕ	phase.
Φ	total magnetic flux.

B APPENDIX

DEFINITIONS

The following definitions are added for the convenience and information of students and engineers using this book. All of the terms defined here are either used or implied in the text but are not defined there. Terms defined in the text are omitted here.

Definitions followed by the letters (RHH) are from the *Radiological Health Handbook* compiled and edited by the Division of Radiological Health, U. S. Department of Health, Education, and Welfare, Washington, D. C., 20201.

Alternating-current Distribution—The supplying to points of utilization of electric energy by alternating current from its source or one or more receiving stations (sometimes called distribution stations or substations).

Note—Generally, a voltage is employed which is not higher than that which could be delivered or utilized by rotating electric machinery. Stepdown transformers of a capacity much smaller than that of the line are usually employed as links between the moderate voltage of distribution and the lower voltage of the customer's apparatus.

Alternating-current Transmission—The transfer of electric energy by alternating current from its source to one or more main receiving stations for subsequent distribution.

Note—Generally, a voltage is employed which is higher than that which would be delivered or utilized by electric machinery. Transformers of a capacity comparable to that of the line are usually employed as links between the high voltage of transmission and the lower voltage used for distribution or utilization.

Anion—Negatively charged ion. (RHH)

Anode—Positive electrode; electrode to which negative ions are attracted. (RHH)

Atom—Smallest particle of an element which is capable of entering into a chemical reaction. (RHH)

Atomic Number—The number of orbital electrons surrounding the nucleus of a neutral atom and, according to present theory, the number of protons in the nucleus. (RHH)

Atomic Weight—The weighted mean of the masses of the neutral atoms of an element expressed in atomic weight units. *See* Atomic Weight Unit. (RHH)

Atomic Weight Unit—One-sixteenth of the weighted mean of the masses of the neutral atoms of oxygen of isotopic composition, equivalent to 1.660×10^{-24} grams. (RHH)

Balanced Polyphase Load—A load to which symmetrical currents are supplied when it is connected to a system having symmetrical voltages.

Note—The term "balanced polyphase load" is applied also to a load to which are supplied two currents having the same wave form and rms value and differing in phase by 90 electrical degrees when the load is connected to a quarter-phase (or two-phase) system having voltages of the same wave form and rms value.

Balanced Polyphase System—A polyphase system in which both the currents and voltages are symmetrical.

Note—The term "balanced polyphase system" is applied also to a quarter-phase (or two-phase) system in which the voltages have the same wave form and rms value and in which the currents have the same wave form and rms value and differ in phase by 90 electrical degrees.

Balanced Three-Wire System—A three-wire system in which no current flows in the conductor connected to the neutral point of the supply. *See also* Three-wire System.

British Thermal Unit (Btu)—The quantity of heat required to increase the temperature of one pound of water one degree Fahrenheit at atmospheric pressure; approximately 252 gram-calories. (RHH)

Calorie (Gram-calorie)—Amount of heat necessary to raise the temperature of one gram of water 1° C (from 14.5° to 15.5 ° C). (RHH)

Cathode—Negative electrode; electrode to which positive ions are attracted. (RHH)

Cation—Positively charged ion. (RHH)

Circular Mil—An area equal to the area contained in a circle of one mil in diameter or 7.854×10^{-7} square inch. (RHH)

Compound—A distinct substance formed by a union of two or more ingredients in definite proportions by weight. (RHH)

Connected Load—The connected load on a system, or part of a system, is the sum of the continuous ratings of the load-consuming apparatus connected to the system, or part of the system, under consideration.

Coulomb—Unit of electrical charge in the practical system of units. A quantity of electricity equal to 3×10^9 electrostatic units of charge. (RHH)

Direct-current Distribution— The supplying to points of utilization of electric energy by direct current from its point of generation or conversion.

Direct-current Transmission— The transfer of electric energy by direct current from its source to one or more receiving stations. *Note*— For transmitting large blocks of power, high voltage such as is obtained with generators in series, rectifiers, etc., may be used.

Edison Distribution System—A three-wire direct-current system, usually about 120–240 volts, for combined light and power service from a single set of mains.

Note—This system has also been adapted to alternating current at the same voltages. *See* Three-wire System.

Efficiency— The ratio of the input to the output. Efficiency may be expressed either as a decimal or as a per cent of the input.

Electrode—Either terminal of an electrical apparatus. (RHH)

Electromotive Force—Potential difference across electrodes tending to produce an electric current. (RHH)

Electron— Negatively charged particle which is a constituent of every neutral atom. Unit of negative electricity equal to 4.8×10^{-10} electrostatic units or 1.6×10^{-19} coulomb. Its mass is 0.000549 atomic mass units. (RHH)

Electrostatic Field— The region surrounding an electric charge in which another electric charge experiences a force. (RHH)

Element— Pure substance consisting of atoms of the same atomic number which cannot be decomposed by ordinary chemical means. (RHH)

Gram Atomic Weight— A mass in grams numerically equal to the atomic weight of an element. (RHH)

Gram Molecular Weight (Gram-mole)—Mass in grams numerically equal to the molecular weight of a substance. (RHH)

Ion— Atomic particle, atom, or chemical radical bearing an electrical charge, either negative or positive. (RHH)

Ionization— The process or the result of any process by which a neutral atom or molecule acquires either a positive or a negative charge. (RHH)

Isomer— One of several nuclides having the same number of neutrons and protons but capable of existing, for a measurable time, in different quantum states with different energies and radioactive properties. Commonly, the isomer of higher energy decays to one of lower energy by the process of isomeric transition. (RHH)

Note— The quantum is an energy level. Isomeric transition is a decaying process involving isomers.

Isotope— One of several nuclides having the same number of protons in their nuclei, and hence having the same atomic number, but differing in the number of neutrons, and therefore in the mass number. Almost identical chemical properties exist between isotopes of a particular element. The use of this term as a synonym for nuclide is to be discouraged. (RHH)

Note— Some isotopes are radioactive and some are not. For example, hydrogen and heavy hydrogen (deuterium, which has an extra neutron in the nucleus) are not radioactive. Tritium, which is a hydrogen isotope with two extra neutrons in the nucleus, is radioactive. The normal hydrogen atom has no neutrons in the nucleus.

Low-voltage System— An electric system having an operating voltage less than 750 volts.

Mass— The material equivalent of energy—different from weight in that it neither increases nor decreases with gravitational force. (RHH)

Mass Number—The number of nucleons (protons and neutrons) in the nucleus of an atom. (RHH)

Mil— Term equal to one-thousandth of an inch. (RHH)

Molecular Weight— The sum of the atomic weights of all the atoms in a molecule. (RHH)

Molecule—Ultimate unit quantity of a compound which can exist by itself and retain all the properties of the original substance. (RHH)

Neutron— Elementary nuclear particle with a mass approximately the same as that of a hydrogen atom and electrically neutral; its mass is 1.008982 mass units. (RHH)

Nucleon—Common name for a constituent particle of the nucleus. At present applied to protons and neutrons, but will include any other particle found to exist in the nucleus. (RHH)

Nucleus (Nuclear)—That part of an atom in which the total positive electric charge and most of the mass are concentrated. (RHH)

Nuclide—A species of atom characterized by the constitution of its nucleus. The nuclear constitution is specified by the number of protons Z, number of neutrons N, and energy content; or, alternatively, by the atomic number Z, mass number A $(=N+Z)$, and atomic mass. To be regarded as a distinct nuclide, the atom must be capable of existing for a measurable time; thus nuclear isomers are separate nuclides, whereas promptly decaying excited nuclear states and unstable intermediates in nuclear reactions are not so considered. (RHH)
Note—The word "decaying" refers to the radioactive decay of a radioactive element.

Potential Difference—Work required to carry a unit positive charge from one point to another. (RHH)
Note—"Difference in potential" and "potential difference" are identical terms.

Proton—Elementary nuclear particle with a positive electric charge equal numerically to the charge of the electron and a mass of 1.007594 mass units. (RHH)

Regulation—The per cent rise in voltage from the full-load condition to the no-load condition.

Three-phase Four-wire System—A system of alternating-current supply comprising four conductors, three of which are connected as in a three-phase three-wire system, the fourth being connected to the neutral point of the supply, which may be grounded.

Three-phase Seven-wire System—A system of alternating-current supply from groups of three single-phase transformers connected in Y so as to obtain a three-phase four-wire grounded neutral system for lighting and a three-phase three-wire grounded neutral system of a higher voltage for power, the neutral wire being common to both systems. The most common systems of this type are the 120–208 volt and 277–480 volt systems.

Three-phase Three-wire System—A system of alternating-current supply comprising three conductors between successive pairs of which are maintained alternating differences of potential successively displaced in phase by one-third of a period.

Three-wire System (direct current or single-phase alternating current)— A system of electric supply comprising three conductors, one of which (known as the "neutral wire") is maintained as a potential midway between the potential of the other two (referred to as the outer conductors).

Note— Part of the load may be connected directly between the outer conductors, the remainder being divided as evenly as possible into two parts, each of which is connected between the neutral and one other conductor. There are thus two distinct voltages of supply, the one being twice that of the other.

Two-phase Five-wire System— A system of alternating-current supply comprising five conductors, four of which are connected as in a four-wire two-phase system, the fifth being connected to the neutral point of each phase.

Note— The neutral is usually grounded. Although this type of system is usually known as the two-phase five-wire system, it is strictly a four-phase five-wire system.

Two-phase Four-wire System— A system of alternating-current supply comprising two pairs of conductors between one pair of which is maintained an alternating difference of potential displaced in phase by one-quarter of a period from an alternating difference of potential of the same frequency maintained between the other pair.

Two-phase Three-wire System— A system of alternating-current supply comprising three conductors between one of which (known as the common return) and each of the other two are maintained alternating differences of potential displaced in phase by one-quarter of a period with relation to each other.

Two-wire System (direct current or single-phase alternating current)— A system of electric supply comprising two conductors between which the load is connected.

Ungrounded System (Insulated Supply System)— A system in which no point is deliberately connected to earth except through potential or ground detecting transformers or other very high impedance devices.

Voltage Drop (in a supply system)— The difference between the voltages at the transmitting and receiving ends of a feeder, main, or service.

Note— With alternating current, the voltages are not necessarily in phase, and hence the voltage drop is not necessarily equal to the algebraic sum of the voltage drops along the several conductors.

INDEX